COMPREHENSIVE BIOCHEMISTRY

SOLE DISTRIBUTORS FOR THE UNITED STATES AND CANADA:

AMERICAN ELSEVIER PUBLISHING COMPANY, INC.

52, VANDERBILT AVENUE, NEW YORK 17 N.Y.

SOLE DISTRIBUTORS FOR GREAT BRITAIN

ELSEVIER PUBLISHING COMPANY LIMITED

12B, RIPPLESIDE COMMERCIAL ESTATE

RIPPLE ROAD, BARKING, ESSEX

Library of Congress Catalog Card Number 62–10359

With 26 illustrations and 36 tables

PRINTED IN THE NETHERLANDS BY

DRUKKERIJ MEIJER — WORMERVEER AND AMSTERDAM

COMPREHENSIVE BIOCHEMISTRY

COMPREHENSIVE
BIOCHEMISTRY

SECTION I (VOLUMES I–4)

PHYSICO-CHEMICAL AND ORGANIC ASPECTS
OF BIOCHEMISTRY

SECTION II (VOLUMES 5–11)

CHEMISTRY OF BIOLOGICAL COMPOUNDS

SECTION III

BIOCHEMICAL REACTION MECHANISMS

SECTION IV

METABOLISM

SECTION V

CHEMICAL BIOLOGY
GENERAL INDEX

COMPREHENSIVE
BIOCHEMISTRY

EDITED BY

MARCEL FLORKIN

Professor of Biochemistry, University of Liège (Belgium)

AND

ELMER H. STOTZ

*Professor of Biochemistry, University of Rochester, School of Medicine
and Dentistry, Rochester, N.Y. (U.S.A.)*

VOLUME 7
PROTEINS (PART 1)

ELSEVIER PUBLISHING COMPANY
AMSTERDAM · LONDON · NEW YORK

1963

CONTRIBUTORS TO THIS VOLUME

ROBERT L. BALDWIN, B.A., Ph.D.

Professor of Biochemistry, Stanford University, School of Medicine,
Palo Alto, Calif. (U.S.A.)

H. FRAENKEL-CONRAT, Ph.D., M.D.

Professor of Virology, Department of Virology and Virus Laboratory,
University of California, Berkeley 4, Calif. (U.S.A.)

E. GORDON YOUNG, B.A., M.Sc., Ph.D., D.Sc., F.R.S.C., F.C.I.C.

Director, Atlantic Regional Laboratory, National Research Council of Canada,
Halifax (Canada)

D. W. GREEN, B.Sc. (CAMBRIDGE), Ph.D. (LONDON)

Davy Faraday Research Laboratory, The Royal Institution, 21, Albemarle Street,
London, W.1 (Great Britain)

KAI O. PEDERSEN, Ph.D., M.D. (H.C.)

Associate Professor of Physical Chemistry, Institute of Physical Chemistry,
University of Uppsala (Sweden)

HAROLD A. SCHERAGA, B.S., A.M., Ph.D. (DUKE UNIV.),
Sc.D. (HON.) (DUKE UNIV.)

Professor of Chemistry and Chairman of the Department, Cornell University,
Ithaca, N.Y. (U.S.A.)

RODES TRAUTMAN, B.E.E., Ph.D.

Principal Research Physicist, Plum Island Animal Disease Laboratory, Animal Disease
and Parasite Research Division, Agricultural Research Service, U.S. Department of
Agriculture, P.O.Box 848, Greenport, Long Island, N.Y. (U.S.A.)

GENERAL PREFACE

The Editors are keenly aware that the literature of Biochemistry is already very large, in fact so widespread that it is increasingly difficult to assemble the most pertinent material in a given area. Beyond the ordinary textbook the subject matter of the rapidly expanding knowledge of biochemistry is spread among innumerable journals, monographs, and series of reviews. The Editors believe that there is a real place for an advanced treatise in biochemistry which assembles the principal areas of the subject in a single set of books.

It would be ideal if an individual or small group of biochemists could produce such an advanced treatise, and within the time to keep reasonably abreast of rapid advances, but this is at least difficult if not impossible. Instead, the Editors with the advice of the Advisory Board, have assembled what they consider the best possible sequence of chapters written by competent authors; they must take the responsibility for inevitable gaps of subject matter and duplication which may result from this procedure.

Most evident to the modern biochemist, apart from the body of knowledge of the chemistry and metabolism of biological substances, is the extent to which he must draw from recent concepts of physical and organic chemistry, and in turn project into the vast field of biology. Thus in the organization of Comprehensive Biochemistry, the middle three sections, Chemistry of Biological Compounds, Biochemical Reaction Mechanisms, and Metabolism may be considered classical biochemistry, while the first and last sections provide selected material on the origins and projections of the subject.

It is hoped that sub-division of sections into volumes will not only be convenient, but will find favour among students concerned with specialized areas, and will permit easier future revisions of the individual volumes. Toward the latter end particularly, the Editors will welcome all comments in their effort to produce a useful and efficient source of biochemical knowledge.

Liège/Rochester
March 1962

M. FLORKIN
E. H. STOTZ

PREFACE TO SECTION II

(Volumes 5–11)

Section II on the Chemistry of Biological Compounds deals with the organic and physical chemistry of the major organic constituents of living material. A general understanding of organic and physical chemistry is presumed, but the reader will find the special topics in Section I of value in the fuller understanding of several parts of Section II. The Editors have made special effort to include a sound treatment of the important biological high polymers, including sections on their shape and physical properties. A number of substances peculiar to plants, certain isoprenoids, flavonoids, tannins, lignins, and plant hormones, often omitted from text-books of biochemistry, are included. Nevertheless, it is inevitable that some omissions, hopefully minor ones, have occurred. The only intentional omission is the chemistry of the coenzymes and certain components of biological oxidation, which will be covered in connection with their function in Section III.

The previous policy of dividing the section into smaller volumes has been continued, resulting in seven volumes for Section II. Two of the volumes each contain a complete area, namely Carbohydrates (Volume 5) and Sterols, Bile Acids and Steroids (Volume 10). Comments from readers will be appreciated by the Editors and be most helpful for possible future revisions.

Liège/Rochester   M. FLORKIN
December 1962   E. H. STOTZ

CONTENTS

VOLUME 7

PROTEINS – PART 1

Chapter I. Occurrence, Classification, Preparation and Analysis of Proteins

by E. GORDON YOUNG

Chapter II. Chemistry of Proteins

by H. Fraenkel-Conrat

Chapter III. Acid–Base Properties and Electrophoresis of Proteins

by R. Trautman

Chapter IV. Reactions of Proteins; Denaturation

by H. A. Scheraga

Chapter V. Thermodynamic Properties of Proteins Found From Osmotic Experiments

by R. L. Baldwin

Chapter VI. Sedimentation, Diffusion and Partial Specific Volume

by K. O. Pedersen

Chapter VII. Spacial Configuration in Proteins

by D. W. Green

Chapter I

Occurrence, Classification, Preparation and Analysis of Proteins

E. GORDON YOUNG

*Atlantic Regional Laboratory, National Research Council,
Halifax (Canada)*

1. Introduction

Of all known chemical compounds proteins are the most complex and, at the same time, the most characteristic of living matter. All viable cells contain them. They are the compounds which, as nucleoproteins, are essential to the process of cell division, and, as enzymes and hormones, control many chemical reactions in the metabolism of both plant and animal cells. As the major, if not the only, constituent of viruses, nucleoproteins are synonymous with the most elementary form of living matter.

The word protein first appeared in scientific literature in 1838 in an article by the Dutch chemist, G. J. Mulder. It is derived from the Greek adjective πρωτειος (*prote*–first and *eidos*–like) which may be translated as of the first rank or position. While Mulder was investigating an organic substance which contained nitrogen, sulfur and phosphorus and appeared to be widely distributed in biological material, he received a letter from the great Swedish chemist Berzelius who suggested the term to him[1,2]. Thus as early as 1838 the fundamental importance of protein in living matter was recognized. Liebig, a few years later, investigated the composition of several plant and animal proteins. Later, the German term *Eiweisskörper* and the English modification *proteid* came into general use. The latter has now disappeared.

During the second half of the nineteenth century and the early years of the twentieth investigators were concerned with the separation of proteins from their complex environment and the determination of their constituent amino acids. The names of Osborne, Abderhalden, Kossel, Ritthausen,

References p. 53

Hammarsten, Schmiedeberg, Emil Fischer, Levene, Sörensen, and Van Slyke, may be recalled as the founders of the modern chemistry of the proteins. In those days the determination of the amino acids in a protein required esterification, fractional distillation, and frequently isolation of each amino acid —a task which required many weeks, in contrast to the present mechanized procedure which requires less than a day.

The first protein to be crystallized was haemoglobin, in 1840, by evaporation of the blood of the earthworm[3]; probably the second was the globulin[4] from the Brazil nut in 1877, and the third ovalbumin[5] in 1889. The first enzyme to be crystallized was urease, isolated by Sumner[6] in 1926. Abel[7] crystallized the first protein hormone, insulin, in 1926, and Stanley[8] the first virus, tobacco mosaic virus, in 1935. Crystalline proteins now are numbered by the score.

In the earlier part of this century investigators turned their attention to the physico-chemical characteristics of a few proteins. These studies have formed the basis for our present conceptions of colloidal behavior, hydrodynamic properties, size and shape of protein particles. The invention of the ultracentrifuge in 1923 by Svedberg and the extensive modification of the electrophoretic cell by Tiselius in 1930 were significant milestones in the progress of protein chemistry. The advent of modern chromatography has made possible a new approach to the structure of proteins in the classical study of the sequence of amino acids in insulin by Sanger[9] in 1955. The initial attempts of Emil Fischer to synthesize polypeptides have now led to a synthesis of the pituitary hormones, oxytocin and vasopressin, by du Vigneaud[10] and his colleagues. So rapid has been the advance and so voluminous the amount of work that there is a yearly volume *Advances in Protein Chemistry* dating back to 1944, a comprehensive treatise on proteins in four volumes[11], the classical monograph of Cohn and Edsall[12], and several smaller text books[13].

2. Occurrence

Proteins are believed to occur in all living matter – viruses, bacteria, plants and animals. In addition they are found, sometimes in high concentration, in such animal products as urine, blood, lymph, milk, eggs, in epidermal structures such as hair, feathers, and hoofs, in internal secretions such as the digestive juices, cerebrospinal, ocular, and synovial fluids, and in external secretions, such as uterine, seminal, prostatic, and testicular. Rather special cases are the secretion of the silkworm and the cobweb of the spider. In plants they occur in solution in the circulating fluids such as the cell sap. In the undissolved state, sometimes as crystals, they are found in seeds, spores, tubers, bulbs, and roots. The concentration in seeds is very high, especially in the endosperm and this is of particular importance to man in nuts, in grains and in some legumes, such as peas and beans. A very poisonous protein, ricin, occurs in the castor bean. The greater part of the protein in leaves or fronds is in a rather insoluble form.

Within the structure of the cell, proteins constitute part of the cell wall or membrane and all of cilia or flagella. Both in solution and in granular or crystalline form they are present in the cytoplasm and in vacuoles. They probably constitute the major portion of mitochondria and plastids. It is especially in the nucleus and nucleolus that they attain their greatest biological importance as the substance of chromosomes. In the submicroscopic structures known as phages or viruses they constitute all or the greater part of the particle[14, 15].

3. Classification

Classifications, as efforts to systematize knowledge in science, are useful. In biology this approach is axiomatic and from such efforts came the theory of evolution. In organic chemistry classification is indispensable. It is therefore not surprising that in the early days of biochemistry proteins were classified, and, indeed, national committees were appointed to standardize the nomenclature in 1907. At that time little was known about proteins and the most distinctive properties were differences in solubility, coagulability, and the presence or absence of a "prosthetic" group as distinct from that portion made up of amino acids. The differences between the two classifications proposed in 1907 were minor and have no significance today. These classifications are now used to a limited degree because of the many exceptions which are known. They are reproduced below. Proteins are so classified because, basically, they are polypeptides made up of α-amino acids. But when does a polypeptide become a protein with increasing size of particle? There is no authoritative answer to this question but general practice places it at a molecular weight of about 5000, which includes the simplest native group, the protamines, but excludes, for example, oxytocin and vasopressin, the hormones of the posterior pituitary gland, as polypeptides.

A subdivision of proteins[16] into simple and conjugated was proposed in 1907 on the basis of the following definitions, (1) simple proteins are those which yield only α-amino acids or their derivatives on hydrolysis; (2) conjugated proteins are those which contain a protein molecule united to some other molecule or molecules otherwise than as a salt. The definition of a conjugated protein should now be modified to read that the other or "prosthetic" molecule be organic in character and possibly in combination with the protein moiety as a salt. The French use the terms holoproteins and heteroproteins to distinguish these main subdivisions.

The distinctive physical and chemical characteristics of these groups will now be described.

Simple proteins	Conjugated proteins
Protamines	Phosphoproteins
Histones	Mucoproteins (glycoproteins)
Albumins	Chromoproteins (metalloproteins)
Globulins	Nucleoproteins
Prolamins (alcohol-soluble)	Lipoproteins
Glutelins	
Scleroproteins (albuminoids)	

(a) Simple proteins

(i) Protamines

These are the simplest native proteins. They occur in mature spermatozoa and have been isolated mainly from fish sperm. The first to be recognized was discovered by Miescher in 1874 in the spermatozoa of the salmon and named by him *protamin*[17]. Kossel[18] and his collaborators carried out many investigations of this group. The protamines are distinctive for their low molecular weights of about 5000, a limited variety of amino acids with a preponderance of the basic ones, especially arginine. These properties account for their relatively high value of nitrogen (18–25 %), their basic isoelectric points (pH 10–12) and the absence of any sulfur. They are moderately soluble in water and ammonia and basic in character but difficult to prepare as the free base. They form insoluble sulfates and chloroplatinates which are frequently crystalline. They are not coagulable by heat. Because of their basicity they form protein–protein compounds and combine with nucleic acids to form nucleoproteins[19]. This property has found practical application in the form of protamine insulinate for which salmine, scombrine, clupeine, and cyclopterine have been used as they form insoluble compounds with insulin. They are hydrolyzed by trypsin, trypsin-kinase, cathepsin, and papain but not by pepsin. They dissociate in concentrated aqueous salt solutions.

Salmine and clupeine have been most thoroughly studied but the most recent observations indicate heterogeneity in the preparations[20]. The distribution of amino acids as percentages of the total protein is as follows.

	Ala	Arg	Gly	Ileu	Pro	Ser	Thr	Val
Salmine	1.5	88.4	3.3	1.2	7.9	7.0	0.0	4.1
Clupeine	4.7	87.1	0 0	1.0	8.2	3.4	1.9	3.6

The following protamines have been isolated after liberation from their respective nucleoproteins:

clupeine from the herring, *Clupea harengus*, and *C. pallasii*,
cyclopterine from *Cyclopterus lumpus*, and *Salmo iridens*,
cyprinine from the carp, *Cyprinus carpio*,
galline from the cockerel, *Gallus domesticus*,
percine from the perch, *Perca flavescens*, and the pike, *Stizostedion vitreum*,
salmine from the salmon, *Salmo salar*, and other species,
sardinine from the sardine, *Sardinia caerulea*,
scombrine from the mackerel, *Scomber scomber*, and *S. japonicus*,
sturine from the sturgeon, *Acipenser sturio*.

Numerous other protamines have been prepared and named but their individuality has not yet been established.

(ii) Histones

The isolation of a protein from the nuclei of the erythrocytes of the goose led Kossel in 1884 to differentiate this group[21]. The few proteins in it are rather similar to the protamines but with a larger variety of amino acids. They also contain a high concentration of basic amino acids and are therefore basic in character. They contain no tryptophan and little cystine or methionine. Present indications are that they occur in the nuclei of the somatic cells of most organisms, probably combined with nucleic acid as nucleoproteins[22]. They are soluble in water and dilute acids but insoluble in dilute ammonia. In neutral saturated solutions of ammonium chloride, sodium chloride, or magnesium sulfate, they are insoluble. They combine readily with other proteins to form sparingly soluble compounds. Unlike protamines and nucleoproteins they are soluble in a solution of mercuric sulfate in dilute sulfuric acid. They are not coagulable by heat. It appears to be established that histones are hydrolyzable with pepsin and trypsin[22]. Physiologically they are closely related to the protamines and a search for them in tissues other than those examined at present seems definitely desirable. Stedman and Stedman[23] consider them to be cell-specific, to act as inhibitors capable of suppressing the activities of specific groups of genes, and to be in intimate relationship within the chromosome. Those which have been best characterized are: histone of nucleated erythrocytes, histones of thymus and of lymphocytes, histone from liver, histones in haemoglobins.

It would seem simpler to designate these histones by the use of a prefix indicative of their origin, such as erythrocytohistone, thymohistone, hepatohistone, etc. Globin has been the most carefully studied of the histones. It was first prepared from crystalline haemoglobin by Preyer[24] in 1868. Other histones have been obtained in crude form from spermatozoa of fish and echinoderms. The so-called haptoglobins of blood, discovered by Polonovski and Jayle[25] which combine with haemoglobin and exhibit peroxidase activity, appear to contain carbohydrate and to belong to the mucoproteins.

(iii) Albumins

These proteins are typically soluble in water and dilute saline solutions. They are precipitable by saturation with ammonium sulfate. They are coagulable by heat and other agents which bring about denaturation. Most have been obtained in crystalline form. They are rather widely distributed and are found in the interstitial fluids of animals, such as blood and lymph, in muscle, in eggs, in milk, and in the seeds of angiosperms, especially of grains and legumes. The distribution of constituent amino acids includes all eighteen of the commoner ones, although glycine is sometimes low. In addition carbohydrate has been detected in ovalbumin as a polysaccharide which contains mannose, glucosamine, and possibly other constituents[26]. It accounts for less than 5 % of the molecule and may still be shown to be due to contaminating mucoprotein. Likewise a fraction has been separated from serum albumin which contained carbohydrate[27]. Earlier workers had detected the presence of glucosamine, mannose, and galactose in serum albumin.

The albumins which have been most carefully characterized are ovalbumin and conalbumin of egg white, α-lactalbumin, the serum albumins, leucosin of cereals, myoalbumin and the myogens of muscle of which some behave as enzymes.

(iv) Globulins

This is a large and important group which is widely distributed in plants and animals. These proteins resemble the albumins in some respects. They are generally insoluble in water although a few, designated as pseudo-globulins, are soluble. They may all be dissolved in dilute saline solutions and precipitated at high concentrations of inorganic salts, such as near to or at saturation of sodium chloride or sodium sulfate or magnesium sulfate, and at about half-saturation of ammonium sulfate. They are coagulable by heat and other denaturing agents. Many, especially those of plant origin, have been obtained in crystalline form. They contain all of the common amino acids and are relatively rich in the dicarboxylic acids, aspartic and glutamic. In animals they occur in interstitial fluids such as blood, lymph and seminal fluid, in muscle, in eggs, in milk, in the lens of the eye, and perhaps in all cytoplasm. In plants they are deposited as reserve protein in nuts and seeds. In plasma some are associated with lipid as lipoproteins. Several appear to contain carbohydrate.

Some well recognized globulins in plants are arachin and conarachin of the peanut, edestin of hempseed, excelsin of the Brazil nut, legumin and vicilin of the common pea, phaesolin of beans, and amandin of almonds. In animals there are fibrinogen and other globulins of blood plasma and lymph, the ovoglobulins and lysozyme of avian egg white and the livetins of the yolk, the myosins of muscle, the α-and β-crystallins of the ocular lens of vertebrates, β-lactoglobulin and the "immune" globulins of milk and the Bence-Jones proteins associated with some pathological states such as *myelomatosis*.

On cooling sera from some pathological states a deposit of protein may form as crystals, precipitate or gel. These proteins have been designated as cryoglobulins. They differ widely in properties and are considered to be abnormal proteins although somewhat similar to normal γ-globulins[28]. Another group of proteins has been designated as macroglobulins because of their relatively large molecular weights (> 160,000) and sedimentation constants (> 7 S). They are generally of the γ-globulin type and precipitable from serum by dilution.

(v) *Prolamins*

This group is characterized by their solubility in the lower aliphatic carbinols, especially ethanol, and in some aromatic carbinols as phenol, *p*-cresol, and benzyl alcohol. They have been detected only in the seeds of the grasses; they were first recognized in wheat by Taddei in 1819 and named by Osborne[29]. They are also known as the alcohol-soluble proteins and as gliadins. They contain a relatively high proportion of glutamic acid, proline and ammonia as the amide radical in asparagine and glutamine. They are deficient in lysine and contain few free α-amino or carboxyl radicals. The prolamins, as isolated, are readily soluble in 50–90 % of aqueous ethanol with maximum at about 70 %. They also exhibit slight solubility in buffer solutions such as acetate and salicylate, in urea and in some detergents. They are usually isolated as "gluten" in association with a glutelin. Whether gluten is a mixture or a true chemical compound of these two proteins is not yet established[30]. All preparations of prolamins have shown marked polydispersity on sedimentation and in electrophoresis. The principal prolamins are gliadin from wheat, secalin from rye, hordein from barley, zein from corn, and kafirin from sorghum.

(vi) *Glutelins*

These proteins are present in the seeds of dicotyledonous plants. They are characteristically soluble in dilute acids and alkalis but insoluble in neutral saline solutions. They occur in largest amount in the grains of cereals. They are comparatively rich in the amino acids arginine, proline and glutamic acid. By modern criteria of purity the glutelins are heterogeneous and poorly characterized. Progressive extraction of gluten with solvents has not proved the existence of distinct proteins. The subject and the pertinent literature have been discussed critically by McCalla[31] who was convinced that prolamins and glutelins have no separate existence in plants. Those proteins of this group which have been isolated and studied are glutenin of wheat, zeanin of corn, hordenin of barley, oryzenin of rice, secalinin of rye, and avenin of oats.

(vii) Scleroproteins

This is a large and important group which occurs mostly in ectodermal and mesodermal tissues of animals. They are also known as albuminoids but this is a peculiarly unsuitable name in that they are definitely not albumin-like. Their function is architectonic in character and they are highly resistant to all ordinary solvents and most enzymes. They occur in skin, hair, horn, hoofs, nails, quills, feathers, turtle scutes, pelican excrescences, cartilage, bone, ligaments, tendons, and connective tissues generally, in silk, in egg casings, in corals, and in sponges. They are essentially fibrous proteins and exhibit characteristic X-ray diffraction patterns which permit them to be classified as at least partially crystalline. They are subdivided into two main classes, keratins and collagens, which differ sharply in chemical reactivity and content of amino acids.

The keratins are found in epidermal structures as listed above, although neurokeratin occurs in nerve tissue as the frame of the sheath. Block and Vickery[32] suggested subdivision of the keratins into eukeratins and pseudokeratins. Eukeratins may be defined as the keratins insoluble in the conventional solvents, resistant to hydrolysis by pepsin and trypsin, relatively rich in cystine and with the basic amino acids, histidine, lysine, and arginine, in the ratio of about 1:4:12. Most of the keratins are included in this subgroup. Pseudokeratins are keratin-like proteins with relatively greater solubility, less resistance to enzymic hydrolysis, with much less cystine and with histidine, lysine and arginine in a ratio of about 1:2:3. This group would include the keratins of nerve tissue, horse burrs, whale baleen, pelican excrescences, and egg casings[33]. Keratins may be solubilized by treatment with a reducing agent, such as sodium or calcium sulfide or bisulfite, thioglycol, thioglycollic or thiolactic acids. The product, keratein, contains many more sulfhydryl radicals.

The collagens occur in the skin of many animals, in scales, fins, and swim bladders of fishes, in the byssus threads of molluscs, in connective tissue, in cartilage, and in bone[34]. While mostly insoluble in neutral aqueous solvents, collagen may be dissolved at ordinary temperature in acidic buffer solutions which contain acetic, lactic, tartaric or citric acid at pH about 3–4, and recovered as typical microscopic cross-striated fibers. Collagen may also be solubilized and degraded by prolonged treatment with hot water when gelatin is formed. The distribution of amino acids is rather characteristic in the large amounts of glycine, alanine, proline, and hydroxyproline that are present. Hydroxyproline is distinctive of collagen in animal proteins. While collagens are relatively resistant to alimentary hydrolysis, a specific collagenase is known. The collagen from fish skin and swim bladder is known as ichthyocol. Elastin in the yellow fibers of connective tissue is so similar in distribution and properties that it may be classified as a collagen. Gelatin must be regarded as a product of degradation of collagen.

Additional scleroproteins are fibroin and sericin of silk, spongins of sponges, and gorgonins of corals. They have been known for many years but their classification is uncertain. In many properties they resemble collagens. They contain large amounts of glycine, alanine, serine and tyrosine. Spongins and gorgonins are remarkable for their contents of iodotyrosine and bromotyrosine[35].

(b) Conjugated proteins

(i) Phosphoproteins

Few of this group are known. They contain orthophosphoric acid in ester linkage with the hydroxyamino acids serine and threonine. They occur in milk and eggs, and probably in certain organs such as liver. The only well recognized ones are the caseins of milk and the vitellins of egg yolk. They contain about 1 % of phosphorus which is readily split off from the molecule by alkali or enzymes. They are soluble in saline solvents but insoluble at their isoelectric points. In that they contain phosphoric acid, other than as a salt, the phosphoproteins should be classed as conjugated proteins. The prosthetic group in casein has been isolated as a dipeptide, glutamyl-serine phosphate and also as serine phosphate which probably exists in casein both as the mono- and diester[36].

$$
\begin{array}{ccc}
\mathrm{CH_2 \cdot CH \cdot COOH} & \qquad & \mathrm{CH_2 \cdot CH \cdot COOH} \\
\mid \quad\ \ \mid & & \mid \quad\ \ \mid \\
\mathrm{O} \quad\ \ \mathrm{NH_2} & & \mathrm{O} \quad\ \ \mathrm{NH_2} \\
\mid & & \mid \\
\mathrm{HO-P{=}O} & & \mathrm{HO-P{=}O} \\
\mid & & \mid \\
\mathrm{OH} & & \mathrm{O} \quad\ \ \mathrm{NH_2} \\
& & \mid \quad\ \ \mid \\
& & \mathrm{CH_2 \cdot CH \cdot COOH}
\end{array}
$$

The free ionizable groups of the phosphoric acid make the phosphoproteins relatively strong acids as is shown in electrometric titration. The heterogeneity of ordinary casein has been established by electrophoretic analysis and three components are now recognized, as α, β, and γ caseins. They differ quantitatively in distribution in different mammals and in other ways[37].

References p. 53

The phosphoproteins are coagulable by heat with some decomposition and loss of phosphorus. They are readily hydrolyzed by the alimentary protein-ases, pepsin and trypsin. The distribution of amino acids is not distinctive.

The vitellin of egg yolk has been shown to be heterogeneous and to contain at least two components[38]. They exist however as lipoproteins in the yolk and in the blood of laying hens. In fish eggs the major protein is known as ichthulin. Meecham and Olcott[39] have isolated an unusual phosphoprotein from hen's egg yolk which contained about 10 % of phosphorus and which they named phosvitin. It was remarkably stable to heat within the limits of pH 4–8 at 100°. It contained 33 % of serine. Indirect evidence has sug-gested the presence of protein which contained phosphorus other than as nucleoprotein in various tissues.

(ii) Mucoproteins

The members of this group of conjugated proteins are widely distributed in nature and complex in character. They are described more fully in Vol. 8, Chapter Ib. The class was initially known as the gluco- or glycoproteins to designate a prosthetic group which contained carbohydrate. Meyer[40] has suggested a detailed system of classification which, however, is not entirely satisfactory in that the differences between sub-groups are rather arbitrary: (1) Mucoids ($> 4 \%$ hexosamine), (a) Neutral soluble—α-ovomucoid, sero-mucoid, gonadotropins, blood group substances, (b) Insoluble—β-ovomucoid, (c) Acid soluble—submaxillary mucoid; (2) Glycoproteins ($< 4 \%$ hexos-amine)—α and β of blood plasma.

We now know a range of substances from those with little carbohydrate ($< 4 \%$) to those which are predominantly carbohydrate in composition, such as blood group substances. All mucoproteins contain at least hexosamine in the prosthetic group. Mucopolysaccharides, such as chondroitin and mucoitin sulfuric acids, hyaluronic acid and heparin, which are strongly acid in character, can and do combine in nature with proteins to form salts or esters. These substances probably are the mucins of the older nomenclature. The haptoglobins, referred to under histones, are probably mucoproteins.

Two mucoproteins have been obtained in crystalline form, the α_1-glyco-protein of plasma and a choline esterase.

In general mucoproteins are stable to heat, i.e., non-coagulable, readily soluble in water and saline solvents, and precipitable by acidification, by salting out, or by ethanol. Their solutions are usually highly viscous. Some are not readily precipitated by such agents as trichloroacetic acid or sulfo-salicylic acid.

They occur in skin, cartilage, bone, connective tissue, eggs, blood, urine, several body fluids such as the digestive juices, cerebrospinal, ocular, and synovial fluids, and in pathological cysts of several types, especially ovarian.

The prosthetic group most frequently contains a polysaccharide made up of an acetyl hexosamine, a hexuronic acid or hexose, with or without sulfuric acid as a half-ester. The percentages of carbohydrate in various mucoproteins are as follows,

salivary mucoid	20–25%
gastric mucoid	55%
mucoid from ovarian cyst	50–67%
urinary gonadotropin	19–24%
α-ovomucoid	9–10%
β-ovomucoid	12–15%
α-glycoprotein	29%
β-glycoprotein	17%

The hormones of the anterior pituitary gland, metakentrin and thylakentrin, are probably to be classed as mucoproteins in that they contain both glucosamine and mannose with over 4 % of each.

(iii) Chromoproteins

This class was originally named the haemoglobins. The prosthetic group accounts for the colour which is one of the reasons for the name and sub-division. This property is hardly a sufficient reason for classification and as a result the group is very heterogeneous. It includes the respiratory pigments of vertebrates and invertebrates, the haemoglobins, haemocyanins, haem-erythrins, chlorocruorins, and erythrocruorins, of blood and haemolymph, the myoglobins of muscle, and the cytochromes of many tissues. It includes also a few plant pigments such as the phycocyanins and phycoerythrins of the brown and red algae whose prosthetic group is presently unknown. A substance very similar to, if not identical with, haemoglobin has been isolated from the root nodules of some legumes such as clover and alfalfa. In it also are the pigments of the retina, rhodopsin and porphyropsin, with a carotenoid as prothetic group, and several yellow flavoproteins which contain riboflavin or a derivative. The ferritins of bone marrow, etc., have also been classified as chromoproteins; they contain a high concentration of iron as a basic ferric phosphate. The pigments of hair and skin have been referred to as melanoproteins with melanin as prosthetic group but they have not been adequately studied to be recognized as chemical entities.

Haemoglobin is very widely distributed, not only in the blood of all vertebrates, but also in many species of invertebrates. It is now established that there may be several haemoglobins in the same species and of genetic significance[41]. Haemocyanins occur principally in molluscs, crustaceans, and arachnids. Haemerythrins are found in sipunculien worms; chlorocruorins occur in polychaete annelid worms, and erythrocruorins in other worms and many other invertebrates. Most of the chromoproteins contain a heavy metal, such as iron or copper, which is responsible for their remarkable respiratory character. Many of the chromoproteins have been crystallized[42]. They are highly soluble in water or dilute saline solvents and insoluble in concentrated salt solutions. They possess characteristic absorption spectra over a wide range of wavelength. They are readily denatured and degree of resistance to alkali has been used to differentiate the haemoglobins. The cytochromes are exceptionally stable, while visual purple (rhodopsin) is very unstable. The molecular weights vary widely from about 12,000 for cytochrome c up to several millions for some haemocyanins and erythrocruorins. The protein portion as globin in the haemoglobins has been quite well investigated but many are largely unknown. With the exception of globin as a histone, the distribution of amino acids is not distinctive. This group of proteins is more fully discussed in Vol. 8, Chapter 1c and d.

(iv) Nucleoproteins

While of great biological importance and assumed general distribution in all cells, few if any nucleoproteins have been prepared in a state of homogeneity. They are generally considered to be a compound of nucleic acid in salt linkage with a protamine, histone, or other protein. They occur in cytoplasm and in nuclei where they constitute in greater part the material of the chromosomes. They now appear to form all or a large part of plant and animal viruses and phages. The prosthetic group is a nucleic acid and the investigation of the nucleic acids is one of the most active fields of investigation in biochemistry today (see Vol. 8, Part B).

In the earlier investigations only two types of nucleic acid were recognized, (1) the plant, with D-ribofuranose as carbohydrate, adenine (6-aminopurine) and guanine (2-amino-6-hydroxypurine) as purines, uracil (2,6-dihydroxypyrimidine) and cytosine (2-hydroxy-6-aminopyrimidine) as pyrimidines, and orthophosphoric acid, and (2) the animal, with 2-deoxy-D-ribofuranose as carbohydrate, adenine and guanine as purines, thymine (5-methyluracil) and cytosine as pyrimidines, and orthophosphoric acid. This distinction between plant and animal nucleoproteins is no longer held and it now appears established that the ribose type of nucleic acid (RNA) is usually cytoplasmic in distribution and the deoxyribose type (DNA) is usually nuclear. There are exceptions.

The simplest unit in a nucleic acid is a nucleotide which contains H_3PO_4—pentose—purine or pyrimidine and there are therefore many different mononucleotides. A new pyrimidine, 5-methylcytosine, has been discovered in some deoxyribonucleic acids. In cellular nucleoproteins the nucleic acid constitutes about 40–70 % of the molecule while in viruses it varies between 5 and 40 %. The concentration of P varies between 4 and 6 % and of N between 16.6 and 20.3 %. The value for P in tobacco mosaic virus is only 0.5 %, and in turnip yellow mosaic virus 3.4 %. The particle size is large and may be enormous as in tobacco mosaic virus at about $40 \cdot 10^6$. The following nucleoproteins have been isolated and characterized to a varying degree of completeness—nucleosalmine, nucleoclupeine, nucleotruttine, and nucleosturine as deoxyribose nucleoprotamins; thymonucleohistone, and hepatonucleohistone, as nucleohistones; nucleotropomyosin, tobacco mosaic virus, tomato bushy stunt virus, and turnip yellow mosaic virus as the RNA type, and several bacteriophages. The animal viruses of influenza, vaccinia, and rabbit papilloma are of the DNA type. Pollister[43] suggested that the approximate composition of nucleoprotein of the nucleus of a mammalian liver cell in the interphase of mitosis might be as follows: DNA 9%, RNA 1%, histone 11%, residual protein 14%, non-histone protein 65%. The nucleoproteins are moderately soluble in aqueous saline solvents, e.g., 10% NaCl, and precipitable at varying concentrations of the usual salts and by weak acids. They are readily denatured and dissociated. They may be hydrolyzed by acids or by enzymes, such as ribonuclease or deoxyribonuclease.

(v) Lipoproteins

This is the most recent group to be added to the classification of the proteins. Compounds of proteins with fatty acids have been synthesized which can be regarded as true lipoproteins[44,45]. Lecithin associated with vitellin in egg yolk has been dignified by the name of lecitho- or lipo-vitellin for many years. In a delightful review Chargaff[46] discusses arguments for and against the existence of this group of proteins. Lipoproteins have been claimed to be present in some cellular grana, in mitochondria, in blood serum and some tissue extracts, in egg yolk, in plastids, in bacteria, and in animal viruses.

No lipoprotein has been obtained in crystalline form. As a class the lipoproteins tend to be soluble in aqueous saline solutions (e.g., 10% NaCl) and to be precipitated on dilution. Constancy of composition in various preparations has been notably lacking for most of the lipoproteins. The partial specific volume is low as compared to ordinary proteins and the rate of flotation, rather than sedimentation, is used as a physical constant. The lipid portion is readily removed from the protein by exposure to a critical concentration of methanol or ethanol (7–20%) but not by other common organic solvents.

The prosthetic group in lipovitellin appears to be lecithin, cephalin, and possibly other lipids attached to the phosphoprotein, vitellin. It accounts for about 18–20% of the molecule. Another less well characterized lipoprotein in egg yolk is lipovitellinin which contains 36–41% of lipid.

The lipoproteins of blood plasma have been designated α_1 and β_1. The α_1-lipoprotein was first isolated and classified by Macheboeuf in 1929. It has been shown to contain 30–40 % of lipids as glyceride, phosphatide and cholesterol. Its solubility in water is remarkable because of its high lipid content. The β_1-lipoprotein was obtained in the ethanolic fractionation of plasma proteins. It contained 75 % lipid as cholesterol, phosphatide, and possibly glyceride. The amount of total cholesterol present at more than 30 % is remarkable. The protein moiety in these serum lipoproteins appears to be a globulin.

(c) Other methods of classification

Few enzymes have been mentioned in the classification discussed above although a large number have been crystallized and prepared in a homogeneous state. This is because their investigators have been content to group them on the basis of their enzymic activity rather than as proteins. Two other methods of distinguishing proteins should be mentioned. One is the division of proteins into fibrous or globular from their native state and molecular dimensions. In the former group are placed keratin, myosin, epidermin and fibrin, abbreviated as the k-m-e-f group, all with α- or β-keratin structure from X-ray diffraction patterns. Epidermin is an ill-defined keratin of the epidermal layer of mammalian skin. A second group of fibrous proteins includes fibroin, collagen, and elastin with characteristic diffraction pattern different from that of keratin. Few of the globular proteins are truly spherical as judged by their axial or frictional ratios as shown in Table IX. However, the division is probably useful as distinguishing the proteins with particular dissymmetry[47, 48]. The subject is more fully explained later and in Chapter VII. The frictional ratio f/f_0 should be unity if the molecules are spherical and not hydrated. Hydration tends to diminish the degree of symmetry. From Table IX (p. 50) it is evident that there is no break in the continuity of numerals for either the axial ratio or the frictional ratio from unity to relatively high figures. It may be concluded that fibrous proteins exhibit axial ratios of 10 : 1 or higher and that this is not related to the magnitude of the molecular weight. Thus some viruses are globular and some fibrous in character.

An interesting attempt at the classification of proteins based on similarity of distribution of their amino acids has been made by Bailey[49]. He constructed a series of histograms in which he plotted the proportions of various groups (i.e., number of residues per 10^5 g protein, which total about 900) against the number of proteins considered, which included about twenty representative ones. While a few distinctive conclusions can be drawn on this basis, the general picture supports the similarity of proteins in one or more superimposable distribution curves. It points to the difficulty of classifying proteins solely on the property of their content of amino acids. Nevertheless, it is now accepted that every individual protein has a fixed and probably constant content of amino acids. The process of such an analysis is spoken of as "finger printing" the particular protein. The reasons remain obscure why valine, phenylalanine, proline and tyrosine are always present, why glycine, tryptophan and methionine may be absent, why leucine is usually present in large amount and tryptophan in rather small amount.

There has been a tendency over the past decade to group proteins according to the medium of their occurrence, *e.g.*, milk, egg, serum, plant, or on the basis of some biological activity, *e.g.*, enzymic, toxic, hormonal, respiratory. Such a classification shows no fundamental similarities in physical or chemical properties of the individual proteins. The further development of the older system of classification is to be preferred. Progress in the determination of the sequences of amino acids in more proteins may lead to a truly fundamental classification based on structure in the framework of organic chemistry.

4. General methods of preparation

While many different methods of isolation of individual proteins have been used, only a few properties serve for their separation from their natural environment[50]. Consideration must be given to the labile character of most proteins toward heat, extremes of acidity or alkalinity, contact with organic solvents, and sometimes toward light and mechanical shock. Undue exposure to one or more of these conditions causes denaturation as defined in Chapter IV, and a change in basic molecular configuration, frequently with loss of solubility. The more concentrated the protein in solution the less likely is it to undergo denaturation or dissociation. It has long been recognized that proteins are relatively stable in the solid state. It should be appreciated that the separation of a mixture of proteins is a difficult chemical task in the light of present methods of appraising homogeneity of a protein. The possible complexity of the task is indicated by the fact that in 1948 Cohn listed twenty-five or more proteins in mammalian blood[51].

Occasionally the solubility of a protein decreases with purification as in the case of papain. This may be due to denaturation or to dissociation of protein–protein complexes.

The susceptibility of most proteins to decomposition by bacteria and fungi constitutes a problem that is nearly always present during the procedure of isolation.

(a) Liberation from cellular material

The close association, both chemical and physical, of proteins in their natural habitat with the architecture of the cell, nucleus, plastid, mito-

References p. 53

chondrium, or granule, is only partially understood, especially in muscular and connective tissues. It is not known, for example, whether collagen is combined with mucopolysaccharide in the "ground substance" and what is the actual state of collagen in tendon or cartilage.

The initial problem is comminution of the tissue to be extracted. Blendors of various forms are available with speeds of cutting blades up to 45,000 rev./min. This procedure generates heat and adequate cooling must be maintained. A milder procedure is the use of the Potter-Elvehjem homogenizer[52] or a modification of it[53]. In this apparatus a plastic pestle is caused to rotate in a glass tube, made in different diameters, which is raised and lowered such that the shearing force is exerted at the sides and bottom of the tube in the presence of the material suspended in a liquid. The Wiley cutting mill is particularly useful for dry plant material. Comminution to a powder of > 100 mesh is frequently essential for adequate extraction.

Ordinary and refrigerated centrifuges are invaluable tools in the preparation of proteins because the slimy character of many precipitates often defies ordinary filtration. Clarification is sometimes possible only at relatively high speeds. For some preparations, such as the proteins of egg yolk, a Sharples centrifuge is necessary.

The technique of freeze-drying is frequently employed. It is based on the principle of evaporation of water from the frozen state *in vacuo* such that the latent heat of vaporization keeps the temperature low until the solute becomes a solid.

(b) Effect of temperature

In general, temperature should be kept low because many proteins are denatured over 60°. Some proteins, such as casein, insulin, protamines and mucoids, are stable at higher temperatures and this property permits the removal of more readily coagulable ones. A few, like cod ichthyocol and many proteins of muscle, are unstable even at 20°, although the great majority of proteins may be kept for long periods at 20°. When in contact with ethanol a temperature below 0° is necessary, as in the fractionation of plasma proteins. The seed globulins, like edestin, may be crystallized by the simple procedure of preparing a concentrated solution by extraction of the crushed seeds with 10 % of sodium chloride at 65° and cooling to 4° with or without dilution.

(c) Effect of hydrogen ion concentration

The isoelectric point of many proteins is used in their separation because it is the point of minimum solubility and sometimes of complete insolubility. Casein is thus precipitated from skim milk at pH 4.8. In general, exposure to acidity under pH 4 or to alkalinity over pH 9 is undesirable. Frequently proteins are separated by adjustment of the pH of their solutions in the presence of a neutral salt. The commercial preparation of crystalline insulin is a good example of the application of this principle. Haemoglobin is also easily obtained in crystalline form in this manner.

(d) Extraction with aqueous solvents

This is the commonest method of separation and it is based on the use of varying concentrations of such neutral inorganic salts as sodium chloride, sodium sulfate, sodium sulfite, sodium thiosulfate, potassium phosphate, sodium citrate, magnesium sulfate, or ammonium sulfate. Fractionation with ammonium sulfate was apparently first used by Méhu[54] in 1878 and it is still one of the most frequently used salts because of its great solubility in water. It has the disadvantage that determination of total nitrogen cannot be used to follow the separation. The curve of solubility *vs.* ionic strength indicates in its first part the effect of "salting in" and in its second part that of "salting out". It is possible to separate proteins in both portions. Control of the pH and the temperature of the solution is necessary. The proteins of egg white, milk whey, blood serum, and many other fluids are susceptible to fractionation by this method. Globulins are removed from diluted egg white at half saturation of ammonium sulfate after which adjustment of the pH to 4.6 causes ovalbumin to crystallize. This is also true for serum albumin. The crude fractionation of plasma proteins with ammonium sulfate is indicated in Table I in terms of molality and degree of saturation[55]

TABLE I

FRACTIONATION OF PLASMA PROTEINS WITH AMMONIUM SULFATE

Conc. of $(NH_4)_2SO_4$		Nature of precipitate
M	Saturation	
1.01	0.25	fibrinogen
1.39	0.34	largely γ-globulin
1.64	0.40	α-, β-, and γ-globulins
2.05	0.50	α- and β-globulins
2.57	0.62	albumin
2.80	0.68	albumin, hemocuprein, mucoprotein, etc.

at 20° and pH 7. Sodium sulfate at 37° has also been used for this purpose in clinical application with separation of γ-globulin at 13.5 %, β-globulin at 17.4 %, α-globulin at 21.5 %, and serum albumin is left in solution.

References p. 53

Jager et al.[56] compared the electrophoretic patterns of such precipitates obtained with six different salting-out procedures and concluded that magnesium sulfate was the most efficient, but in no case could the result be considered quantitative. In a series of papers between 1944 and 1951 Derrien and his co-workers[57] have attempted similar close fractionations by salting out with potassium phosphates at 24° and pH 6.5 in many steps.

Crystalline chymotrypsin and trypsin were prepared from bovine pancreas by the use of ammonium sulfate at different concentrations and acidities[58]. The proteins of milk are usually fractionated in this manner as in the preparation of crystalline α-lactalbumin and β-lactoglobulin and the proteins of muscle have been thus separated into many crystalline albumins and globulins.

(e) Use of organic solvents

Ethanol at −5° can serve to fractionate the proteins of blood plasma and this method was used in bulk to provide material for intravenous use during World War II. The conditions for pH and concentration of ethanol are given in Table II with fibrinogen distinguished as φ-globulin[59]. It is apparent that complete separation of single proteins is not achieved in such initial treat-

TABLE II

DISTRIBUTION OF PLASMA PROTEINS IN ETHANOLIC FRACTIONATION

Fraction	pH	Ethanol (M)	Percentage distribution in fractions				
			Albumin	Globulins			
				α	β	ø	γ
I	7.2	0.027	7	8	15	61	9
2 + 3	6.8	0.091	4	6	48	5	37
4−1	5.2	0.062	0	88	10	0	2
4−4	5.8	0.163	16	47	38	0	0
5	4.8	0.163	95	4	1	0	0

ment. In England a similar fractionation was carried out with ether[60]. Ethanol is also used in the preparation of some pituitary hormones, such as prolactin and somatotropin. The crystallization of urease was accomplished by Sumner[6] by extracting jack beans with aqueous acetone (31.6 %) at 22° and cooling to 2°. Acetone is also used in the preparation of crystalline pepsin, and of globin.

Prolamins are extracted from grains with 70 % aqueous ethanol or with 60 % propanol at 20°. The remaining glutelins may be dissolved in 60 % isopropanol which contains 0.2 % sodium bisulfite. Wheat glutin may also be solubilized at 60° with 4 M dimethylformamide. The use of other organic solvents, such as formamide, dioxane, phenol, hydrazine, formic acid, dichloroacetic acid, ethylenediamine, etc., is very limited because of the great danger of degrading the protein.

(f) Dialysis

The separation of inorganic salts from proteins by the use of semi-permeable membranes has been used ever since Thomas Graham introduced the concept of colloids in 1854. Various types of membrane have been employed for this purpose from parchment to cellophane. For a long time films of cellulose nitrate or acetate were prepared with different permeabilities. Sörensen and Höyrup[61] devised an apparatus for this purpose which made use of thicker and stronger membranes and which was operated in a vacuum to permit concentration of the protein within the membrane. Commercial cellophane of different thicknesses has now replaced all other membranes. Sometimes unwarranted faith is placed in the uniformity of behavior of this commercial product. It is the current concept that mechanical stirring of the inner or outer fluid, or rotation of the whole bag, accelerates dialysis. Ogston[62] has questioned the efficacy of this procedure and placed it at about a two-fold increase. Increase in the viscosity of the inner fluid tends to decrease the rate of dialysis. When possible, frequent changes of the external fluid are desirable to increase the speed of dialysis. Continuous circulation of the inner fluid through narrow tubing or through a series of compartments separated by flat membranes is also used. By the slow removal of electrolytes some proteins such as acid-soluble collagen may be caused to crystallize.

Electrolytes may be removed more completely by electrodialysis when an apparatus of three compartments is used with electrodes of carbon plates in the two outer chambers. A current is passed through the central one which contains the protein. Adequate circulation of water through the outer compartments is necessary to prevent overheating.

(g) Adsorption

Up to the present time comparatively few proteins have been prepared by the use of adsorbants[50]. Lysozyme may be separated from other proteins in egg white by adsorption on bentonite and elution with aqueous pyridine. Ribonuclease has also been prepared by this technique. Salmine has been purified by passage through a column of Dowex 2 resin. Likewise a separation of the two components of degradation of acid-soluble collagen can be achieved on carboxymethyl cellulose at 37°. The use of ion-exchange resins has been of importance in the purification of pituitary hormones such as adrenocorticotropin (ACTH). Adsorption on a column of a resin or other substance may thus serve the purpose of removing impurities or of selective removal of the desired protein with its later elution from the column. There is some danger of denaturation of the protein by this procedure. The method has been used very extensively in the examination of hydrolytic products, both peptides and amino acids. The method deserves more extensive investigation as applied to proteins. Media most frequently used are alumina gel, calcium phosphate gel, diatomaceous earth, ferric hydroxide, benzoic acid, starch, and different forms of cellulose[63].

(h) Electrophoresis

The possibility of separating proteins on the basis of different mobilities in electrophoresis has been explored and applied successfully to several systems both by the moving boundary and zonal gradient methods. Different forms of apparatus are available commercially. The medium may be paper, glass beads, or a special electrophoretic cell for the removal of fractions[50]. In a mixture of several proteins immobilization of one is achieved by electrophoresis at its isoelectric point and separation from others is thus made feasible. Electrophoretic methods are much simpler than other methods of fractionation but the quantities made available tend to be smaller.

(i) Counter-current distribution

While this principle has been applied very successfully to many mixtures, it has not been used with many proteins. Crystalline insulin has been purified in this manner. Partition is achieved in a two-phase liquid–liquid system of immiscible solvents, such as an aqueous buffer and butanol or ethyl acetate. Equilibrium is established by shaking in a special apparatus of ingenious design on the basis of partition ratios. Craig's method, however, depends upon performing a large number of successive extractions and determining the distribution of the components of the mixture during fractionation[50, 64]. This method has been particularly useful in the separation of peptides, as for the hormones of the posterior pituitary gland.

(j) Use of enzymes

In a few cases digestion of a tissue either by autolysis or by added proteolytic enzymes facilitates the extraction of a specific protein which is itself resistant to such hydrolysis. This applies particularly to the insoluble scleroproteins such as the eukeratins. It has also been used in the isolation of crystalline enzymes from yeast.

(k) Specific precipitants

In a few instances a protein may be precipitated directly from solution as an insoluble compound. This is possible for the basic protamines as sulfate, picrate, flavianate, or chloroplatinate. The use of metallic cations such as zinc, mercury, iron, and calcium, in the separation of proteins is an interesting development[65]. The fractionation of plasma proteins is facilitated by conversion to their zinc salts because of the wider range of solubilities, especially in aqueous ethanol. Mercury reacts with sulfhydryl groups while zinc combines with imidazole radicals. Iron is bound specifically to several proteins and has been used to precipitate the proteins of whey. Uranyl acetate facilitates the preparation of pure α_1- and γ-globulins from human serum.

5. Criteria of purity

The definition of purity or homogeneity as applied to proteins is difficult because of their diverse nature. Pirie[66] postulated that the preparation should contain particles which were identical in size, chemical composition, and physical properties, and, in those proteins with biological activity, each particle should carry such activity in undiminished degree as in the native state. This is the definition of an ideal state. It cannot be applied to insoluble proteins, such as many of the scleroproteins which require chemical modification to be solubilized and examined. It disregards the phenomenon of association or dissociation, as in the case of insulin which may exist as dimer, trimer or tetramer, and which may otherwise conform to the definition. The polymer thus provides a real problem in considering homogeneity of a protein.

The usual criteria of purity of organic compounds, such as the melting point, are not applicable to proteins. Crystalline insulin is the only protein to give a sharp melting point (233° with decomposition). Some physical constants such as density, specific refractive increment, partial specific volume, and optical rotation, are of limited value. Even crystalline form has been shown many times to be a fallacious criterion of purity, as with haemoglobin, ovalbumin, serum albumin, pepsin, and β-lactoglobulin, all of which were considered homogeneous until recently.

The isoelectric point represents a special physico-chemical constant of value but one which requires careful definition as to ionic concentration of solvent. As amino acids exhibit isoelectric points (pI), so do proteins. When one amino and one carboxyl group are present in the molecule of an amino acid the value for pI varies between 5.68 and 6.90. With two carboxyl radicals it is about 3 and with one or more basic groups it varies between 7.59 and 10.76. The presence of hydroxyl, sulfhydryl, amide, iodo, or other

TABLE III

ISOELECTRIC POINTS OF VARIOUS PROTEINS

Protein	pI	$\Gamma/2$	Protein	pI	$\Gamma/2$
Protamines			*Phosphoproteins*		
Salmine	12.1		α-Casein	4.0–4.1	0.10
Clupeine	12.1		β-Casein	4.5	0.10
Sturine	11.71		γ-Casein	5.8–6.0	0.05
Histones			*Mucoproteins*		
Thymohistone	10.8		α-Ovomucoid	3.83–4.41	
Globin (human)	7.5	0.10	α_1-Mucoprotein	1.8–2.7	
			Vitellomucoid	5.5	
Albumins			Urinary gonadotropin	3.2–3.3	
Ovalbumin	4.59	0.10	Lysozyme	11.0–11.2	0.01
	4.71	0.01			
Conalbumin	6.8	0.10	*Chromoproteins*		
	7.1	0.01	Myoglobin	6.99	
Serum albumin	4.7–4.9	0.02	Haemoglobin (human)	7.07	
Myoalbumin	3.5		Haemoglobin (hen)	7.23	
Myogen A	6.3		Haemoglobin (horse)	6.92	
			Haemocyanins	4.6–6.4	
Globulins			Haemerythrin	5.60	
β-Lactoglobulin	5.1–5.3	0.10	Chlorocruorin	4.3–4.5	
	4.7–5.1	0.01	Erythrocruorins	4.6–6.2	
Livetin	4.8–5.0		Cytochrome c	9.8–10.1	
γ_1-Globulin (human)	5.8	0.10	Rhodopsin	4.47–4.57	
	6.6	0.01			
γ_2-Globulin (human)	7.3	0.10	*Lipoproteins*		
	8.2	0.01	Thromboplastin	5.2	
Myosin A	5.2–5.5		α_1-Lipoprotein	5.5	
Tropomyosin	5.1		β_1-Lipoprotein	5.4	
Thyroglobulin	4.58		β-Lipovitellin	5.9	
Siderophilin	5.9				
Fetuin	3.4–3.5		*Nucleoproteins*		
Fibrinogen	5.5–5.8		Thymonucleohistone	*ca.* 4	
α-Crystallin	4.8		Bushy stunt virus	4.11	0.02
β-Crystallin	6.0		Turnip yellow virus	3.75	
Arachin	5.1		Vaccinia virus	5.3	
Conarachin	3.9				
			Unclassified		
Scleroproteins			Somatotropin	6.85	
Keratins	3.7–5.0		Prolactin	5.73	
Keratein	4.6–4.7		Insulin	5.35	
Collagen	6.6–6.8		Pepsin	*ca.* 1.0	
Ichthyocol	4.8–5.2				
Gelatin	4.7–5.0				

pI = Isoelectric point or range.

$\Gamma/2$ = Ionic strength of solvent (buffer).

radicals affects the value obtained. The isoelectric point may be defined as the pH at which the average net electrical charge of the molecule is zero. Hardy defined it as the pH of a buffer of specified composition in which no net migration of the protein is produced in electrophoresis. The isoelectric point may, however, be determined experimentally in several ways as by electrophoresis, titration, diffusion, solubility, etc. As measured by electrophoretic mobility human γ_1-globulin exhibits a value for pI of 5.8 in buffer solution with $\Gamma/2 = 0.1$ and 6.6 for a solution with $\Gamma/2 = 0.01$. The pI of ovalbumin is 4.59 in sodium acetate ($\Gamma/2 = 0.10$) and 4.71 when $\Gamma/2 = 0.01$. The experimental conditions must therefore be considered in comparing the data in Table III which have been taken from many sources. Marked variation between groups is evident and differences between proteins from different species of animals is indicated. As a physical constant, however, the value of pI cannot serve as a sensitive criterion of purity. Lysozyme is a peculiar anomaly in the mucoproteins as is cytochrome c in the chromoproteins.

The most successful physico-chemical procedures as criteria of purity have been those of electrophoresis, ultracentrifugation, solubility in the presence of excess of the solid phase, and chromatography. No single physico-chemical constant is sufficient in itself to establish homogeneity. The biochemist has been deceived too frequently in the past by claims of individuality which later have proved false, as with serum albumin and β-lactoglobulin.

Crystallinity of a protein has been considered a criterion of purity by chemists in the past, but it is now well recognized that this property is unsatisfactory in this respect as applied to proteins. It serves frequently to separate one protein from another but not to remove traces of impurity. The phenomena of mixed crystals or solid solutions enter into the situation. Isomorphism is also encountered as in the chromoproteins. At times it becomes difficult even to differentiate between the amorphous and the crystalline states, as with collagen, myosin, and tobacco mosaic virus. From evidence of X-ray diffraction both may exist in the same molecular structure in that part of the main chain may conform to a crystalline lattice and part may not.

Electrophoretic analysis has contributed much in demonstrating heterogeneity in proteins. The physical separation of small quantities of individual proteins has been accomplished by this method from a mixture, otherwise difficult to fractionate. Fig. 1 shows examples of such separation with lactalbumin and casein. In different buffers at different pH levels and ionic concentrations, preparations such as crystalline ovalbumin, serum albumin, β-lactoglobulin, casein and pepsin have been shown to consist of two or more components. Techniques employed are described in Chapter III. Electrophoresis has furnished a very useful tool by which to judge the efficacy of

References p. 53

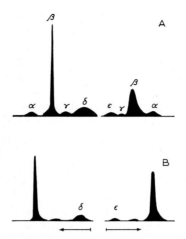

Fig. 1A. Electrophoretic pattern of crude β-casein in barbiturate–chloride buffer of ionic strength 0.1 and pH 7.78 after 3.5 h at 4.5 V/cm. The δ and ε are the starting stationary boundaries. At least two impurities are indicated as α and γ. (From R. C. Warner, *J. Am. Chem. Soc.*, 66 (1944) 1725, by courtesy of the American Chemical Society.)
Fig. 1B. Electrophoretic pattern of crystalline lactalbumin in barbiturate–chloride buffer of ionic strength 0.1 and pH 8.4 after 3 h. A trace of impurity is visible. (From B. D. Polis, H. W. Shmukler and J. H. Custer, *J. Biol. Chem.*, 187 (1950) 349 by permission.)

fractionation as for plasma proteins. With care this method is capable of detecting a few tenths of a per cent of an impurity which has a mobility different from the major component. When the mobility of the impurity is close to that of the major component the method is not as sensitive, and several per cent may be present without being detected. Proteins possessing the same density of ionic charge cannot be separated by this method. The technique of reversible spreading with the determination of the heterogeneity constant is an additional measure of homogeneity in the electrophoretic method[67]. Diffusion or electrophoresis in an agar gel which contains the antibody to the protein under examination provides a very sensitive means of testing the homogeneity of material and the number of components present. Specific precipitates form at the line of reaction as discs or zones. The method was proposed by Oudin and by Ouchterlony[68].

The sedimentation diagram in the ultracentrifuge has been of great value as a criterion of homogeneity. The sedimentation velocity depends on density, size and shape of particle and is described in Chapter VI. Fig. 2 is an example of heterogeneity in the acid-soluble collagen from the cod. Proteins which have approximately the same particle weight and symmetry are not distinguishable by this method. Mixtures containing many proteins,

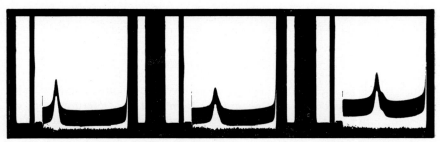

Fig. 2. Ultracentrifugal pattern of collagen from cod skin at a concentration of 0.64% dissolved in 0.1 M citrate buffer of pH 3.3. The presence of a second component is evident as a shoulder in the third photograph after 3.5 h at a speed of 59,780 rev./min.

such as plasma from blood or muscle, can be only partially resolved. Under favourable conditions, it is possible to detect impurities in a preparation in which these comprise 2–3% of the major component. Sedimentation should be carried out at different levels of pH and compared with ordinary spreading by diffusion.

The solubility test provides one of the best criteria of purity of a protein and may distinguish between optical isomers. It involves the measurement of the equilibrium of a substance between two phases, —the liquid solution and the solid itself. The method requires the determination of the quantity of protein dissolved in a constant volume of buffered solvent at constant pressure and temperature, preferably 0–5°, as the total amount of protein only is increased and when the system is in a state of equilibrium. Accuracy is improved by the choice of a solvent which dissolves enough of the material to permit of determination in small volume, (*e.g.*, 0.01–0.1%). A graph with amounts of protein N in solution as ordinates and amounts of total N in the suspension as abscissae is constructed. Before the point of saturation there should be a straight line with unit slope and another straight

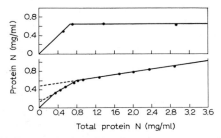

Fig. 3. Solubility diagrams of pure "A" pepsin (upper) and of crystalline pepsin prepared from Cudahy pepsin (lower) in half-saturated magnesium sulfate in 0.05 M acetate buffer, pH 4.6 at 22°. Ordinates: protein N in solution. Abscissae: total protein N in the mixture. (From J. H. Northrop, M. Kunitz and R. M. Herriott, *Crystalline Enzymes*, 2nd ed., Columbia University Press, 1948 by permission.)

line with zero slope after the appearance of a solid phase if a single pure protein is present (Fig. 3). This is an excellent criterion of purity[58].

(a) Chemical analysis

While elementary analysis is regularly employed, the figures obtained only serve to distinguish one group of proteins from another. Determinations of nitrogen, sulfur and phosphorus have been of greatest value. Amino acid analysis is a common method of distinguishing between proteins at present. Newer methods, devised since 1945 and based on chromatographic separation, have improved the sensitivity and the rapidity of estimation[69]. Methods for the determination of carbohydrate in proteins are still far from satisfactory, with the possible exception of glucosamine.

A new form of amino acid analysis aims at the determination of free amino (N-terminal) and carboxyl (C-terminal) end groups in peptide chains[70]. It is based on a reaction of such free amino groups with 1-fluoro-2,4-dinitrobenzene or phenyl isothiocyanate. The labeled protein is then hydrolyzed and the hydrolysate is chromatographed to detect the amino acids which contain the label. Equivalent methods to determine the free carboxyl groups have not yet been developed. However, a method has been proposed which employs crystalline carboxypeptidase. This enzyme specifically attacks C-terminal peptide bonds and the liberated amino acid must then be identified chromatographically. Another method of identification is by reduction to β-amino carbinols with lithium aluminium hydride. After hydrolysis the amino carbinol is extracted with ether and identified chromatographically. These methods have been valuable in distinguishing between insulins from different species and in elucidating the sequence of amino acids in small peptides after the partial hydrolysis of some proteins[71].

(b) Biological methods

A great variety of biological methods may be used with those proteins which have specific biological activity such as viruses, hormones, and enzymes. Constant biological activity may be a very important criterion of purity if the method of assay is sufficiently accurate, but many are not. Great variations in the latter are evident as for the pituitary hormones. Biological methods serve, however, admirably in initial chemical separation. Specificity of a preparation as to species of origin is observed in certain instances, while biological activity may be associated equally with the original substance and its degradation product as in the case of secretin. The most generally used method requires the development of a specific antibody in a suitable animal, such as the rabbit, and the use of its serum for "precipitin" reactions with the antigen. Remarkable specificity can thus be detected but this degree of specificity cannot, however, be achieved with all groups of proteins.

(c) Chemical individuality

A question of fundamental importance in protein chemistry may now be raised. Does a simple protein always possess the same amino acids in exactly the same stereoisomeric arrangement? The answer from our knowledge of insulin as the most completely described protein at present would be in the affirmative. Specificity as to species of origin is accounted for by minor differences in distribution of amino acids. Ogston has boldly set down that the main objective of research of the biochemist in the field of proteins is to discover the biosynthesis and *raison d'être* of proteins in chemical terms. He suggests that this may be achieved by closer specification for the purity and homogeneity of a chemical individual which would include the composition and structure, both physical and chemical, and a correlation with the biological activity. This conception is constructed on the belief that proteins *can* be obtained in a chemically pure state and *are* chemical individuals. Colvin, Smith and Cook[73] have reviewed the major methods of testing homogeneity and concluded in 1954 that the present evidence does not justify the acceptance of any preparation yet achieved as strictly homogeneous. They develop the conception of microheterogeneity and suggest that polydispersity may be a natural phenomenon in the biosynthesis of proteins. Microheterogeneity is defined as a condition in which there is experimental evidence for one or more minor differences between individual protein molecules of a preparation extending well beyond the time of the experiment. This would be a new conception in chemistry as it is an old one in biology. A *species* of protein would permit of some individual variation within the definition of the species, but it would still be, theoretically at least, susceptible of fractionation. Physical constants would thus be legitimately within $\pm$ limitations. This point of view postulates a protein as a population of closely related, but not necessarily identical, molecules. Only a few years ago the view was advanced by Pedersen that to obtain homogeneity a protein might have to be prepared from one individual of a species and that even this might vary when obtained on different occasions. This rather pessimistic approach to the purification of proteins, however, has not been supported by the most recent investigations and such work as that on insulin and ribonuclease tends to define a protein as a chemical individual within the concepts of classical organic chemistry and as defined by Pirie or Ogston.

Description of the physical and chemical techniques used in the study of proteins are available[13,50,72] and many are described in the present volume.

References p. 53

6. General methods of analysis

(a) Elementary composition

Following the usual chemical practice, proteins have been analyzed for their elementary composition since they were first recognized in 1838. In the early period of protein chemistry such analyses were used to calculate empirical formulae. Globin, for example, was expressed as $C_{726}H_{1174}N_{194}O_{214}S_3$ with a calculated molecular weight of 11,322. Except for the simplest proteins, the protamines, and for polypeptides, such calculations are meaningless because differences are mostly so slight as to be within the

TABLE IV

ELEMENTARY COMPOSITION OF SOME TYPICAL PROTEINS
(AS PERCENTAGES OF DRY WEIGHT)

Protein	C	H	N	S	P	Other
Protamines						
Clupeine	48.0	8.6	31.6	0	0	
Salmine	47.0	9.0	31.4	0	0	
Histones						
Thymohistone	52.4	7.5	18.1	0.62	0	
Globin	55.0	7.2	16.9	0.42	0	
Albumins						
Ovalbumin (hen)	52.8	7.1	15.5	1.66	0.12	
Conalbumin (hen)	52.5	7.0	16.6	1.83	0	
α-Lactalbumin (cow)	53.32	7.01	15.9	1.91	0.02	
Serum albumin (horse)	52.99	7.01	15.95	1.96		
Globulins						
β-Lactoglobulin (cow)	53.39	7.22	15.6	1.60	0	
Myosin A	50.67	7.80	16.35	1.15	0.06	
Thyroglobulin (human)	51.9	6.9	15.8	1.9	0	I 0.35–0.74
Fibrinogen (horse)	52.83	6.90	17.0	1.26		
α-Crystallin (ox)	52.50	7.18	16.66	0.61	0	
Bence-Jones protein	52.8	7.0	16.01	1.24	0	
Scleroproteins						
Keratin (wool)	50.23	8.13	16.62	3.68		
Keratin (neuro)	55.53	6.96	14.1	1.98		
Collagen	50.75	6.47	17.9			
Gelatin	50.52	6.81	17.53	0.6		
Elastin	52.4	7.1	17.1	0.16		
Gorgonin			13.7	1.51		I 0.06–8.9 Br 0.10–2.2
Spongin			13.0	0.7		I 0.20–2.4 Br 0.12–1.2

TABLE IV *(continued)*

Protein	C	H	N	S	P	Other
Phosphoproteins						
α-Casein (cow)	53.50	7.13	15.6	0.72	1.00	
Ichthulin	48.8	7.6	14.7	1.17	0.62	
Phosvitin (cow)			11.9	0.1	9.7	
Vitellin	51.24	7.16	15.7	2.2	0.98	
Mucoproteins						
α-Ovomucoid (hen)	49.0	6.9	13.1	2.20	0	
Vitellomucoid (hen)	43.5	9.6	11.6	3.38	0	
Ovarian mucoid	44.2	6.96	5.72			
Lysozyme (hen)	48.7	6.4	18.6	2.53	0	
α$_2$-Mucoprotein	45.94	7.24	12.3	1.68		
Urinary mucoprotein	48.80	6.65	12.24	3.09		
Chromoproteins						
Haemoglobin (horse)	54.64	7.09	17.38	0.39	0	Fe 0.34
Myoglobin			16.94	0.57		Fe 0.34
Haemocyanin (octopus)	53.4	6.95	15.9	1.04	0	Cu 0.25
Haemerythrin (*Sipunculus*)	53.34	6.54	16.78	1.74		Fe 1.01
Chlorocrurin (*Spirographis*)	47.2	7.3	15.4	2.6		Fe 1.2
Haemocuprin (ox)			14.35	1.12		Cu 0.34
Ferritin			11.1		1.42	Cd 2.74
						Fe 19.7
Yellow enzyme	51.5	7.37	15.9	0.48	0.04	
Cytochrome *c*	49.2	7.33	14.4	1.18		Fe 0.34
Lipoproteins						
Lipovitellin (hen)			13.0	0.86	1.5	
Lipovitellinin (hen)			10.0	0.60	1.7	
Thromboplastin			7.8		1.6	
Nucleoproteins						
Nucleosalmine			20.25	0	5.39	
Nucleosturine			19.72	0	5.47	
Tobacco mosaic virus	51.37	6.95	16.35	0.2	0.45	
Bushy stunt virus	47.50	7.5	16.1	0.6	1.5	
Unclassified						
Somatotropin	46.25	7.07	15.6	1.30	0	
Prolactin	51.11	6.76	14.38	1.77	0	
Insulin	53.00	6.68	15.4	3.25	0	Zn 0.33–0.77
Crotoxin	50.77	6.41	15.85	4.00		
Urease	51.6	7.10	16.0	1.20		

experimental error of the method. All proteins contain carbon, hydrogen, oxygen and nitrogen, most contain sulfur, and a few contain an appreciable amount of phosphorus. It is usual to express these values on a moisture and ash-free basis although in nature most proteins exist as salts and there is therefore a true value for ash. The variation in percentage is approximately as follows:

C, 46–55 %; H, 6.4–9.0 %; O, 12–30 %; N, 10–32 %; S, 0–4 %; P, 0–5 %. Oxygen is calculated by difference. It is apparent that the analyses of nitrogen, sulfur, and phosphorus may be sufficiently different to be significant in characterization. Some typical analyses are shown in Table IV taken from many sources. In those proteins which contain only small amounts of other elements, such as iron, copper, zinc, or iodine, equivalent weights may be calculated.

The figure for nitrogen has been particularly valuable in protein chemistry because it can readily be determined by the classical Kjeldahl method. The amount of nitrogen in most simple proteins, such as the albumins and globulins, is about 16 % as can be seen in Table IV. Multiplication of the percentage of N by the factor 6.25 (100 ÷ 16) thus permits calculation of the approximate amount of protein present. In special cases, such as collagen, where the value for N is higher (ca. 18 %), a different factor, viz., 5.50, must be used. The conjugated proteins show greater variation in elementary composition because of the prosthetic groups present. In fact a point is reached at which there is the dilemma as to whether to classify as a protein or as a polysaccharide or lipid. This is true of the mucoids from ovarian cysts which should probably be classified as mucopolysaccharides and of thromboplastin which contains more lipid than protein.

(b) Qualitative analysis

There are several qualitative reactions which are useful to detect the presence of protein in general or of particular groups in the protein molecule. They are known as the color reactions of proteins and differ markedly in their sensitivity. Some have been adapted to quantitative procedures.

(i) Millon's reaction

The reagent, which contains a mixture of mercurous and mercuric nitrates and nitrites in excess of nitric acid, is added to a solution of protein, and the mixture is boiled for about one minute (Millon, 1849). If the protein is coagulable, a white precipitate forms which then may turn yellow and finally red; otherwise a red color appears. The reaction is probably due to the formation of a nitro derivative of the protein as in the xanthoproteic reaction and subsequently to a mercury phenolate with the phenol radical in tyrosine. It is thus specific only for the hydroxyphenyl group but frequently used as a general reaction for protein.

(ii) Xanthoproteic reaction

When concentrated nitric acid is added to a protein solution and the solution is boiled for a short time a white coagulum may appear which then turns yellow and may redissolve due to hydrolysis to form a yellow solution (Fourcroy and Vauquelin, 1805). Addition of concentrated ammonia changes the colour to orange. The reaction is believed to be due to nitration of the phenyl radical in tyrosine, phenylalanine and tryptophan.

(iii) Glyoxylic acid reaction

This reaction is known under several names such as Adamkiewicz (1875) or Hopkins-Cole (1901) and is due to the indole nucleus in tryptophan in reaction with the aldehyde group of glyoxylic acid, $CHO \cdot COOH$. In the presence of concentrated sulfuric acid a deep violet or purple color appears slowly at room temperature. It is thus a specific test for tryptophan.

(iv) Ehrlich benzaldehyde reaction

This is another specific test for the indole nucleus in tryptophan (Rhode, 1905). It is given by p-dimethylaminobenzaldehyde in the presence of strong hydrochloric acid as an intense blue color. It may be considered a modification of the general reaction of proteins with aldehydes. Rosenheim made use of formaldehyde and an oxidizing agent such as sulfuric acid or ferric chloride. Formaldehyde is also the reactant in the Denigès-Mörner modification of the test. Benzaldehyde and salicylaldehyde have also been used in other similar tests.

(v) Sakaguchi reaction

In an alkaline medium α-naphthol reacts with the guanidine radical of arginine and a bright red color develops on the addition of sodium hypochlorite or hypobromite. The chemistry of the reaction is uncertain but it is a very sensitive test which has been used for the quantitative estimation of arginine in proteins[74]. Methylguanidine and guanidoacetic acid also give this reaction but creatine, creatinine, urea, guanidine, dimethylguanidine, and glycocyamidine do not. It appears to be due to the presence of the radical $NH_2 \cdot C = NH \cdot NHR$ where R is a fatty acid or alkyl group[75].

(vi) Sulfur reaction

On heating a protein which contains a disulfide or sulfhydryl radical, as in cystine or cysteine, with strong alkali in the presence of lead acetate, a brown or black color is formed; later a black precipitate appears. This is due to the formation of lead sulfide with the decomposition of the cystine and liberation of hydrogen sulfide. Methionine does not give this reaction.

References p. 53

(vii) Sullivan reaction

This is a specific test for cysteine. The reaction is carried out in a strongly reducing atmosphere with cyanide, alkaline sodium sulfite and sodium 1,2-naphthoquinone-4-sulfonate. It is a very sensitive test and used for the quantitative estimation of cystine[76]. It requires the presence of free thiol, carboxyl, and amino groups. Glutathione must be present in several times the quantity of cystine to interfere.

(viii) Molisch's reaction

This is the common reaction for carbohydrate applied to protein (Molisch, 1888). An ethanolic solution of α-naphthol is added and the mixture treated with concentrated sulfuric acid as a ring test. A purple-red ring appears in the presence of carbohydrate due to the formation of a condensation product of α-naphthol with the furfural produced by dehydration of a monosaccharide.

(ix) Knoop's reaction

This is a specific test for histidine. It is carried out in a faintly acidic solution by oxidation with bromine water and the removal of excess bromine by shaking with chloroform. On heating for a few minutes in a boiling water bath and on the addition of ammonia a purplish red color develops followed by a black precipitate. The reaction is specific for the imidazole ring (Knoop, 1908). The reaction has been adapted to a quantitative procedure for histidine[77,78].

(x) Lang's reaction

This is a specific test for hydroxyproline. In a protein hydrolysate the hydroxyproline is oxidized and decarboxylated to pyrrol with sodium hypochlorite in sodium carbonate. The pyrrol is then condensed with isatin or p-dimethylaminobenzaldehyde in concentrated sulfuric acid to form a colored compound (Lang, 1933). Hydrogen peroxide has been used as oxidant in place of hypochlorite. Several modifications of the commonly used quantitative method of Neuman and Logan have been proposed[79].

(xi) Folin's reaction

Folin (1922) proposed β-naphthoquinone sulfonic acid as a general reagent for the colorimetric estimation of amino acids. A red color develops on heating protein with the reagent and strong alkali. Ammonia and alkaloids interfere with the test. A more sensitive reaction is obtained with the "phenol" or Folin-Ciocalteu reagent which contains phosphotungstic and phosphomolybdic acids. It gives a blue color of unknown nature with phenols, such as tyrosine, and some other non-phenolic compounds. Of special importance in this respect are cysteine, tryptophan, and the purines, guanine, xanthine, and uric acid. The quantitative application is discussed below.

(xii) Biuret reaction

This is described under the quantitative procedure for total protein in the following section.

(c) Quantitative analysis

Several procedures have been proposed for the quantitative determination of total protein. They are based on quite different basic principles, both physical and chemical, and vary greatly in sensitivity. They, however, find many applications in practical biochemistry and a description of the principles employed follows. The subject has been reviewed by Kirk[80]. It is frequently desirable to determine the total protein in such fluids as plasma or serum, cerebrospinal fluid, pleural or peritoneal fluid, urine, in foods of various kinds, in animal and plant tissues, and in many special investigations, frequently with a specific protein. The procedure is thus of considerable practical importance but the nature of the proteins to be determined may vary greatly, and in consequence the standard to be used must be carefully selected.

Direct precipitation by coagulation may be used in many cases but it presents difficulties of washing free from salts and of drying to constant weight. Yet it is important to realize that any ultimate standard must be based on the weight of dry pure protein with the inaccuracies involved. This applies for instance to the specific refractive increment and to the value of total nitrogen of a protein. At present it is not possible to state under what conditions all of the associated water is removed without any water of decomposition. Most proteins become more and more actively hygroscopic as water is removed. Probably the best method of desiccation is in vacuum over phosphorus pentoxide in an Abderhalden "pistol" drying apparatus with the boiling temperature of the fluid under reflux selected to the stability of the protein under examination.

(i) Biuret method

The simplest method for the analysis of total protein is by the use of the quantitative biuret reagent. The reaction is produced by adding a dilute solution of cupric sulfate in strongly alkaline tartrate to a protein solution (20–40 mg) and a purplish-violet color is formed. With gelatin and polypeptides the color is pinkish-purple. The reaction is given by all proteins, the larger polypeptides, and by biuret, succinimide, malondiamide, and

α-amino acid amides. The intensity of the color is determined in a spectrophotometer at about 540 mμ and the concentration of protein by comparison with
a standard curve of the protein to be estimated[81]. The nature of the color
is uncertain but it is probably due to the formation of a tetra-coordinated
cupric ion with two adjacent —CO—NH— groups; three or more amino
acids in peptide linkage must usually be present[82]. The complex with
leucinamide has been given the following formula

$$
\begin{array}{ccc}
NH_2 & & NH_2 \\
| & & | \\
R \cdot CH & & CH \cdot R \\
| & Cu^{++} & || \\
C—O^- & & C—O^- \\
|| & & || \\
NH & & NH
\end{array}
$$

A color is formed with α-amino acid amides which is due to [Cu(amino acid
amide)$_2$]$\cdot x$H$_2$O in the absence of alkali. The reaction is not very sensitive
but is applicable in the presence of ammonium salts. Plekan and his associates
have made an extensive study of this reaction with simple peptides[83].

(ii) Kjeldahl method

This has been one of the most common procedures in biochemistry. It
seems to determine organic nitrogen as encountered in most biochemical
substances. The nitrogen in nitrate does not interfere in the determination.
The procedure is divided into two operations. Organic matter is oxidized
with boiling concentrated sulfuric acid and a catalyst such as cupric sulfate,
mercuric oxide, or selenium oxychloride. Carbon and hydrogen are driven
off as carbon dioxide and water vapor. The nitrogen is converted into ammonia. Prolonged boiling is required to complete the oxidation after disappearance of carbonization. The variety of chemical reactions involved
must be considerable if one considers the heterocyclic nuclei present as
indole, imidazole, pyrrol, purine, pyrimidine, and the basic groups of the
alkaloids. This may require several hours. The second stage involves distillation of the ammonia from an alkaline medium into standard acid or boric
acid and back titration. There have been many modifications of this method.
The most important has been the micro-Kjeldahl procedure of Pregl with
the use of the Parnas and Wagner distillation apparatus and a micro-burette.
About 0.10 mg or even less of N may be thus estimated. A commonly used
modification is that of Ma and Zuazaga[84]. As the absolute value of nitrogen
in specific proteins is frequently uncertain and varies from one protein to
another, the use of the factor 6.25 to calculate the content of total protein

in an unknown mixture must be regarded as an approximation with considerable possible error.

Direct nesslerization of the Kjeldahl digest is frequently carried out in place of distillation. This procedure is common in the analysis of blood serum or lymph for urea and non-protein nitrogen. As a sensitive colorimetric procedure it permits greater rapidity by use of a photoelectric colorimeter. The chemical reaction is between ammonia and the potassium mercuric iodide of the Nessler reagent with the formation of a yellowish-orange color as follows

$$NH_4OH + 2\ HgI_2 \cdot 2\ KI + 3\ KOH \longrightarrow NHg_2I + 7\ KI + 4\ H_2O$$

The dimercuric ammonium iodide is colloidal and therefore the conditions of formation must be carefully standardized. Several formulae for the preparation of Nessler's reagent are available.

(iii) Ninhydrin method

The ninhydrin reaction is also used for the determination of total protein and as a general test for protein. It is given by ninhydrin (triketohydrindene hydrate) in a buffered solution on heating with protein or amino acids as a blue color. Ammonium salts also respond to this test. It is very sensitive and is commonly used in the analysis of the amino acids in hydrolysates by the procedure of Moore and Stein[85]. Ruhemann[86] explained the reaction as a dehydrogenation of the amino acid to an imino acid by the ninhydrin, decomposition of the imino acid to the lower aldehyde, carbon dioxide and ammonia, and condensation of the ammonia with excess ninhydrin and the secondary alcohol to form the colored compound, diketohydrindene diketohydrindamine.

Proline and hydroxyproline react in a somewhat different manner.

References p. 53

(iv) Kingsley and Getchell method

Tetrabromophenolphthalein ethyl ester as its potassium salt reacts with protein to form a color which may be measured in a spectrophotometer at 600 mμ and 25°. This provides a method for measuring the small quantities of protein in lymph and cerebrospinal[87] fluid (0.03–0.04 %).

(v) Ultraviolet absorption

Because all proteins, except the protamines, exhibit an absorption band in the region about 280 mμ due to the presence of aromatic amino acids, measurement of its intensity furnishes a convenient and rapid method of estimation[88]. Standardization presents difficulties in that there is considerable variation in the content of the aromatic amino acids in different proteins.

(vi) Refractive index

It is possible to determine the concentration of protein in solution simply and rapidly with the refractometer. The procedure was introduced by Reiss in 1903 and used extensively by T. B. Robertson. It is based on a known value for the specific refractive increment of the protein to be determined. This constant may be defined as the difference in the refractive index N of a solution containing 1 g of solute per 100 ml of solution and the refractive index of the solvent for light of a specific wavelength, when

$$\alpha = \frac{N_{solution} - N_{solvent}}{\text{conc. (g per 100 ml)}}$$

and a linear relationship is obtained. The sensitivity will depend upon the precision of the refractometer or interferometer employed. The dipping refractometer is commonly used for this purpose with ordinary white light. The temperature must be kept constant. Some values for the specific refractive increments of various proteins are shown in Table V. The general applicability of this method is rather limited because the solvent must be available as a blank.

(vii) Turbidity method

Most proteins in solution can be precipitated by addition of a 3–10 % solution of trichloroacetic or sulfosalicylic acids. The resulting turbidity may then be measured by direct comparison, or in a photoelectric colorimeter or nephelometer, and the amount of light transmitted or reflected compared with a standard series for the protein under examination. This method is used occasionally but has obvious limitations when applied to mixtures.

TABLE V

SPECIFIC REFRACTIVE INCREMENT OF VARIOUS PROTEINS

Protein	Solvent		Specific refractive increment (α)
Casein	dilute acid or alkali		0.00152 ± 5
Edestin	dilute acid or alkali		0.00174 ± 6
Gliadin	ethanol (70%)		0.00152 ± 6
Globin	dilute acid or alkali		0.00169 ± 5
Ovalbumin	water		0.00181
Ovomucoid	water		0.00160 ± 4
Ovovitellin	dilute alkali		0.00130 ± 10
Salmine sulfate	water		0.00174 ± 7
Serum albumin	water		0.00185 ± 6
β-Lactoglobulin	0.5 M NaCl at	366 mμ	0.00196
		436 mμ	0.00189
		546 mμ	0.00182
		579 mμ	0.00181
Myosin A	0.6 M KCl + 0.01 M K$_2$HPO$_4$ at 25° and pH 6.5	546 mμ	0.00171 ± 7
Keratin	as complex with Na dodecylbenzene sulfonate at pH 7.8	589 mμ	0.00199

It serves, however, as a rapid method for the assay of total protein in urine and cerebrospinal fluid.

(viii) Folin method

One of the most sensitive methods available for the determination of total protein is the spectrophotometric one based on the blue color formed by the reaction of phenolic (*e.g.*, tyrosine) and other compounds with the Folin "phenol" reagent. The procedure has been modified many times. It is both rapid and sensitive but, due to its empirical character, requires careful standardization for the particular purpose to which it is to be applied. The intensity of color differs markedly with different proteins. The method has been stated to be one hundred times more sensitive than the biuret, ten to twenty times more sensitive than by ultraviolet absorption, several fold more sensitive than the ninhydrin, and about as sensitive as the Nessler procedure. It requires no initial hydrolysis. By the micro modification as little as 0.2 μg of protein may be determined[89].

Many of the more important properties of proteins have been referred to above and some will be presented at greater length in the following chapters of this volume. Certain aspects of proteins, however, require an introductory treatment.

References p. 53

7. Crystalline state

Only some thirty years ago very few proteins had been obtained in crystalline form with the exception of the haemoglobins. Now many have been crystallized. There are, however, marked differences in the ease of crystallization between different groups of proteins. Albumins and plant globulins are readily prepared in this condition. Most of the chromoproteins and many enzymes can be crystallized. The protamines form crystalline salts but are amorphous as the free base. The scleroproteins exhibit patterns by X-ray diffraction which indicate the presence of a crystalline lattice but they are difficult to crystallize in the conventional way because of their insolubility. Acid-soluble collagen can be obtained as microscopic needles which on greater magnification in the electron microscope show a characteristic banded structure (Fig. 4) and a characteristic X-ray diffraction pattern[91]. Histones, prolamins, glutelins, phosphoproteins and lipoproteins have never been

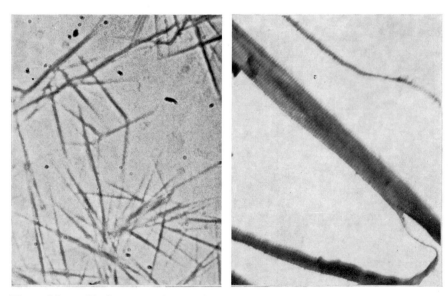

Fig. 4. "Crystalline" collagen from cod skin. Left: under ordinary microscope × 850. Right: under electron microscope shadowed with gold × 9,000. (From E. G. Young and J. W. Lorimer, *Arch. Biochem. Biophys.*, 88 (1960) 373.)

obtained in crystalline form. Likewise only two mucoproteins and comparatively few nucleoproteins have been crystallized.

The conditions for crystallization vary greatly and have been described under general methods of preparation. Control of total ionic strength and

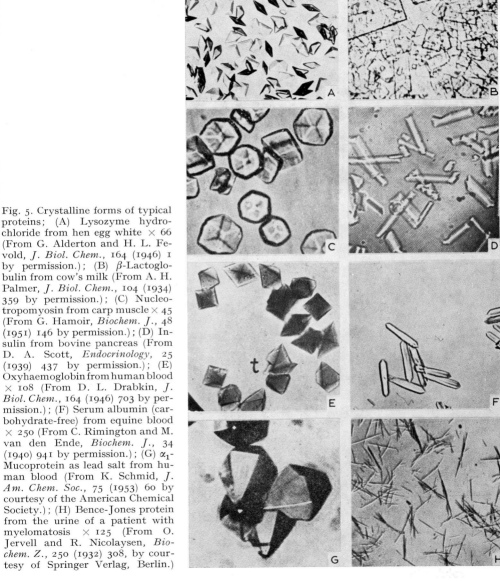

Fig. 5. Crystalline forms of typical proteins; (A) Lysozyme hydrochloride from hen egg white × 66 (From G. Alderton and H. L. Fevold, *J. Biol. Chem.*, 164 (1946) 1 by permission.); (B) β-Lactoglobulin from cow's milk (From A. H. Palmer, *J. Biol. Chem.*, 104 (1934) 359 by permission.); (C) Nucleotropomyosin from carp muscle × 45 (From G. Hamoir, *Biochem. J.*, 48 (1951) 146 by permission.); (D) Insulin from bovine pancreas (From D. A. Scott, *Endocrinology*, 25 (1939) 437 by permission.); (E) Oxyhaemoglobin from human blood × 108 (From D. L. Drabkin, *J. Biol. Chem.*, 164 (1946) 703 by permission.); (F) Serum albumin (carbohydrate-free) from equine blood × 250 (From C. Rimington and M. van den Ende, *Biochem. J.*, 34 (1940) 941 by permission.); (G) α_1-Mucoprotein as lead salt from human blood (From K. Schmid, *J. Am. Chem. Soc.*, 75 (1953) 60 by courtesy of the American Chemical Society.); (H) Bence-Jones protein from the urine of a patient with myelomatosis × 125 (From O. Jervell and R. Nicolaysen, *Biochem. Z.*, 250 (1932) 308, by courtesy of Springer Verlag, Berlin.)

hydrogen ion concentration is essential. The high degree of polarity of most proteins assists the orientation for crystallization but the slow rate of diffusion and the relatively large size of the molecules tend to retard the process so that it is usually slow. Some typical crystals are shown in Fig. 5. The phenomenon of isomorphism or mixed crystals is encountered frequently, especially in the chromoproteins. Tiselius and Horsfall[92] in an experiment with the haemocyanins from *Helix* and *Littorina* showed that these proteins of molecular weight about 7,000,000 could be dissociated into two, four or eight particles per molecule beyond their stable range of pH 3.8–8.5. On re-association in a solution of the two haemocyanins and re-crystallization a new type of mixed crystal was obtained. Repeated recrystallization affords no assurance of a chemical individual by the modern physical methods of determining homogeneity.

8. Solubility

The characteristic solubilities of the various groups of proteins have been described previously. The use of the solubility constant as a test for purity has already been explained. While few, such as albumins and chromoproteins, are soluble in water, most are dispersed in the presence of varying amounts of simple inorganic salts. A few are soluble only in dilute acids or alkalis. A few, such as the prolamins, are readily soluble only in a limited number of organic solvents. The scleroproteins are generally insoluble and require special solvents to be dispersed, probably in a form different from that of their native state. This characteristic solubility is not only of practical importance but is also evidence of their internal structure. Proteins are amphoteric electrolytes as will be discussed in Chapter III. They possess both acidic and basic groups as is demonstrable by titration, by electrophoresis, and by their characteristic isoelectric points. This is also evident from inspection of analyses of their content of amino acids and analysis of terminal groups. There are free amino and carboxyl groups as well as acidic phenolic and basic guanidino and imidazole groups in most proteins and these have been estimated. Thus in β-lactoglobulin there are 61 carboxyl, 37 amino, 9 phenolic, 4 imidazole, and 7 guanidino groups per molecule of 42,000 molecular weight, or approximately 48 cationic and 64 anionic, distributed over the surface of the molecule. Such a molecule is therefore ionic and polar in character and attracts water of hydration. Many of the side chains are non-polar. The prolamins, which are soluble in media of low dielectric constant, have few ionic groups. The insoluble keratins are heavily crosslinked through disulfide bonds due to their high content of cystine. They may be solubilized by rupture of these bonds with reducing agents to form soluble keratin.

In that the number of free acidic and basic groups will be controlled by the reaction of the medium, the effect of the pH of the solvent on solubility will be great and solubility will be at a minimum at the isoelectric point. The effects of the total ionic strength and of pH on solubility are shown in Fig. 6.

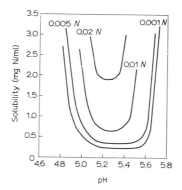

Fig. 6. Solubility of β-lactoglobulin as a function of the concentration of sodium chloride and hydrogen ions. (From A. Grönwall, *Compt. rend. trav. lab. Carlsberg, Sér. chim.*, 24 (1942) 185, by courtesy of the Danish Science Press Ltd.)

Addition of an organic solvent such as ethanol usually causes precipitation of protein from aqueous solution. Ethanol lowers the dielectric constant. This leads to an increase of ionic attraction and favours insolubility. Basic theory can now explain the solubility of proteins in the phenomena of salting-in and salting-out[12]. In general the solubility increases with ionic strength at constant pH, passes through a maximum, and then decreases. This is shown diagrammatically in Fig. 7 but curves for various proteins

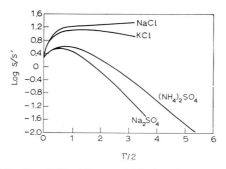

Fig. 7. The solubility (log S/S') of haemoglobin in salt solutions of varying ionic concentrations ($\Gamma/2$) where S is solubility in g/l and S' is solubility in salt-free 25% aqueous ethanol at $-5°$. (From E. J. Cohn, *Chem. Revs.*, 19 (1936) 241, by courtesy of the American Chemical Society.)

differ in detail as to shape and point of maximum solubility. The effects of salts on proteins is spoken of as salting-in as at low concentrations and salting-out as at high concentrations. These effects are particularly applicable to the globulins. Salts differ in this respect on an equimolar basis with valency (Fig. 7). Polyvalent ions are more effective than monovalent ions. Valency, however, is not the only factor involved in the phenomenon. Ions possess varying potencies as is shown in the Hofmeister or lyotropic series in the swelling, gelation, precipitation and other properties of colloids in the following descending order of magnitude: (1) anions—citrate > tartrate > F > sulfate > acetate > Cl > NO_3 > ClO_3 > Br > I > CNS; (2) cations—Th > Al > Ba > Sr > Ca > Mg > NH_4 > K > Na > Li. The effect has been explained as related to the hydration of the ion but more specific effects may be involved. The order is not rigid and varies with the particular phenomenon.

9. Viscosity

Viscosity is the internal friction of a liquid in flow. It is frequently measured for solutions of protein as an index of molecular weight, axial ratio, and state of hydration. Some proteins, especially those classified as fibrous, exhibit very high relative and intrinsic viscosities. Others, such as the simpler globular proteins, have a viscosity little greater than that of the aqueous solvent. The relative viscosity is dependent upon both concentration and temperature. Thus some proteins tend to pass into the gel state at relatively low concentration which may be thixotropic in character. In this type of gel simple agitation restores its liquid character and prolonged standing is required to reform a gel. In some instances measurement of viscosity becomes very difficult if not impossible. Viscosity is expressed quantitatively in the equation

$$\eta = Cdt$$

where η is the viscosity, C a constant governed by the experimental conditions of measurement, d the density of the solution, and t the time of flow. The velocity of flow will depend upon the force which produces the flow and other factors, expressed in Poiseuille's law, such as the radius and length of the capillary tube. The unit is the poise, expressed usually as centipoises. The *relative* viscosity is defined as the ratio of the viscosity of the solution to that of the solvent

$$\eta_{rel} = \frac{\eta}{\eta_0} = \frac{tp}{t_0 p_0}$$

where t and t_0 are the times of flow and p and p_0 the densities of solution and solvent respectively. The numerical value of η_{rel} is always greater than one because the viscosity of a protein solution is always greater than that of the solvent. The *specific* viscosity (η_{sp}) is $\eta_{rel} - 1$ and the *reduced specific* viscosity is η_{sp}/c where c is the concentration in g/ml of protein in the solution. A plot of η_{sp}/c against c permits extrapolation to infinite dilution $(c = 0)$ which value is known as the *intrinsic* viscosity $[\eta]$ or H_0. Proteins may thus be compared as to viscosity independent of concentration. However, it has been shown with several proteins, *e.g.*, conalbumin, that this value is dependent upon the ionic strength and the pH of the solvent. The Einstein equation for very dilute solutions of globular proteins is

$$\eta = \eta_0 \left(1 + 2.5 \, Nv/V\right)$$

where N is the number of particles, v the volume of each particle, and V the total volume of solution. It permits a determination of either the state of hydration or the particle weight if v or N is known. This equation has a limited application to proteins as most are non-spherical. However, data on viscosity have been of assistance in arriving at both the weight and shape of protein particles. Values for $[\eta]$ of several typical proteins are listed in Table VI. In many proteins the viscosity observed varies with the velocity

TABLE VI

INTRINSIC VISCOSITY OF VARIOUS PROTEINS

Protein	$[\eta]$	Protein	$[\eta]$
Serum albumin	0.012–0.044	α_1-Lipoprotein	0.066
Lysozyme	0.030	α_1-Mucoprotein	0.069
Myoglobin	0.031	Lipovitellin	0.070
Conalbumin	0.035–0.16	γ-Casein	0.122
Haemoglobin (horse)	0.036	α-Casein	0.140
Pepsin	0.039	β-Casein	0.205
β_1-Lipoprotein	0.041	Fibrinogen	0.23–0.30
Ovalbumin	0.042	Tobacco mosaic virus	0.28
β-Lactoglobulin	0.045	Tropomyosin	0.52
Haemocyanin (*Helix*)	0.052	Myosin A	2.00
Siderophilin	0.055	Ichthyocol	11.5–13.2
γ-Globulin	0.060–0.14	Actomyosin	14.0

gradient and is designated as non-Newtonian. It is interpreted as due to interference or interaction of the molecules which is decreased with increasing gradients. The presence of anions and cations in protein solutions

References p. 53

gives rise to electrostatic effects in the measurement of viscosity. This electro-viscous effect may be lowered or eliminated by use of an inorganic salt solution as solvent of such concentration as to yield a constant value for η_{sp}.

Viscosity may be measured in several ways. The commonest is by the use of the simple Ostwald viscosimeter which serves to measure the time of flow of a fixed volume of fluid through a capillary tube of chosen dimensions in a constant temperature bath. The Ubbelohde and Fenske modifications of this instrument are frequently used. Another type of instrument is the Couette viscosimeter which employs a rotating cylinder under controlled torque and the measurement of the time required for a fixed number of rotations as in the Stormer model, or driven electrically as in the Brookfield instrument.

10. Light scattering

The visibility of light which is made to pass through a colloidal solution is well known as the Tyndall effect. The ultramicroscope and the nephelo-meter are examples of applications of the principle. This scattering of light is characteristic of proteins in solution and is due to the reflection of the incident beam by the protein particle if it is sufficiently large. Lyophilic sols vary from those which exhibit a weak Tyndall effect to those which are practically optically clear. The phenomenon has been adapted to quantitative estimation and is used to obtain information on the size and shape of protein particles. Up to the present time this method has been used as complementary to other methods of determining molecular weights. While the actual measurement is rapid, the precautions required in the mani-pulation and preparation of the solutions are great. Results have not always been in agreement with those by other methods. The intensity of scatter will increase with the number and the size of the particles. Thus the "turbidity" (τ), defined as the fractional decrease of the intensity of light passing through unit distance, may be expressed in the equation

$$\tau = HcM = \frac{32\pi^3 n_0^2 \left(\dfrac{n - n_0}{c}\right)^2}{3N\lambda^4} cM$$

where H is a proportionality constant, M the molecular weight, c the con-centration in g/cm^3, n and n_0 the refractive index of solution and solvent respectively, N the Avogadro number, and λ the wave length of the light used. All of the values in the equation are known or can be determined experimentally except M which may be calculated. Table VIII records some molecular weights obtained by this method in comparison with those by other methods. The intensity of scatter I_θ is usually observed between 38 and 135 angular degrees (θ) defined by the direction of scattering and the transmitted beam. The angular distribution of intensity can indicate the shape and characteristic dimensions of the particle as between spheres, coils, and rods. The scattered light may be measured by a photomultiplier tube movable to different angles with the incident beam. From the equation it is evident that the turbidity will be greater as the wave length decreases and also as the difference between the refractive indices of solvent and solution increases. When the diameter of particle is one tenth or less of the wave length of the incident light, I_θ will be the same in all directions. If the diameter is of the same order or greater, I_θ will not be uniform over all angles and the situation becomes complex. A more accurate method known as the Zimm plot is frequently used when a large dissymmetry of scatter obtains. A graph of c/I_θ vs. $\sin^2 1/2\,\theta + Kc$ is drawn where K is a constant chosen to separate the distribution of intensity for each concentration. The value for c/I_0 when $c = 0$ and $\theta = 0$ is found by extrapolation. The value of $(c/\tau)_{c\,=\,0}$ is obtained from its equality to

$$C(c/I_\theta)_{\substack{\theta=0 \\ c=0}}$$

where C is the calibration factor determined with a standard suspension. The subject is a rather special one in protein chemistry and the interested reader is referred to the review by Doty and Edsall[90].

11. Size and shape of protein molecules

The classical methods of chemistry for the determination of molecular weight, such as the lowering of the freezing point or elevation of the boiling point, do not apply to proteins mainly for two reasons. Most proteins would undergo denaturation in the process and few are soluble in water alone. The second and more important reason is the small effect of the protein as compared with that of inorganic material usually present. Traces of mineral salts are notoriously difficult to remove and the error introduced by their presence would be excessive if considered on the basis of molality. Thus a 0.01 M solution of sodium chloride would be 0.079 % and of ovalbumin 43 % with an equal number of molecules. The effect with a protein of molecular weight more than 43,000 would be proportionately greater.

The method of "combining" or "containing" weights is applicable and has been used many times to obtain minimum molecular weights. The presence in a few proteins of small amounts of metals, such as the iron or copper in chromoproteins, permits calculation of a minimum value on the assumption of one atom per molecule. Thus a concentration of 0.335 % of iron in equine haemoglobin provides a minimum molecular weight of 16,700

TABLE VII

MOLECULAR WEIGHT OF β-LACTOGLOBULIN FROM
ANALYSES OF AMINO ACIDS[*]

Amino acid	Percent of		Moles per 10^5 g protein	Minimum mol. wt.	Assumed no. of residues	Mol. wt. calculated
	Amino acid	Amino acid residue				
Arginine	2.89	2.59	16.5	6,015	7	42,105
Histidine	1.54	1.36	10.2	10,080	4	40,290
Lysine	9.75	8.53	66.7	1,498	28	41,970
Tyrosine	3.78	3.40	20.9	4,790	9	43,110
Tryptophan	1.94	1.77	9.5	10,520	4	42,090
Methionine	3.22	2.83	21.6	4,633	9	41,700
Cystine	2.29	1.95	19.1	10,500	4	41,980
Cysteine	1.10	0.94	9.2	10,920	4	43,670
Glutamic acid	21.50	18.88	146.3	684	62	42,400
Aspartic acid	9.88	8.56	79.5	1,346	31	41,730
Amide NH_3	1.29	1.22		1,318	32	42,160
						42,110
Glycine	1.4	1.06	18.7	5,370	8	42,900
Alanine	6.2	4.95	69.6	1,454	29	41,700
Valine	5.83	4.93	49.8	2,008	21	42,200
Leucine	15.6	13.46	118.9	840	50	42,100
Isoleucine	8.4	7.25	64.0	1,159	27	42,200
Proline	4.1	3.46	35.6	2,803	15	42,100
Phenylalanine	3.54	3.15	21.4	4,667	9	42,000
Serine	5.0	4.14	47.6	2,101	20	42,000
Threonine	5.85	4.97	49.1	2,032	21	42,800
Terminal H_2O		0.20				
Total	115.10	99.60	874.2		394	42,160

[*] from Brand[93] and Chibnall[94].

$(0.335 : 100 = 55.85 \text{ (Fe)} : x)$ on the assumption of one atom of iron per molecule. Physical methods, however, indicate a molecular weight of 66,000 so that four atoms of iron must be present per molecule. Some amino acids are susceptible of sufficiently accurate determination and are present in small amounts in proteins. This is particularly true of cystine, tryptophan, histidine, and sometimes of tyrosine. Minimum molecular weights are of value in checking those obtained by physical methods and the accuracy of other determinations of constituent amino acids which can be treated in the same manner. Brand[93] and Chibnall[94] have examined the data for several proteins in this manner and the results for β-lactoglobulin are reproduced in Table VII. The average weight of amino acids present calculated as the residue $(R \cdot CH \cdot NH_2 \cdot COOH - H_2O)$ is 112.4. A minimum containing weight of about 10,500 is indicated from the figures for cystine, cysteine, tryptophan and histidine. By calculating the molar ratios to tryptophan amongst the more accurately determined amino acids as shown in the upper portion of the table whole numbers are obtained at 4 for the amino acids mentioned. This establishes the minimum molecular weight at 42,100 which agrees with the values of 41,600 by sedimentation velocity and 38,000 from sedimentation equilibrium but is higher than the value of about 35,000 indicated by osmotic pressure, light scattering, and X-ray diffraction as shown in Table VIII.

Several physicochemical methods have been used for the determination of the molecular weight of proteins. They are based on different principles and the results are not always in good agreement. This is because factors other than mass, such as shape and electrical charge, affect the results. The shape is of importance when the rate of movement as in diffusion or sedimentation is measured and fibrous proteins behave differently from globular proteins. Likewise the degree of hydration of the particle is another factor which may affect its motion if the cross-sectional area is increased. Measure-

TABLE VIII

MOLECULAR WEIGHTS OF CRYSTALLINE PROTEINS DETERMINED BY VARIOUS METHODS

Method	Ovalbumin	Serum albumin	Haemoglobin	Lysozyme	β-Lactoglobulin	Insulin
Containing weight	43,000	70,000	66,700	14,700	42,000	6,000
Osmotic pressure	45,000–46,600	66,000–76,000	67,000	17,500	35,050–38,000	12,000–48,000
Diffusion	34,500		68,600	13,000	40,000	40,900
Sedimentation	43,800–45,000	65,360–70,200	68,000	14,000–17,000	38,000–41,500	12,000–48,000
Light scattering	45,700–46,000	72,500		14,700	33,700–35,500	12,000–48,000
X-radiation		65,600–66,200	66,700	13,900	33,000–35,600	36,000–52,400

ments of osmotic pressure, of rate of sedimentation and of diffusion, of viscosity, and of light scattering have been applied to proteins. Some proteins have been examined by streaming birefringence, by X-ray analysis, in the electron microscope, and a few as monolayers by interfacial spreading. The techniques employed in most of these methods will be explained in later sections. A comparison of the various results obtained with six purified proteins is shown in Table VIII. Some, like those for ovalbumin and haemoglobin, are in reasonably good agreement. A considerable variation is evident with β-lactoglobulin, serum albumin, and lysozyme. Insulin provides an interesting example of results which, in the past, have shown marked disagreement until the phenomenon of association and dissociation was considered. The minimum molecular weight from our present knowledge of the detailed structure is approximately 6,000. Association is known to be controlled by the pH and the nature of the buffer salts so that molecules of 12,000, 24,000, 36,000 and 48,000 may occur. This serves to explain the discrepancies and variation in results of different investigators. When it is considered that the proteins of Table VIII are some of the most homogeneous known it is evident that present methods are able to indicate an order of magnitude accurate in some cases to 5–10 %, rather than an exact figure. The range in the selected group listed in Table IX is from 12,000 to $40 \cdot 10^6$; most proteins have molecular weights greater than 40,000. The method to be used for the determination of the molecular weight will depend on the size of the particle.

As pointed out in discussing classification of proteins as globular and fibrous, most protein molecules are non-spherical as shown by measurements of their frictional ratios, viscosity, streaming birefringence, and dielectric dispersion. Whether a protein molecule is spherical or not may be determined by combined measurements of sedimentation and diffusion. It is usually assumed that the particle is an ellipsoid of revolution with a long axis (a) and two shorter axes (b). The axial ratio, a/b, is greater than one for a prolate ellipsoid and less than one for an oblate ellipsoid. The axial ratio can be calculated if M, the molecular weight, and f/f_0 are known. However, the frictional constant also depends upon the extent of solvation of the molecule and usually this is considerable, *viz.*, $\sim$ 0.3 (0.2–0.6) g water per g protein. The relationship is shown in Fig. 8.

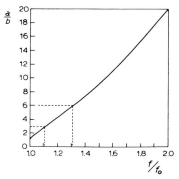

Fig. 8. Graph relating the axial ratio, a/b, to the frictional ratio, f/f_0, for protein molecules as prolate ellipsoids of revolution from Perrin's equation. (From D. M. Greenberg, *Amino Acids and Proteins*, by courtesy of Charles C. Thomas, Springfield, Ill., U.S.A., 1951.)

The dissymmetry constant or frictional ratio, f/f_0, is defined as the ratio of the molar frictional constant, determined experimentally, to the molar frictional constant calculated for an unsolvated spherical particle of the same mass. This ratio is an index of asymmetry and may be calculated from the values for the partial specific volume V, the sedimentation constant s, the diffusion coefficient D, the molecular weight M, the viscosity η, and the density of the solution ρ, in non-oriented particles

$$f = M\,(\mathrm{I} - V\rho)/s \quad \text{or} \quad RT/D$$

$$f_0 = 6\pi\eta N \left(\frac{3VM}{4\pi N}\right)^{\frac{1}{3}}$$

when

$$f/f_0 = \mathrm{IO}^{-8} \left(\frac{\mathrm{I} - V\rho}{D_{20}^2 \cdot s_{20} V}\right)^{\frac{1}{3}}$$

where N is the Avogadro constant, R the gas constant, and T the absolute temperature. Certain factors, such as degree of hydration and the nature of the ellipsoid, alter the numerical results quite markedly. By a combination of the equation for f/f_0 with that of Perrin for the linear diffusion of ellipsoidal molecules, the relative dimensions of particles may be calculated[95]. The relationship is shown graphically in Fig. 9. A selection of data for representative proteins is shown in Table IX in ascending magnitude of f/f_0 and taken

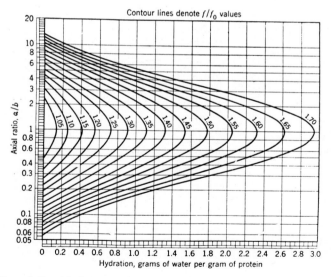

Fig. 9. The relationship between the axial ratio, degree of hydration, and the frictional ratio. (From J. L. Oncley, *Ann. N.Y. Acad. Sci.*, 41 (1941) 121, by courtesy of the author and the N.Y. Academy of Sciences.)

TABLE IX

MOLECULAR DIMENSIONS AND FRICTIONAL RATIOS OF VARIOUS PROTEINS
(IN ASCENDING MAGNITUDE OF f/f_0)

Protein	Molecular weight	Major axis (Å)	Minor axis (Å)	Axial ratio	Frictional ratio
α-Bence-Jones protein	35,000	43	43	1	1.0
β₁-Lipoprotein	1,300,000	185	185	1	1.0
Ribonuclease	12,700				1.04
Pepsin	35,500	84	31	2.7	1.08
Bushy stunt virus	7,600,000	250	250	1	1.09
Myoglobin	17,100	70	24	2.9	1.11
Ferritin	465,000			3	1.14
Ovalbumin	43,800	63	23	2.7	1.16
Haemoglobin (man)	68,000	57	34	1.7	1.16
Prothrombin	62,700	119	34	3.5	1.17
Insulin—tetramer	47,800	102	31	3.3	1.18
Edestin	310,000	237	55	4.3	1.21
Haemocyanin (*Helix*)	8,670,000	820	240	3.4	1.24
Turnip yellow virus	4,970,000	200	200	1	1.25
β-Lactoglobulin	38,000	122	28	4.4	1.26
Serum albumin (man)	69,000	150	38	4.0	1.28
Cytochrome *c*	15,600	98	18	5.4	1.29
Lysozyme	14,100	60	24	2.5	1.3
α-Ovomucoid	27,000			6.1	1.35
Siderophilin	90,000	190	37	5.1	1.37
α₁-Lipoprotein	200,000	300	50	6.0	1.38
γ-Globulin (human)	156,000	235	44	5.3	1.38
Globin (horse)	37,000				1.47
Thyroglobulin	650,000	498	54	9.2	1.50
Mucoid (salivary)	87,000			10	1.51
Meromyosin (H)	232,000	435	29	15	1.78
Fetuin	48,700			11	1.80
Fibrinogen (human)	580,000	700	38	18	1.98
Gelatin	69,700	400	20	20	2.03
Thymonucleohistone	2,150,000			35	2.5
Tobacco mosaic virus	40,000,000	2,700	152	18	2.9
Fibroin	84,000				3.0
Tropomyosin	92,700	385	15	25	3.1
Mucoid (blood group A)	260,000				3.2
Myosin A	1,500,000	2,000	23	87	5.5
α-Casein	121,800	2,200	82	27	
Actomyosin	14,000,000	11,600	60	193	
Collagen (cod)	280,000	2,810	15	192	

from various sources. It must be realized that the dimensions calculated are subject to considerable error and several inconsistencies are to be found in the table due to the different sources of the data.

The dimensions of tobacco mosaic virus have been determined by various methods which are in relatively good agreement[96] as shown in Table X.

TABLE X

Method	Molecular weight	Length (Å)	Diameter (Å)
Sedimentation and viscosity	$33.2 \cdot 10^6$	2760	136
Sedimentation and diffusion	$31.6 \cdot 10^6$	2560	138
Viscosity and diffusion	$36.0 \cdot 10^6$	2830	140
Electron microscope	$40.0 \cdot 10^6$	2700	152

The electron micrographs are an interesting direct confirmation of dimensions obtained by indirect means but can only be applied to particles greater than 50 Å because of lack of resolving power below this limit. This technique also has the disadvantage of applying only to dry mounts in a high vacuum.

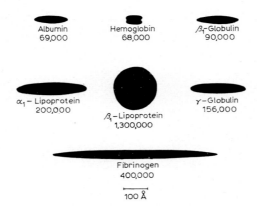

Fig. 10. Size and shape of some proteins in human blood. (From J. L. Oncley in *The Preservation of the Formed Elements and of the Proteins of the Blood*, p. 79, Washington, D.C., 1949, by courtesy of the author and American National Red Cross.)

It is possible to measure the length of asymmetric particles by subjecting them to a strong velocity gradient as achieved between concentric cylinders one of which is rotated. Under such circumstances the molecules will tend to be oriented with the long axis parallel to the direction of flow as contrasted with natural random orientation and the solution becomes doubly refractive, *i.e.*, birefringent. The magnitude of birefringence and the optical axis can be measured from which the length of large molecules can be calculated. By this method the length of some fibrous protein particles have been determined, *e.g.*, rabbit myosin 11,600 Å, tobacco mosaic virus 7,200 Å, *Helix* haemocyanin 890 Å, human fibrinogen 700 Å, human γ-globulin 230 Å.

The evidence presented above as to the size and shape of protein molecules points to a long series of particles from a few truly spherical to several which consist of long chains or spirals, some of indefinite length. There appears to be no sharp division between those proteins designated as fibrous and those as globular. The difference is quantitative rather than qualitative except that the fibrous proteins possess an extreme asymmetry of shape and tend to be insoluble. The shapes of some typical plasma proteins are shown in Fig. 10 as approximations of their possible structures.

REFERENCES

[1] H. B. VICKERY, Yale J. Biol. Med., 22 (1950) 387.
[2] H. HARTLEY, Nature, 168 (1951) 244.
[3] F. L. HÜNEFELD, Der Chemismus in der tierischen Organisation, Brockhaus, Leipzig, 1840, p. 160.
[4] O. SCHMIEDEBERG, Z. physiol. Chem., Hoppe-Seyler's, 1 (1877) 205.
[5] F. HOFMEISTER, Z. physiol. Chem., Hoppe-Seyler's, 14 (1889) 163.
[6] J. B. SUMNER, J. Biol. Chem., 69 (1926) 435.
[7] J. J. ABEL, Proc. Natl. Acad. Sci. U.S., 12 (1926) 132.
[8] W. M. STANLEY, Science, 81 (1935) 644.
[9] H. BROWN, F. SANGER AND R. KITAI, Biochem. J., 60 (1955) 556.
[10] V. DU VIGNEAUD, CH. RESSLER, J. M. SWAN, C. W. ROBERTS, P. C. KATSOYANNIS AND S. GORDON, J. Am. Chem. Soc., 75 (1953) 4879; 76 (1954) 3115.
[11] H. NEURATH AND K. BAILEY (Eds.), The Proteins, Academic Press, New York, 1953–1954, 4 Vols.
[12] E. J. COHN AND J. T. EDSALL, Proteins, Amino Acids and Peptides, Reinhold, New York, 1943.
[13] F. HAUROWITZ, Chemistry and Biology of Proteins, Academic Press, New York, 1950, 374 pp.
D. M. GREENBERG, Amino Acids and Proteins, C. C. Thomas, Springfield, Ill., 1951, 950 pp.
H. D. SPRINGALL, The Structural Chemistry of Proteins, Butterworths, London, 1954, 376 pp.
S. W. FOX AND J. F. FOSTER, Introduction to Protein Chemistry, Wiley and Sons, New York, 1957, 459 pp.
[14] H. FRAENKEL-CONRAT AND L. K. RAMACHANDRAN, Advances in Protein Chem., 14 (1959) 175.
[15] F. W. PUTNAM, Advances in Protein Chem., 8 (1953) 175.
[16] J. Biol. Chem., 4 (1908) xlviii.
[17] F. MIESCHER, Ber. ,7 (1874) 376.
[18] A. KOSSEL, The Protamines and Histones, Longmans, Green and Co., London, 1928.
[19] P. ALEXANDER, Biochim. Biophys. Acta, 10 (1953) 595.
[20] T. ANDO AND F. SAWADA, J. Biochem. (Tokyo), 46 (1959) 517.
[21] A. KOSSEL, Z. physiol. Chem., Hoppe-Seyler's, 8 (1884) 511.
[22] M. M. DALY, A. E. MIRSKY AND H. RIS, J. Gen. Physiol., 34 (1951) 439.
[23] E. STEDMAN AND E. STEDMAN, Trans. Roy. Soc. (London) B, 235 (1951) 565.
[24] W. PREYER, Arch. ges. Physiol., Pflüger's, 1 (1868) 395.
[25] M. POLONOVSKI AND M. F. JAYLE, Bull. soc. chim. biol., 21 (1939) 66.
[26] P. G. JOHANSEN, R. D. MARSHALL AND A. NEUBERGER, Biochem. J., 77 (1960) 239.
[27] T. L. MCMEEKIN, J. Am. Chem. Soc., 62 (1940) 3393.
[28] F. W. PUTNAM AND A. MIYAKE, Arch. Biochem. Biophys., 65 (1956) 39.
[29] T. B. OSBORNE, Science, 28 (1908) 417.
[30] A. G. MCCALLA AND N. GRALÉN, Can. J. Research, C, 20 (1942) 130.
[31] A. G. MCCALLA, Ann. Rev. Biochem., 18 (1949) 615.
[32] R. J. BLOCK AND H. B. VICKERY, J. Biol. Chem., 93 (1931) 113.
[33] E. G. YOUNG AND D. G. SMITH, J. Biol. Chem., 219 (1956) 161.
[34] M. H. MARKS, R. S. BEAR AND C. H. BLAKE, J. exptl. Zool., 111 (1949) 55.
[35] J. ROCHE AND R. MICHEL, Advances in Protein Chem., 6 (1951) 253.
[36] G. E. PERLMANN, Advances in Protein Chem., 10 (1955) 1.
[37] N. J. HIPP, M. L. GROVES AND T. L. MCMEEKIN, J. Am. Chem. Soc., 74 (1952) 4822.
[38] W. G. MARTIN, K. J. TURNER AND W. H. COOK, Can. J. Biochem. Physiol., 37 (1959) 1197.
[39] D. A. MEECHAM AND H. S. OLCOTT, J. Am. Chem. Soc., 71 (1949) 3670.
[40] K. MEYER, Advances in Protein Chem., 2 (1945) 249.
[41] H. A. ITANO, Advances in Protein Chem., 12 (1957) 216.
[42] E. T. REICHERT AND A. P. BROWN, The Crystallography of Haemoglobins, Carnegie Inst. Washington, Publ. No. 116, Washington, D.C., 1909.

[43] A. W. POLLISTER, *Exptl. Cell Research*, Suppl. 2 (1952) 59.

[44] P. D. BOYER, G. A. BALLOU AND J. M. LUCK, *J. Biol. Chem.*, 167 (1947) 407.

[45] D. S. GOODMAN, *J. Am. Chem. Soc.*, 80 (1958) 3892.

[46] E. CHARGAFF, *Advances in Protein Chem.*, 1 (1944) 1.

[47] W. T. ASTBURY, *Proc. Roy. Soc. (London), B*, 141 (1953) 1.

[48] F. H. C. CRICK AND J. C. KENDREW, *Advances in Protein Chem.*, 12 (1957) 134.

[49] K. BAILEY, *Chem. & Ind. (London)*, (1950) 243.

[50] P. ALEXANDER AND R. J. BLOCK, *Analytical Methods of Protein Chemistry*, Vol. 1, The Separation and Isolation of Proteins, Pergamon Press, New York, 1960.

[51] E. J. COHN, *Blood*, 3 (1948) 471

[52] V. R. POTTER in *Methods in Enzymology*, Vol. 1, Academic Press, New York, 1955, p. 10.

[53] W. N. ALDRIDGE, R. C. EMERY AND B. W. STREET, *Biochem. J.*, 77 (1960) 326.

[54] C. MÉHU, *J. Pharm. chim.*, 4th Ser., 28 (1878) 159.

[55] E. J. COHN, J. A. LUETSCHER JR., J. L. ONCLEY, S. H. ARMSTRONG JR. AND B. D. DAVIS, *J. Am. Chem. Soc.*, 62 (1940) 3396.

[56] B. V. JAGER, T. B. SCHWARTZ, E. L. SMITH, M. NICKERSON AND D. M. BROWN, *J. Lab. Clin. Med.*, 35 (1950) 76.

[57] Y. DERRIEN-TABUSSE, G. LAURENT AND J. REYNAUD, *J. chim. phys.*, 48 (1951) 651.

[58] J. H. NORTHROP, M. KUNITZ AND R. M. HERRIOTT, *Crystalline Enzymes*, 2nd ed., Columbia University Press, New York, 1948.

[59] E. J. COHN, L. E. STRONG, W. L. HUGHES JR., D. J. MULFORD, J. N. ASHWORTH, M. MELIN AND H. L. TAYLOR, *J. Am. Chem. Soc.*, 68 (1946) 459.

[60] R. A. KEKWICK AND M. MACKAY, *Med. Res. Council Spec. Rep. No. 286*, H.M. Stationery Office, London, 1954.

[61] S. P. L. SÖRENSEN AND M. HÖYRUP, *Compt. rend. trav. lab. Carlsberg*, 12 (1917) 12.

[62] A. G. OGSTON, *Arch. Biochem. Biophys.*, 89 (1960) 181.

[63] S. MOORE AND W. H. STEIN, *Advances in Protein Chem.*, 11 (1956) 191.

[64] P. VON TAVEL AND R. SIGNER, *Advances in Protein Chem.*, 11 (1956) 237.

[65] F. R. N. GURD AND P. E. WILCOX, *Advances in Protein Chem.*, 11 (1956) 311.

[66] N. W. PIRIE, *Biol. Revs. Cambridge Phil. Soc.*, 15 (1940) 377.

[67] R. A. ALBERTY, E. A. ANDERSON AND J. W. WILLIAMS, *J. Phys. & Colloid Chem.*, 52 (1948) 217.

[68] P. GRABAR, *Advances in Protein Chem.*, 13 (1958) 1.

[69] D. H. SPACKMAN, W. H. STEIN AND S. MOORE, *Anal. Chem.*, 30 (1958) 1190.

[70] H. FRAENKEL-CONRAT, J. I. HARRIS AND A. L. LEVY in D. GLICK (Ed.), *Methods of Biochemical Analysis*, Vol. 2, Interscience, New York, 1955, p. 359.

[71] F. SANGER, *Advances in Protein Chem.*, 7 (1952) 1.

[72] L. C. CRAIG *et al.* in A. C. CORCORAN (Ed.), *Methods in Medical Research*, Vol. 5, Year Book Publishers, Chicago, 1952, pp. 1–133.

[73] J. R. COLVIN, D. B. SMITH AND W. H. COOK, *Chem. Revs.*, 54 (1954) 687.

[74] K. SATAKE AND J. M. LUCK, *Bull. soc. chim. biol.*, 40 (1958) 1743.

[75] S. SAKAGUCHI, *J. Biochem. (Tokyo)*, 5 (1925) 25, 133, 143, 159.

[76] M. X. SULLIVAN, W. C. HESS AND H. W. HOWARD, *J. Biol. Chem.*, 145 (1942) 621.

[77] G. HUNTER, *Biochem. J.*, 16 (1922) 637.

[78] R. KAPELLER-ADLER, *Biochem. Z.*, 264 (1933) 131.

[79] D. J. PROCKOP AND S. UDENFRIEND, *Anal. Biochem.*, 1 (1960) 228.

[80] P. L. KIRK, *Advances in Protein Chem.*, 3 (1947) 139.

[81] A. G. GORNALL, C. J. BARDAWILL AND M. M. DAVID, *J. Biol. Chem.*, 177 (1949) 751.

[82] M. B. RISING AND P. S. YANG, *J. Biol. Chem.*, 99 (1933) 755.

[83] M. I. PLEKAN, *Zhur. Obshchei Khim.*, 28 (1958) 3133.

[84] T. S. MA AND G. ZUAZAGA, *Anal. Chem.*, 14 (1942) 280.

[85] S. MOORE AND W. H. STEIN, *J. Biol. Chem.*, 176 (1948) 367.

[86] S. RUHEMANN, *J. Chem. Soc.*, 99 (1911) 792, 1306, 1486.

[87] G. R. KINGSLEY AND G. GETCHELL, *J. Biol. Chem.*, 225 (1957) 545.

[88] J. B. MURPHY AND M. W. KIES, *Biochim. Biophys. Acta*, 45 (1960) 382.

[89] O. H. LOWRY, N. J. ROSEBROUGH, A. L. FARR AND R. J. RANDALL, *J. Biol. Chem.*, 193 (1951) 265.

[90] P. DOTY AND J. T. EDSALL, *Advances in Protein Chem.*, 6 (1951) 35.
[91] R. S. BEAR, *Advances in Protein Chem.*, 7 (1952) 69.
[92] A. TISELIUS AND F. L. HORSFALL, *J. Exptl. Med.*, 69 (1939) 83.
[93] E. BRAND, *Ann. N.Y. Acad. Sci.*, 47 (1946) 187.
[94] A. C. CHIBNALL, *Proc. Roy. Soc. (London) B*, 131 (1942) 136.
[95] H. NEURATH, *J. Am. Chem. Soc.*, 61 (1939) 1841.
[96] M. A. LAUFFER, *J. Am. Chem. Soc.*, 66 (1944) 1188.

Chapter II

Chemistry of Proteins

H. FRAENKEL-CONRAT

Department of Virology and Virus Laboratory,
University of California, Berkeley, Calif. (U.S.A.)

The development of our present concepts of protein chemistry started about 100 years ago, and is mostly due to the pioneering studies of such men as Curtius, Hofmeister, Miescher, Kossel, but most prominently to Emil Fischer. Fischer was convinced that proteins represented peptide-bonded condensation products of many amino acids and he set about to synthesize long peptide chains and thus to prove his point[1]. Since his time a few more amino acids were discovered and the methodology of handling proteins and their degradation products has been enormously enriched. But Fischer's fundamental ideas and experiments were rarely and never successfully questioned. Thus protein chemistry begins with the chemistry of the amino acids.

1. The amino acids as components of proteins

Almost all amino acids have the basic structure $H_2N-CHR-COOH$, the only exceptions being the imino acids proline and hydroxyproline. The proximity of two reactive and ionizable groups greatly affects the chemical behavior of this class of compounds. Actually the formula in aqueous neutral solution is not as written, but dissociation of a proton from the carboxyl group, and binding of a proton by the amino group makes this a zwitter (or hybrid) ion which is better formulated as $^+H_3N-CHR-COO^-$. However, since this chapter is devoted to the chemistry of proteins, and since the amino and carboxyl groups are lost upon entry of an amino acid into the protein structure we will not systematically discuss the chemistry of the free amino acids. The part of the amino acids which is of greatest importance for protein structure is the nature of the side chain or R group in the above formula. Table I lists the amino acids which occur in proteins; a few listed at the bottom of the table have been found in only one small group of proteins or another; many other amino acids, not listed, have not been detected in proteins, but only in free form in plants or in some special products of microbial metabolism. Upon consideration of the structure of amino acids it is evident that all but glycine have at least one asymmetric carbon atom, *i.e.* one carrying four different substituents. This means that each exists in the form of two isomers showing opposite optical rotation, as ascertained in a polarimeter. The actual angle and sign of rotation varies for different amino acids and depends on the solvent; however, it has been established that all or very nearly all amino acids derived from proteins have the same configuration and because this can be related to L-glyceraldehyde (*levorotatory*) the amino acids are given the prefix L-; a (+) or (—) sign after the L indicates the actual observed dextro or levo-rotation. The configuration of the L- and D-form, as presented in a plane is as shown; actually if the H atom is visualized at the top of the pyramid, the other 3 substituents of the carbon are arranged in clockwise manner around the base in the L-form, and counter-clockwise in the D-form.

$$
\begin{array}{cc}
\text{L} & \text{D} \\[1em]
\text{COO}^- & \text{COO}^- \\
| & | \\
{}^+\text{H}_3\text{N—C—H} & {}^+\text{H}_3\text{N—C—R} \\
| & | \\
\text{R} & \text{H}
\end{array}
$$

While proteins appear to contain only L-amino acids, the D-forms occur not infrequently in nature, particularly in the lower forms of life.

The chemical nature of the R group of the amino acids varies considerably, and will now be briefly discussed (Table I). The two simplest members, glycine and alanine, lack striking characteristics. As the aliphatic chain gets longer and more complex (valine, leucine, isoleucine) the R group acquires a distinct hydrophobic character which tends to make the polymer less water-soluble; such groups attract and bind aliphatic compounds, such as soaps and detergents.

In contrast, alcoholic side chains (serine and threonine) contribute to the hydrophilic properties of the protein. Peptides of the imino acids (proline and hydroxyproline) are mainly characterized by the lack of an —NH group which usually plays an important role in inter-peptide bonding (see later).

The aromatic residues (phenylalanine, tyrosine, tryptophan) have their special hydrophobic flavor, and in addition they are set apart by their

TABLE I

THE AMINO ACIDS OF PROTEINS

Name	$\begin{array}{c}HOOC \\ HC-R \\ H_2N \end{array}$	Symbol	Mol. wt.
Glycine	R = H	Gly	75
Alanine	R = $-CH_3$	Ala	89
Valine	R = $-CH\begin{smallmatrix}CH_3 \\ CH_3\end{smallmatrix}$	Val	117
Leucine	R = $-CH-CH\begin{smallmatrix}CH_3 \\ CH_3\end{smallmatrix}$	Leu	131
Isoleucine	R = $-CH-CH_2-CH_3$ with CH_3	Ileu	131
Phenylalanine	R = $-CH_2-$⬡	Phe	165
Tyrosine	R = $-CH_2-$⬡$-OH$	Tyr	181
Tryptophan	R = $-CH_2-$(indole ring)	Try	204
Serine	R = $-CH_2OH$	Ser	105
Threonine	R = $-CHOH-CH_3$	Thr	119
Cysteine	R = $-CH_2-SH$	CySH	121
Cystine	R = $-CH_2-S-S-CH_2-$	CyS-SCy	240
Methionine	R = $-CH_2-CH_2-S-CH_3$	Met	149
Aspartic acid	R = $-CH_2-COOH$	Asp	133
Asparagine	R = $-CH_2-CONH_2$	Asp(NH$_2$)	132
Glutamic acid	R = $-CH_2-CH_2-COOH$	Glu	147
Glutamine	R = $-CH_2-CH_2-CONH_2$	Glu(NH$_2$)	146
Lysine	R = $-CH_2-CH_2-CH_2-CH_2-NH_2$	Lys	146
Arginine	R = $-CH_2-CH_2-CH_2-NH-C(NH_2)=NH$	Arg	174
Histidine	R = $-CH_2-$(imidazole ring)	His	154

TABLE I *(continued)*

Name		Symbol	Mol. wt.
Proline	HOOC—CH—CH$_2$ / HN—CH$_2$ / CH$_2$ (ring)	Pro	115
Hydroxyproline	HOOC—CH—CH$_2$ / HN—CHOH / CH$_2$ (ring)	HyPro	131
Hydroxylysine	R= —CH$_2$—CH$_2$—CH—CH$_2$ with OH and NH$_2$	HyLy	162
Thyroxin	R= —CH$_2$— (diiodophenyl)—O—(diiodophenyl)—OH	Thy	777
Ornithine[a]	R= —CH$_2$—CH$_2$—CH$_2$—NH$_2$	Orn	132
Citrulline[a]	R= —CH$_2$—CH$_2$—CH$_2$—NH—CO—NH$_2$	Cit	175

[a] Doubtful whether these ever occur in proteins.

ability to absorb ultraviolet light, owing to their conjugated double bond system. As a function of the number of double bonds and the presence of auxochromic groups, such as >NH and —OH groups, the molar extinction coefficient increases markedly from phenylalanine to tyrosine, and tryptophan, and the wave length of maximal absorption rises from about 260 to 280 mμ. The phenolic group distinguishes tyrosine from all other common amino acids. The sulfur-containing amino acid residues (cystine, cysteine, methionine) are susceptible to oxidizing and reducing agents (but so are some of the others); cystine plays a particular structural role because its R group forms a crosslink between two chains (Formula I)

$$
\begin{array}{ccc}
| & & | \\
NH & & NH \\
| & & | \\
HC—CH_2—S—S—CH_2—CH \\
| & & | \\
CO & & CO \\
| & & | \\
& (I) &
\end{array}
$$

The acid nature of aspartic and glutamic acid is of obvious importance in determining the properties of the polymer; on the other hand the corresponding amides, asparagine and glutamine, are neutral and not particularly reactive except as possible hydrogen-bonding sites.

Finally we come to the basic amino acid residues. Arginine carries the very strongly basic guanidyl group which is always fully ionized over the stability range of most proteins. The amino group of lysine represents a very characteristic protein group, both because of its chemical reactivity and its tendency to become protonated at pH's below 10.5. The imidazole group of histidine, finally, dissociates or releases its proton at just about neutral pH; this residue appears to play an important role in many protein enzyme reactions.

The amino acid residues of a peptide chain are frequently represented by the 3 or 4-letter symbols introduced by Brand[2] and included in Table I.

(a) The peptide bond and other primary bonds of proteins

The amino acids occur in proteins in peptide linkage, the result of a condensation reaction with loss of water between an amino and a carboxyl group. The condensation of 4 amino acids to a so called tetrapeptide can be represented as follows (Formula II):

$$
\begin{array}{cccc}
\text{R} & \text{R'} & \text{R''} & \text{R'''} \\
| & | & | & | \\
\text{H}_2\text{N--CH--COOH} + & \text{H}_2\text{N--CH--COOH} + & \text{H}_2\text{N--CH--COOH} + & \text{H}_2\text{N--CH--COOH}
\end{array}
$$

$$-\big\| +\text{H}_2\text{O} \qquad -\big\| +\text{H}_2\text{O} \qquad -\big\| +\text{H}_2\text{O}$$

$$
\begin{array}{cccc}
\text{R} & \text{R'} & \text{R''} & \text{R'''} \\
| & | & | & | \\
\text{H}_2\text{N--CH--CO--NH--CH--CO--NH--CH--CO--NH--CH--COOH}
\end{array}
$$

$$\text{(II)}$$

The resultant —CO—NH— linkage, the peptide bond, takes the place of the two characteristic polar groups of all amino acids, and thus greatly changes their character. The peptide bond, weakly acidic in nature, contributes definite new properties to the macromolecule and its ability to acquire a three-dimensional structure, which will be discussed in a later chapter.

The peptide bond structure of proteins is often referred to as a hypothesis, but it has received so much new supporting evidence since the days of Emil Fischer that this no longer seems necessary, even though it is true that each piece of evidence by itself is not conclusive. To list some of the evidence:

(1) Titrations show that proteins contain relatively few —COO⁻ and —NH₃⁺ groups, some proteins almost none of either or both types of groups; and that upon hydrolytic degradation of the protein both types of groups appear at the same rate. This is as would be expected from the reaction scheme of Formula II.

(2) Incomplete hydrolytic degradation yields some di- or tri-peptides which can be shown to be identical with synthetic peptides of known structure. Syntheses of bigger peptides, some approaching protein chains in length, have also yielded products identical with the natural peptides in all respects including biological (*i.e.* hormonal) activity[3].

(3) Specific reactions of —CO—NH— compounds, such as the biuret test and the chlorine–starch–iodine test (see later) are given by proteins.

(4) Enzymes which specifically attack the —CO—NH— bonds of certain synthetic peptides attack with similar affinity the corresponding sites in proteins.

(5) Proteins show infrared as well as far-ultraviolet ($\sim$ 200 mμ) absorbance characteristics typical for the peptide bond.

The peptide bond is usually defined as an imide linkage between the α-carboxyl and α-amino groups of two amino acids. However, the possibility exists that amino acids such as lysine, glutamic and aspartic acid are bonded through their respective ε, γ, and β groups, be it instead of, or in addition to the α-peptide linkage. Some of the evidence just cited for the peptide bond rules out the possibility that such bonds are common or frequent. Other evidence against this will later be reported. Nevertheless, there are strong indications, and in some instances even proof, that such bonds do occur in specific cases and it is not impossible that their occurrence in small numbers (*e.g.* one or two) is more frequent and has been overlooked in typical proteins. The specific cases are (1) in collagen and related proteins, some of the lysine, possibly about one-third, is bound both by its α- and its ε-amino group to other amino acids, thus forming branches or crosslinks between chains[4], and, (2) a bacterial polyglutamic acid, not a protein, composed of D- rather than L-glutamic acid, is largely held together through γ-imide linkages[5]. Indirect indications for the occurrence of free α-carboxyl and α-carboxamido groups (—CO—NH₂) in many proteins were also obtained by two different techniques[6].

Another type of bond that could well occur in proteins is an ester bond between the hydroxyl groups of serine and threonine and either any α-carboxyl or the β- and γ-carboxyl groups of aspartic and glutamic acids. Such ester bonds could replace the peptide linkage of the main chain, but this is extremely unlikely, since esters of this type, when artificially produced by a rearrangement reaction known as the acyl shift, are known to be very labile (Formula III).

References p. 105

$$\begin{array}{cc} HO-CH_2 & R \\ | & | \\ -CO-NH-CH-CO-NH-CH-CO- \end{array} \underset{OH^-}{\overset{H^+}{\rightleftharpoons}} \begin{array}{c} -CO-O-CH_2 \\ | \\ H_2N-CH-CO-NH-CH-CO- \\ | \\ R \end{array} \qquad (III)$$

The alternate possibility, ester bonds as branch points or crosslinks, are somewhat more probable and definite evidence in their favor has been reported in the case of collagen, which in various respects has proven to be an unusual protein[7]. But the more we learn about proteins, the more we find that most of them are usually unusual. It was also demonstrated that many mucin-like proteins carry ester-bound disaccharide side chains containing neuraminic acid[8].

Other potential crosslinks which have been suggested but not proven are through imide linkages involving carbonic acid. Bicarbonate definitely adds to amino groups and condensation to a second amino group would seem a distinct possibility (Formula IV a,b). Imide crosslinks between carboxyl groups must also be considered (Formula IVc).

$$\begin{aligned} &(a) \quad R-NH_2 \; + H_2CO_3 \rightleftharpoons R-NH-COOH + H_2O \\ &(b) \; 2\,R-NH_2 \; + H_2CO_3 \longrightarrow R-NH-CO-NH-R + 2\,H_2O \\ &(c) \quad R-COOH + H_2N-CO-R' \longrightarrow R-CO-NH-CO-R' + H_2O \quad (IV) \end{aligned}$$

All these represent means of establishing crosslinking bonds in proteins which may well occur occasionally. Another crosslink which has been postulated as present in phosphoproteins is through doubly esterified serine phosphate groups[9] (Formula Va,b).

$$\begin{array}{cccc}
| & & | & \\
CO & O & CO & O & NH \\
| & \parallel & | & \parallel & | \\
CH-CH_2-O-P-OH & CH-CH_2-O-P-O-CH_2-CH \\
| & | & | & | & | \\
NH & O^- & NH & O^- & CO \\
| & & | & & | \\
(Va) & & (Vb) & \\
\end{array}$$

The ability of divalent metals (mercury, iron, etc.) to form specific crossbonds in proteins is well established, and will be discussed in a later chapter. Finally there is the cystine disulfide bond (Formula I) which, beyond any doubt acts as crosslink between chains and which will be repeatedly mentioned.

Cyclic peptides have occasionally been observed in microorganisms, and their existence in typical proteins is not excluded. One example[10] is the antibiotic gramicidin S(VI). These must be clearly differentiated from ring structures formed by a disulfide linkage, which definitely occur in typical proteins. One example of the occurrence of such a ring in a relatively small peptide is the structure of the hormone oxytocin[3] (Formula VII).

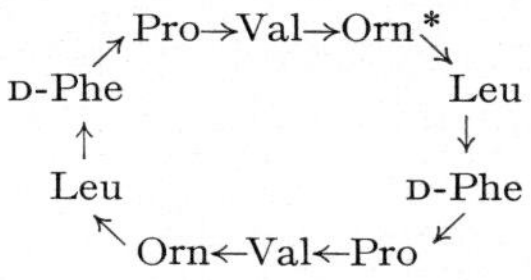

$$H_2N—Cy \longrightarrow Tyr \longrightarrow Ileu$$

$$
\begin{array}{c}
\nearrow Pro \rightarrow Val \rightarrow Orn^* \searrow \\
\text{D-Phe} \qquad\qquad \text{Leu} \\
\uparrow \qquad\qquad\qquad \downarrow \\
\text{Leu} \qquad\qquad \text{D-Phe} \\
\nwarrow Orn \leftarrow Val \leftarrow Pro \swarrow
\end{array}
$$

(VI)

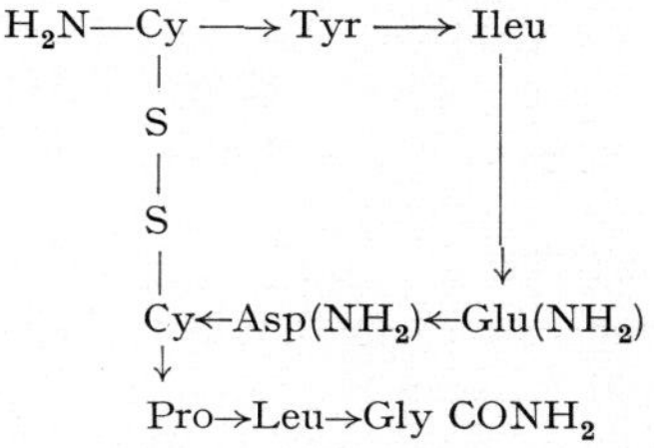

$$
\begin{array}{c}
H_2N—Cy \longrightarrow Tyr \longrightarrow Ileu \\
| \qquad\qquad\qquad\qquad | \\
S \qquad\qquad\qquad\qquad | \\
| \qquad\qquad\qquad\qquad | \\
S \qquad\qquad\qquad\qquad | \\
| \qquad\qquad\qquad\qquad \downarrow \\
Cy \leftarrow Asp(NH_2) \leftarrow Glu(NH_2) \\
\downarrow \\
Pro \rightarrow Leu \rightarrow Gly \; CONH_2
\end{array}
$$

(VII)

* Ornithine, $NH_2—CH—CH_2—CH_2—CH_2—NH_2$
$\qquad\qquad\qquad |$
$\qquad\qquad COOH$

In the representation of peptide chains it is customary to start with the free amino end (N-terminal group) and proceed from left to right towards the free carboxyl group (C-terminal group; see Formula II). Frequently, and particularly in cyclic peptides, arrows are used to indicate the direction $(—CO—NH = \rightarrow)$. The suffix -yl indicates an

$$
\begin{array}{c}
R \\
| \\
X—NH—CH—CO—
\end{array}
$$

group, while the name of the amino acid stands for

$$
\begin{array}{c}
R \\
| \\
X—NH—CH—COOH, \; (X = H \; or \; —CO):
\end{array}
$$

thus seryl glycine (Ser–Gly, Ser $\rightarrow$ Gly) is

$$
\begin{array}{c}
CH_2OH \\
| \\
NH_2—CH—CO—NH—CH_2—COOH
\end{array}
$$

and glycyl serine (Gly–Ser, Gly $\rightarrow$ Ser)

$$
\begin{array}{c}
CH_2OH \\
| \\
NH_2CH_2—CO—NH—CH—COOH
\end{array}
$$

(b) The hydrolysis of proteins

The formation and hydrolysis of peptide bonds is shown in Formula II as an equilibrium reaction. Actually the equilibrium favors the top (open) state so greatly that this condensation probably does not take part in any biosynthetic pathway. Nature, as well as the organic chemist must activate the carboxyl group for synthetic purposes. While the equilibrium favors hydrolysis of peptides, the rate of the reaction is extremely slow, unless catalysts are employed. Useful catalysts for hydrolysis of peptides and proteins are, (i) strong acids, (ii) strong alkali and (iii) enzymes.

(i) Acid hydrolysis

Any strong acid can be used; constant-boiling hydrochloric acid (about 6 N) is most frequently employed; this is preferably twice redistilled from glass to remove trace metals. Boiling under reflux is often convenient. For greatest accuracy the sample, suspended in a 10–100 fold of the acid is frozen, and the container, usually a test tube, evacuated by means of a vacuum pump, and sealed. It is then held at 110° for 12–96 h. Tryptophan completely decomposes during the acid hydrolysis of most proteins and must be separately determined. Serine, threonine and in certain proteins certain other amino acids slowly decompose during prolonged acid hydrolysis. Thus, when a decrease is noted in comparing the content of any amino acid in a 24-h and a 48-h hydrolysate, then it is customary to plot such data combined with those of additional hydrolysates (e.g. 12, 72 h) and extrapolate the hoped-for line, the decay rate of the given amino acid, back to zero-time. This value is regarded as the best analytical value, although occasionally the procedure is simplified by using only a 24-h hydrolysate and correcting the serine and threonine values by factors of 1.1 and 1.05, respectively[2].

While these amino acids decrease upon prolonged acid treatment the content of others, particularly valine, isoleucine, and leucine often increase in the hydrolysate with time. This is due to the particularly slow rate of hydrolysis of peptide bonds between these hydrophobic residues. It is for that reason that sufficiently long hydrolysis periods are employed to obtain maximal analytical values for these amino acids.

When hydrochloric acid is used for hydrolysis, the excess over that bound by the basic groups in the hydrolysate can be removed by evaporation in vacuo. Sulfuric acid is usually separated from the hydrolysate as barium sulfate by the addition of baryta $(Ba(OH)_2)$.

Acid hydrolysates generally contain varying amounts of so called humin: black material which is more or less insoluble. This is usually the result of the interaction of decomposing tryptophan and carbohydrates (if these are present), or aldehydes as they arise from the decomposition of serine, cysteine, etc. In the absence of any such aldehydes, tryptophan is actually quite resistant to acid, as shown with gramicidin (Dubos), a bacterial antibiotic peptide very rich in tryptophan (40 %) and devoid of serine, threonine, sulfur-containing amino acids, and others. In this peptide no tryptophan is lost and no humin formed upon acid hydrolysis. Proteins lacking trypto-phan also give little if any humin.

(ii) Alkaline hydrolysis

2–4 N sodium hydroxide or saturated baryta hydrolyzes most peptide bonds quite rapidly, so that periods of 4–8 h at 100° are usually adequate. Teflon tubes are advantageous to avoid silicates in the hydrolysate. Alkaline hydrolysis has the following serious disadvantages: it causes the decom-position of certain amino acids (arginine, cystine, cysteine); it causes racemi-zation (loss of optical activity) of most amino acids in contrast to acid which does not significantly affect their steric isomerism; it gradually destroys many amino acids by deamination. Alkali is therefore only used for specific purposes, such as tryptophan analysis.

(iii) Enzymatic hydrolysis

To achieve complete breakdown of a protein by enzymatic means is a difficult and time-consuming process. Several combinations of proteases and peptidases have been suggested. Particularly bacterial proteases might be effective in such combinations. However, at present, enzymes have been used primarily when partial hydrolysis was the object. For this purpose they have distinct advantages over H^+ or OH^- ions. Such applications of enzymes will be frequently referred to in the course of this chapter.

(c) The isolation of amino acids

The earliest methods of amino acid analysis relied on the isolation of the amino acids from the hydrolysate of a protein. Later, isolation was performed mainly for preparative purposes. Some amino acids are so insoluble in water (e.g. leucine, tyrosine) that they can be obtained directly as crystals by appropriate adjustment of the pH of the hydrolysate. Others were caused to precipitate by the addition of reagents of specific affinities. Nowadays there is rarely any need to employ isolation methods.

(d) Amino acid analysis

(i) Column chromatography

The present method of choice relies on ion exchange chromatography for the separation of the amino acids in a mixture, and on the ninhydrin

References p. 105

color reaction (see later) for their detection and quantitative estimation. The ion exchanger most commonly used is a sulfonated polystyrene resin, (Dowex 50 crosslinked to varying extent or Amberlite IR 120), and buffers of increasing pH and ionic strength are employed for the development[11]. By means of an automatic fraction collector, small aliquots of the effluent are collected and subsequently analyzed by the ninhydrin and other tests[12]. Automatic amino acid analyzers are now commercially available which operate on the same principles and plot directly the ninhydrin color intensity of the effluent against time. The resultant analyses, under favorable conditions, may have an error of less than 2 %. By such techniques, therefore, an average size protein containing usually no more than 50 residues of any one amino acid, can be analyzed with sufficient accuracy to allow an expression of its composition in terms of residues of each amino acid per mole protein. As an example, the composition of the protein from tobacco mosaic virus (mol. wt. = 17,500) will be given in such terms, since it is one of the first proteins so analyzed with complete concordance in two independent laboratories (Table II). This protein was also previously analyzed quite

TABLE II

COMPOSITION OF TMV PROTEIN

Residues/mole, mol. wt. = 17,500; 158 residues total

	Asp	Thr	Ser	Pro	Glu	Gly	Ala	Val	Ileu	Leu	Tyr	Phe	Lys	Arg	Try[c]	CyS[c]
Automatic amino acid[82,83] analyzer[a]	18	16	16	8	16	6	14	14	9	12	4	8	2	11	(3)	(1)
Dowex 50 non-automatic[84]	19	17	18	8	17	6	15	14	9	13	4	8	2	11	(2)	(1)
Microbiol.[81]	19	15[b]	13[b]	9	14	5	11	15	9	13	4	9	2	10	(2–3)	(1)
FDNB[85]	19	14	16	8	16	6	14	15		20	4	8	2	10	(3)	(1)

a The same analysis was obtained in two laboratories.
b Uncorrected for decomposition during hydrolysis.
c Separately determined; final value for Try(3) derived from sequence work.

carefully by the non-automatic column technique, and for the purposes of comparison those data will also be given, as well as those obtained yet earlier by the FDNB and the microbiological methods which will be discussed presently (Table II).

(ii) Paper chromatographic methods

A considerable number of simpler though less precise chromatographic methods are also frequently used and will be briefly mentioned. Many of these rely on direct paper chromatographic separation of the amino acids in a hydrolysate which is often developed two-dimensionally. The amino acids are then located by spraying with ninhydrin and analyzed either after elution or directly by photometric methods applied to the spot. Such methods give adequate results in the hands of the originator of a particular technique, but have rarely been transplanted successfully to another laboratory. They are certainly very useful for preliminary or semiquantitative surveys. The characteristic differences in the nuances of color and appearance of different amino acids, particularly when sprayed with a collidin or acetic acid-containing ninhydrin solution, make their identification on two-dimensional chromatograms quite easy[13]. Elution of amino acids from chromatograms and analysis by specific reagents have also at times been employed.

A method which has proven of more wide-spread usefulness, even though limited in precision, consists in transforming all amino acids in the hydroly-sate to their yellow dinitrophenyl derivatives. This is achieved by treatment with 1-fluoro-2,4-dinitrobenzene (FDNB) at pH 8 and 40° for one hour (see later). Most of the yellow amino acid derivatives can be extracted with ether from acid solution. All can be separated two-dimensionally on paper[14]. The plainly visible spots are cut out, eluted, and their absorbance read at 360 mμ and 390 mμ, near the respective maxima for dinitrophenyl (DNP) derivatives of all typical amino acids, and the imino acids proline and hydroxyproline[15].

(iii) Other methods[16]

Methods of purely historical significance will not be listed or described. A series of methods which appear theoretically sound, and yet have been rarely applied, rely on the principles of isotope dilution. These methods require the isotopically labelled amino acids or a labelled reagent and techniques for their measurement. Furthermore they call for isolation of a very pure sample of the amino acid or the derivative though this isolation need not be quantitative. It seems that all methods which require individual handling of each amino acid by specialist's techniques can no longer compete with the chromatographic methods.

The same is probably true for microbiological assays which were the methods of choice until about 1950. The principle of these methods is the use of fastidious strains of bacteria or molds which have definite nutritional amino acid requirements. Such a culture does not grow if deprived of a given amino acid, and upon addition of that amino acid the growth rate is within certain limits proportional to its concentration. The growth rate is determined either turbidimetrically, or by titration of the acid formed by

TABLE III

COMPOSITION OF A FEW SELECTED PROTEINS[a]

	Asp	Thr	Ser	Pro	Glu	Gly	Ala	Val	CyS[a]	Met	Ileu	Leu	Tyr	Phe	Lys	His	Arg	Try	Others	Total	NH₃
Ribonuclease (bovine pancreas) residues/mole	15	10	15	4	12	3	12	9	8	4	3	2	6	3	10	4	4	0		124	16–17
Lysozyme (hen's egg) residues/mole	20	7	9	2	5	~12	~11	6	10	2	6	8	3	3	6	1	11	8		~130	~18
Ovalbumin (hen's egg) residues/mole	32	16	36	14	52	19	35	28	7	16	25	32	9	21	20	7	15	3		387	~33
Collagen (bovine) residues/10⁵ g	47	19	32	131	77	363	106	29	0	5	14	28	5	15	30	5	49	0	HyPro 107 HyLy 7	1069	~47
Silk fibroin (Bombyx mori) residues/10⁵ g	21	13	154	6	15	581	334	31	0	0	8	7	71	10	5	2	6	0		1264	0
Salmine (salmon sperm) residues/mole	0	0	7	4	0	3	1	2	0	0	1	0	0	0	0	0	40	0		58	0

[a] Most recent and reliable data from refs. [16,18].

organisms such as the lactobacilli. This method requires separate handling of each amino acid, but once a suitable organism is found and a reference or standard curve constructed with known amounts of the given amino acid, then analyses for this amino acid can be performed quickly and in a routine fashion[17].

(e) *The composition of proteins*

The composition of proteins in terms of amino acids varies widely. A few proteins are quite exceptionally rich in one or several amino acids; for instance the protamines consist to almost 80 % of arginine; silk fibroin to 57 % of glycine and alanine; collagen to 30 % of those two and 26 % of proline and hydroxyproline. But most proteins fluctuate within narrower limits. The absence of certain amino acids from some proteins is also quite a characteristic property, and useful in their characterization and as evidence for the absence of contaminating proteins. The inspection of such data[16,18,19] (see Table III) is at first sight somewhat disconcerting, for these figures carry meaning only in relation to one another. Such crucial properties as the acidic or basic nature of the protein can be deduced only by much mental arithmetic, namely the subtraction of the amide from the glutamic + aspartic acid value followed by the division of this by the arginine + lysine content. Several of the listed analyses were obtained by methods of limited accuracy and are therefore subject to minor correction. The importance and the role of reliable amino acid analytical data is similar for protein chemistry as is the empirical formula for simpler organic molecules. We do not "recognize" $C_9H_{13}O_3N$ as adrenalin, but we need these figures to interpret its structural analysis. In the same way the amino acid formula of the TMV protein (Table II) is not by itself very illuminating, but is of great comparative value, and is quite essential in the structural analysis of that protein.

It is well to remember that the composition of a protein is of significance only if the protein is pure. The same is true for the aspects of protein chemistry to be discussed below. Methods of purification and criteria for purity were dealt with in the preceding chapter.

2. Reactions of proteins and peptides

Since proteins represent complex polymers carrying the side chains of all component amino acids, they would be expected to react with all amino acid reagents. This is generally so, except for the fact that the 3-dimensional folded structure of a native protein can mask certain groups so effectively that they do not react or react very sluggishly, unless the protein be first denatured. The opposite effect, an unusually increased reactivity or a change in the conditions required for reactivity, has also been observed as a consequence of native structure. Such observations are of great interest because they play an important role in present concepts of the mechanism of enzyme action. In general, however, protein reactions, like those of peptides, are the sum total of the reactions of their component amino acids.

The complexity of the macromolecule, and the fact that all kinds of reactive side chains are usually present makes the specificity of each reagent an important consideration. How can one ascertain whether only the expected reaction is taking place? This question will be ever-present in the forthcoming discussion and will be answered whenever possible.

One particular feature of the reactivity of peptide and protein groups which has acquired great importance in the elucidation of their structure is that of the chain end amino and carboxyl groups, the so-called N-terminal and C-terminal groups and residues, and specific reagents for these groups are thus of singular interest.

(a) Reactions used in detection and analysis of protein groups

(i) Peptide bond reactions

A structural feature common to all peptides and proteins is the peptide bond. Reagents to detect the peptide bond are therefore of great general usefulness for the estimation of such materials. Most specific of these seems to be the biuret reaction[20] which measures colorimetrically the complex of one atom of copper with 4 peptide-NH groups. This method seems to give consistent results with a variety of proteins, but is not very sensitive. A combination of this reaction with the Folin phenol reaction (to be discussed later) gives a 100 fold more sensitive test for proteins[21], but the color here is not only a function of the peptide bond and thus shows some variation from one protein to another. Nevertheless this method is in general use because it represents one of the most sensitive means of detecting proteins or peptides generally. The chlorine–starch–iodide test[22] has been employed primarily for the detection of these substances on paper chromatograms. The U.V. absorption at 200 mμ is also of potential usefulness for the estimation of peptide bonds, but it lacks specificity.

(ii) Amino group reactions

Ninhydrin (oxidation). The ninhydrin reaction is at present the most commonly used method for the detection and measurement of amino compounds[23]. The reagent, ninhydrin or triketohydrindene hydrate is a powerful oxidizing agent which like chloramine T and other similar agents causes the oxidative deamination of an α-amino group to ammonia and an aldehyde. The ammonia forms a deep purple dye by condensing with one mole each of the original and the reduced ninhydrin (VIII). The intensity of the color (at 570 mμ) is nearly proportional to the amount of amino-N present, and not greatly affected by the nature of the R-group, except in the case of cysteine, cystine and tryptophan. Imino groups, such as proline, give end products of a different color (440 mμ = max.).

Ninhydrin

VIII   Blue pigment

Ninhydrin is employed for the purpose of measuring the amino acids in chromatographic methods of analysis (see p. 66). It is also used to detect amino acids or peptides on chromatograms. It is finally used for the determination of amino groups in proteins[24]. This extension of the ninhydrin reaction presupposes that the reagent gives a colored complex even when acting on the ε-amino group of lysine. This appears not to be the case at the pH of 5.5 used in the Moore and Stein procedure; however, at a higher pH and in the presence of pyridine the lysine ε-amino groups definitely are the main chromogenic groups of proteins.

Little has been done to establish the specificity of the ninhydrin reaction. Since it is used only analytically the question is more simply: does it release ammonia and thus generate color with other than amino groups. The fact that none of the amino acids or proteins give unexpectedly high color values suggests that this is not the case. Ninhydrin was used also in a different manner: when acting on free amino acids, and only in that case, the R-group decomposes further and liberates free CO_2 which can be determined manometrically[25].

Dinitrophenylation (alkylation). The reaction of amino acids with 1-fluoro-2,4-dinitrobenzene (FDNB) has previously been mentioned. The amino groups of peptides and proteins react in the same manner, the ε-amino groups because of their higher dissociation constant somewhat more sluggishly than the α-amino groups of the chain end. In addition to the amino groups, the phenolic groups of tyrosine, the imidazole groups of histidine, and the —SH groups of cysteine tend to become alkylated[26]. But the products of these reactions are not yellow and thus do not interfere with the prime use of FDNB as an amino reagent (Formula IX). These side reactions, nevertheless, have found considerable usefulness in studies concerned with the reactivity of the respective residues, particularly of histidine[27].

References p. 105

The introduction of FDNB into protein chemistry by Sanger[26] in 1945 represents a milestone in the history of biochemistry. This reaction supplied the stimulus for an enormously rapid advance in the structural chemistry of proteins which is still in progress. It is this work of Sanger's which focussed the attention of scientists on the end groups of proteins. Others had used similar reagents before, and again others had reported evidence on the end groups of insulin before. But the biochemical world was taken by storm through the combined effect of the pretty yellow DNP (dinitrophenyl) derivatives of the N-terminal amino acids residues of insulin, the

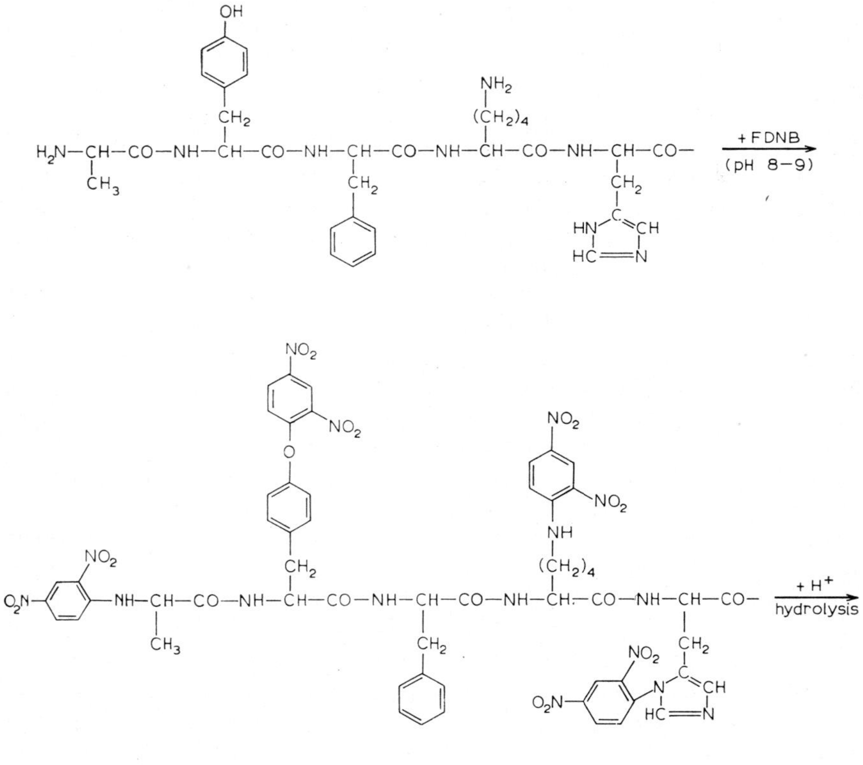

DNP-alanine   +   O-DNP-tyrosine   +   ε-DNP-lysine   +   im. DNP–histidine
(Yellow, ether sol.)   (Colorless)   (Yellow, ether   (Colorless)
                                              insoluble)

+ phenylalanine

IX

fact that there was so much of them (no other protein is as rich in end groups), and Sanger's careful work and self-effacing manner. The particular aim of dinitrophenylation and similar reactions lies in the preparation of derivatives which are resistant to acid hydrolysis. Thus the yellow α-DNP derivatives of the chain end amino acids present in a hydrolysate can be separated from the bulk of the amino acids by ether extraction (except of DNP-arginine), can be purified and isolated by chromatography, and can quantitatively be determined by spectrophotometry[14,15]. Actually, the DNP group of some amino acids is partially lost during the hot acid treatment, and the final analytical values must be corrected according to the lability of the specific DNP-amino acid under the conditions of hydrolysis used.

Apart from the detection of N-terminal residues, FDNB has proven a useful tool for other purposes. Thus, incomplete acid hydrolysis can lead to identifiable DNP-peptides, and by this method Sanger found the first amino acid sequences of the insulin molecule. The ε-DNP-lysine can also be separated from the hydrolysate, identified and determined. In most proteins, the ε-DNP-lysine corresponds well to the lysine content of the protein. This indicates that the lysine amino groups of most proteins are free and not involved in amide crosslinkages. In the collagens[15] part of the lysine did not react with FDNB, and it is in these proteins that the presence of amino acid substituents on the ε-amino groups of lysine residues has since been demonstrated[4]. The same may be the case with other proteins in which the lysine content of the hydrolysate is higher than the number of reactive ε-amino groups.

Other nitrobenzene derivatives have been advocated as advantageous for specific purposes, be it because they act more selectively, or because they form crosslinks, or more water-soluble derivatives[15].

Deamination. The reaction of primary amino groups with nitrous acid leads to the release of an equivalent amount of nitrogen (Formula X)

$$R-NH_3^+ + HONO \longrightarrow R-N=N^+ + 2\ H_2O \longrightarrow R-OH + N_2 + H^+ + H_2O \qquad (X)$$

This reaction was studied extensively, particularly by Van Slyke[25] who designed a volumetric and a manometric apparatus for the determination of the nitrogen and gaseous end products of other reactions such as the CO_2 released from free amino acids by ninhydrin. This method for the analysis of amino-N in amino acids, peptides and proteins has been the mainstay of analytical protein chemistry until recently, and has been abandoned only because the ninhydrin colorimetric method is easier. It is not certain which of the two methods is more accurate, since both have their limitations. Nitrous acid is not very specific since it reacts also with phenolic, sulfhydryl, guanidyl and other groups[28]. However, no rapid release of nitrogen results from any of these reactions. Thus the reaction of nitrous acid with α-amino groups may be too fast (3–5 min) for side reactions to cause noticeable error. The reaction of nitrous acid with ε-amino groups requires 15–30 min to go to completion[24,28].

Isocyanates, isothiocyanates (acylation). Phenyl isocyanate and phenyl isothiocyanate (PTC) add readily to amino and imino groups yielding substituted urea or thiourea derivatives (Formula XI, XII a,b).

(XI)   R—NH$_2$ + O=C=N—C$_6$H$_5$ $\longrightarrow$ R—NH—CO—NH—C$_6$H$_5$

(XIIa) HOOC—CH(R)—NH$_2$ + S=C=N—C$_6$H$_5$ $\xrightarrow{\text{PTC (pH 8-9)}}$ HOOC—CH(R)—NH—HN—C(C$_6$H$_5$)=S $\xrightarrow{H^+}$ OC—CH(R)—NH—N(C$_6$H$_5$)—C=S

(XIIb)
HOOC—CH(R)—NH—CO—CH(R')—NH—CO—CH(R'')—NH$_2$ + PTC, then + H$^+$ $\longrightarrow$

HOOC—CH(R)—NH—CO—CH(R')—NH$_2$ + OC—CH(R'')—NH—N(C$_6$H$_5$)—C=S $\searrow$ Ether soluble phenylthiohydantoins

$\downarrow$ +PTC, +H$^+$

HOOC—CH(R)—NH$_2$ + OC—CH(R')—NH—N(C$_6$H$_5$)—C=S $\nearrow$

The unique aspect of these derivatives is the great tendency of the α-carbamyl compounds to cyclise to hydantoins, or thiohydantoins (XIIb) under the influence of acid catalysts. This occurs not only with the free amino acids, but quite readily also with peptides and proteins, and leads to release of the N-terminal residue in the form of an ether-soluble hydantoin or thiohydantoin, and appearance of a new N-terminal residue, the neighbor of the original one, on the otherwise unaltered chain (XIIb). This sequence of reactions gave the first valid end group data in the archaic days of protein structural chemistry, B.S. (before Sanger). Phenyl isothiocyanate (PTC) is particularly suitable for the purpose of stepwise degradation of peptides[29] and this reaction, used under a variety of conditions, has contributed to a similar extent to the recent rapid advance in protein chemistry as the FDNB method. The two methods actually complement one another since amino acids giving labile DNP derivatives (proline, glycine) represent no problem with PTC, while those giving labile thiohydantoins (*e.g.* serine) are well analyzable as DNP derivatives[15]. The use of these reagents in structural studies will later be discussed.

(iii) Reactions of ionizable groups and of the carboxyl groups

The characteristics of the ionizable groups of proteins will represent the subject of a later chapter. Here we will only list for the sake of completeness those analytical methods which are based on the titration or the complex ion binding by these groups. The most direct procedure is to construct titration curves for proteins and derive the numbers of dissociating carboxyl, imidazole and amino groups from different segments of these curves. The titration between pH 6 and 2.5 is quite representative of typical carboxylate groups. The titration of the amino groups is greatly improved by the use of the formol titration[30]. This consists in back titrating the basic groups lost under the influence of high concentration of formaldehyde (Formula XIII).

$$R—NH_3^+ + 2\ HCHO \rightleftharpoons R—N(CH_2OH)_2 + H^+ \qquad (XIII)$$

Other methods determine the complex binding of large ions by proteins. The extent of binding of an acidic dye (Orange G) at pH 2.2 as an insoluble protein–dye complex, as determined colorimetrically by difference, represents a reliable measure of the sum of guanidine, amino and imidazole groups[24,28]. The corresponding analyses for the total acid group by safranine binding at pH 11.5 is less reliable.

An alternate means of determining and blocking the carboxyl groups is by means of esterification with absolute methanol in the presence of a little HCl (*e.g.*, 0.1 N). Methoxyl analyses supply a measure of the extent of esterification[31]. This reaction, followed by reduction of the esterified protein by a borohydride, supplies additional data of importance in protein structural analysis[32], since the result is the transformation of all protein carboxyl groups into alcoholic groups. Thus the C-terminal amino acid is transformed into an amino-alcohol, and the glutamic and aspartic acid residues in the chain are transformed to hydroxy amino acids (Formula XIV). These reaction products can be isolated after hydrolysis and from their identification and estimation conclusions can be drawn concerning the C-terminal residues of the protein as well as the number of glutamic and aspartic residues with free γ- and β-carboxyl group. When reduction without preliminary esterification has yielded alcohols, this has at times been interpreted as indicative of the pre-existence of ester bonds in a given protein. However, the capacity of certain protein groups to react in unexpected manner casts serious doubt on such conclusions.

$$\text{—NH—CH—CO—NH—CH—CO—NH—CH—CO—NH—CH—COOH} + CH_3OH \xrightarrow{+H^+}$$

with side chains: CH_2–COOH; CH_2–CH_2–$CONH_2$; CH_2–CH_2–COOH; CH_3

$$\text{—NH—CH—CO—NH—CH—CO—NH—CH—CO—NH—CH—}\overset{O}{\underset{\diagdown}{C}}\text{—OCH}_3 \xrightarrow{+ LiBH_4}$$

with side chains: CH_2–$C(\!\!\diagup^O)\!$–OCH_3; $(CH_2)_2$–$CONH_2$; $(CH_2)_2$–$C(\!\!\diagup^O)\!$–OCH_3; CH_3

$$\text{—NH—CH—CO—NH—CH—CO—NH—CH—CO—NH—CH—CH}_2\text{OH} \xrightarrow[\text{hydrolysis}]{+H^+}$$

with side chains: CH_2–CH_2OH; $(CH_2)_2$–$CONH_2$; $(CH_2)_2$–CH_2OH; CH_3

$$\text{H}_2\text{N—CH—COOH, H}_2\text{N—CH—COOH, H}_2\text{N—CH—COOH, H}_2\text{N—CH—CH}_2\text{OH}$$

with side chains: CH_2–CH_2OH; $(CH_2)_2$–COOH; $(CH_2)_2$–CH_2OH; CH_3

$$(XIV)$$

(iv) Reactions of guanidyl, imidazole, phenolic and indole groups

The guanidyl group of arginine reacts specifically with α-naphthol and sodium hypochlorite at high pH, giving a pink color (Sakaguchi reaction). For quantitative purposes a modification proposed by Rosenberg et al.[33] is more reproducible.

The imidazole group of histidine, and with somewhat lesser affinity the phenolic group of tyrosine combine with diazo compounds, e.g., diazotized sulfanilic acid, giving orange to red products. This so called coupling reaction (Formula XV) (or the Pauly reaction) is very sensitive and suitable for the

XV

detection of small amounts of histidine and tyrosine, or peptides containing these residues.

If used for analytical purposes, the respective amino acids must be separated from the bulk[34], since the reaction lacks specificity[28-32].

A specific color reaction of phenols with free *ortho* positions (*e.g.* tyrosine) is with α-nitroso-β-naphthol. This has been used both for detection on paper, and for analysis. Several other reactions involve tyrosine and tryptophan. The xanthoproteic (conc. nitric acid) and Millon reactions (a mixture of mercuric and mercurous salts of nitric and nitrous acid) cause nitration of the aromatic rings, and in the latter case mercury binding. They are used only qualitatively. These three methods require very acid conditions and heat[36]. The Folin phenol reagent (phosphomolybdotungstate) becomes colored as it oxidizes tryptophan, tyrosine, cysteine and possibly other groups, which proceeds under gentle conditions. Notwithstanding its lack of specificity and limited reactivity the Folin reagent has been extensively used in protein chemistry, usually in a comparative manner and with sufficient controls and safeguards to establish the validity of the conclusions[28]. The remarkable synergistic action of the reagent with the biuret reagent for the detection of traces of peptide or proteins has been discussed (peptide bond reagents)[21].

Several aldehydes react with acid-decomposing tryptophan to give bright, usually blue colors with good specificity. The most commonly used are the Hopkins–Cole reagent (glyoxylic acid), and the Ehrlich reagent (dimethyl-amino benzaldehyde). These methods have been used for detection and analysis, but the quantitative aspects leave much to be desired[36].

(v) *Reactions of thiol groups*

The —SH groups of cysteine have probably received more analytical attention than any other group, largely because very frequently they seem to play important structural or functional roles. While of the previously discussed protein groups one may assume that at least a certain fraction will behave normally, this is not the case for —SH groups. For "normal behavior" of thiols (or mercaptans) includes autoxidizability, meaning susceptibility to oxidation by atmospheric oxygen at neutral or alkaline pH, and most proteins are not affected by oxygen. Actually the —SH groups of most native proteins are masked or sterically hindered in such a manner that they are unavailable to some, many, or all of the typical protein reagents. Various denaturing agents may reveal these groups to varying extent. Thus the result of an —SH group analysis of a protein should always include description of the conditions under which the protein reacted to a stated extent with the specified reagent.

The reaction of —SH groups with sodium nitroprusside at alkaline pH is a sensitive method for detecting available —SH groups. This pink color has not proven readily adaptable to direct colorimetry; instead, nitroprusside is used as an indicator while the —SH groups are titrated with the colorless reagents to be described below. Oxidative reagents, like iodosobenzoate, porphyrindene and ferricyanide are now only infrequently employed. This may be attributed to the complexity of the reaction, since the formation of disulfides, the desired end product (Formula XVIa)

(a) 2 R—SH $\xrightarrow{+ \frac{1}{2} O_2}$ R—S—S—R $+$ H$_2$O

(b) R—SH $\xrightarrow{+\frac{1}{2} O_2}$ R—SOH $\xrightarrow{+\frac{1}{2} O_2}$ R—SO$_2$H $\xrightarrow{+\frac{1}{2} O_2}$ R—SO$_3$H   (XVI)

$$(R = H_2N—CH—COOH: \text{ cysteine} \longrightarrow \text{cysteic acid})$$
$$\overset{|}{CH_2}$$
$$|$$

is dependent upon the existence of pairs of —SH groups within reach of one another; otherwise a series of poorly defined oxidative steps leads ultimately to cysteic acid (XVIb).

Alkylating agents react at pH 7–8 much more rapidly with available —SH groups than with other alkylatable groups (imidazole, amino); the most frequently used members of this class are iodoacetic acid and its amide, and their particular advantage lies in the formation of an acid-resistant thio-ether bond, and the ease of isolation and estimation of the resulting carboxymethylcysteine (Formula XVII).

$$\begin{array}{ccccc}
\text{—NH—CH—CO—} & & \text{—NH—CH—CO—} & & \text{H}_2\text{N—CH—COOH} \\
| & \xrightarrow[\text{(iodoacetamide)}]{+\text{ICH}_2\text{CONH}_2} & | & \xrightarrow[\text{(hydrolysis)}]{+\text{H}^+} & | \\
\text{CH}_2 & & \text{CH}_2 & & \text{CH}_2 \quad \text{(XVII)} \\
| & & | & & | \\
\text{SH} & & \text{S—CH}_2\text{—CONH}_2 & & \text{S—CH}_2\text{—COOH}
\end{array}$$

With compounds containing reactive double bonds, such as *N*-ethyl-maleimide, —SH groups react by addition (Formula XVIII).

$$\text{R—SH} + \begin{array}{c} \text{CH—CO} \\ \| \quad\quad \\ \text{CH—CO} \end{array}\!\!\!\!\!\!\!\!\! \diagdown\!\!\!\diagup N\text{—C}_2\text{H}_5 \longrightarrow \begin{array}{c} \text{R—S—CH—CO} \\ | \quad\quad\quad \\ \text{HCH—CO} \end{array}\!\!\!\!\!\!\!\!\! \diagdown\!\!\!\diagup N\text{—C}_2\text{H}_5 \quad \text{(XVIII)}$$

The most frequently used class of reagents exploit the high affinity of mercaptans for *mercury* compounds and *silver* ions. The classical reagent is *p*-chloromercuribenzoate (*p*CMB) (Formula XIX), although a smaller reagent such as methyl mercuric nitrate is often of distinct advantage.

$$\text{R—SH} + \text{ClHgC}_6\text{H}_4\text{COO}^- \longrightarrow \text{R—S—HgC}_6\text{H}_4\text{COO}^- + \text{H}^+, \text{Cl}^- \quad \text{(XIX)}$$

The extent of reaction with these mercurials can be ascertained titrimetrically. Mercury analyses performed on the isolated Hg-derivative of the protein are also feasible. A frequently used measure of the extent of reaction relies on Boyer's finding that the U.V. absorption spectrum of pCMB changes as it becomes bound to a sulfur atom. Thus the amount bound can be approximately derived from differential spectrophotometry (at 250 mμ) although the spectral change is not identical with all proteins, and thus the absolute accuracy of the method is limited[37].

Amperometric titrations with silver or mercuric salts are also frequently used. The former seem to tend to give high values for some proteins. The methods of analysis for —SH and —S—S-groups have recently been critically reviewed[37,38].

(vi) Reactions of disulfide bonds

It is often necessary in protein structural work to abolish the crosslinking disulfide bonds of cystine. *Oxidation* by means of performic acid (HCOOOH) achieves this quantitatively (Formula XXa)

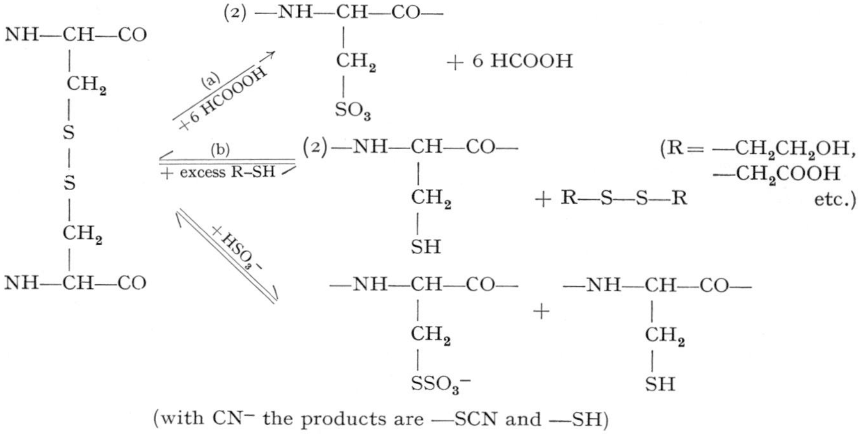

(with CN⁻ the products are —SCN and —SH)

(XX)

and is commonly used, although the concomitant oxidative destruction of the tryptophan and other residues represents a serious drawback of this and similar reactions. Any —SH groups present are also oxidized to sulfonic acids, but this is usually of advantage in structural work, owing to the greater stability and the marked polar nature of the cysteic acid residues.

Alternatively, *reduction* of disulfide bonds can be achieved by a variety of reagents. Some strong reducing agents, like the borohydrides have been employed but suffer from lack of specificity. Thiols, such as mercapto ethanol or cysteine, act quite specifically on the disulfide bonds and so do also the nucleophilic reagents cyanide and sulfite (Formula XXb,c).

References p. 105

These reactions require no drastic conditions, except for the fact that most protein disulfide bridges are so masked or buried that they are not reactive until the protein is denatured. The —SH groups formed upon reduction of denatured proteins are of normal autoxidizability and strictly anaerobic conditions are necessary to maintain the reduced state of the protein. Even a small extent of reoxidation can lead to intermolecular crosslinks and the result is a gelatious precipitation of the protein, which is particularly favored by the so-called disulfide exchange, a chain reaction which occurs when both reactive —S—S and —SH groups are present[39] (Formula XXI)

$$R^a—S—S—R^\beta + R—SH \rightleftharpoons R^a—S—S—R + R^\beta—SH$$

$$R^\beta—SH + R^\gamma—S—S—R^\delta \rightleftharpoons R^\gamma—S—S—R^\beta + R^\delta—SH \qquad (XXI)$$

$$R^\delta—SH + R^a—S—S—R \rightleftharpoons R^a—S—S—R^\delta + R—SH$$

This leads to a complete scrambling of the original disulfide crosslinks which represents a serious problem in protein structural work (see later).

For this reason reductive cleavage of proteins with thiols, *e.g.* mercaptoethanol or thioglycolate is usually coupled with a secondary reaction designed to block the reactive —SH groups and thus prevent their reoxidation. Alkylation by means of iodoacetate or its amide has proven most convenient for this purpose[40] (Formula XVII), although monovalent mercury compounds may be equally suitable.

Another technique achieves complete sulfite substitution by combining the sulfite treatment with copper catalyzed reoxidation of the —SH formed in the reaction (Formula XXII).

$$
\begin{array}{ccc}
R & & R \\
| & & | \\
S + HSO_3^- & \longrightarrow & S—SO_3^- \\
| & & \\
S & & + \\
| & \swarrow^{+O_2(Cu^{++})} & HS—R \\
R & &
\end{array}
\qquad (XXII)
$$

The disadvantage of this, as well as the cyanide reaction lies in the fact that the end products are labile and revert to —SH (and —S—S—) during acid hydrolysis and other manipulations, which is not the case for the carboxymethyl derivatives[40].

(b) Reactions performed for specific modification of protein structure

Whenever a biological function can be attributed to a chemical agent the biochemist is eager to establish the chemical structure of the agent, and the mechanism of its function. The first problem is usually attacked by degrading the molecule and the second by altering it in specific ways and thus de-termining its biologically essential features. The same approaches are used by the protein chemist who wants to elucidate the functional mechanism of a protein enzyme, hormone, toxin or antibody.

We have discussed the principles of protein structure and will take up the detailed structural analysis of peptide chains in a later section of this chapter. We now wish to consider the applicability of controlled chemical modification to the problem of pinning down the mechanism of protein action. This is for obvious reasons a very much more difficult task with proteins than with smaller molecules. Let us presuppose that a given biological activity is localized in a particular site of the protein molecule, and there is evidence favoring such a supposition. Let us further assume that this site consists of a number of specific R-groups of unknown nature. The problem could then be approached by treating the protein with various specific group reagents in the hope of finding one or several which abolished the biological activity under gentle reaction conditions. If this were achieved by an SH-reagent, and if it could be shown that only one mole of reagent had combined with the protein, the working hypothesis that a comparatively reactive —SH group occurred in the active site would be justified. However, in view of the complexity of proteins, many additional experiments would have to be performed to establish this as a fact. For instance it would have to be shown that actually the reagent had combined with an —SH group and that it could be removed in expected manner with regeneration of the —SH group, and of the activity. If several moles of reagents were required for inactivation, considerably more experimental data would be needed before a conclusion could be drawn.

These preliminary suppositions bring out several important points in protein modification studies. (1) Analytical evidence of the extent and nature of the reaction is of greatest importance. (2) Stoichiometric reactions and reversible reactions are of particular advantage. (3) The absence of a certain type of group is more easily and conclusively proven than its presence at the site.

In general, the techniques of modification are quite simple. Obviously denaturation, which by itself causes the loss of most biological activities, should be avoided. This means that reactions which occur at low temperatures and in neutral aqueous solution (pH 4–8) are preferred. Control experiments on the stability of the given protein under the test conditions are always included. After the reaction the protein is separated from any excess reagent, by-products of the reaction, or buffer salts, and analyzed for its biological activity and for the extent of modification. This is done by tests such as those described above, including amino acid analysis whenever the changed R-group should be stable to hydrolysis. For the analysis of the amount of reagent bound it is of great advantage if this carries a recognizable label. Radioactive reagents are therefore preferred whenever possible. U.V. absorption, color, or content in an unusual element may also be useful attributes for a reagent, except for the danger that such usually big reagent molecules can disturb the structure of a protein and thus cause inactivation not through their typical reaction but through their localized denaturing effect.

The state of homogeneity of the protein as ascertained by analyses such as chromatography, electrophoresis, or sedimentation is often very illuminating. In cases of extensive or maximal modification of proteins with introduction of many reagent groups per molecule such analyses usually show only one product although this may well consist of isomers or closely similar molecules. However, with a small protein like insulin which contains only a few groups of each type, products of incomplete reaction (*e.g.* mono- and di-substituted insulin) can often be detected and separated. The same holds for bigger proteins subjected to a limited modification with the purpose of obtaining a monosubstituted product. In the latter case, analysis of the unfractionated reaction mixture may have little significance since all the reagent may have combined with a few partially denatured molecules, the bulk of the protein remaining active and unmodified. It is under such circumstances that it is essential to ascertain the homogeneity of the product which is being analyzed.

In discussing the specificity and selectivity of various reagents, it must be stressed that specificity is always a function of the reaction conditions. Just as everything is poisonous when used in excess, similarly all protein groups react with almost any chemical agent when forced. We should therefore define a specific protein reagent as one which has a more or less marked preferential affinity for one type of protein R-group of average availability and reactivity.

(i) Acetylation, guanidination and other reactions of amino groups

Acetylation by means of acetic anhydride at pH 7–5 and 0° is a frequently employed tool for the transformation of *amino* to acetylamino groups[24, 28]. Maximal reaction leading to acetylation of 80–100 % of the amino groups may in some proteins, but not in others, cause acetylation of a few aliphatic hydroxyl groups (serine); the phenolic —OH groups (tyrosine) of most proteins begin to react only if the reaction is carried out at higher pH's. The resultant ester linkages are considerably more labile than the imide linkage, and can be broken by brief exposure to pH 10–11 either alone (*O*-acetyltyrosine), or in presence of hydroxylamine as the acyl-acceptor (*O*-acetylserine) (Formula XXIII).

An exceptional case is represented by a single serine residue occurring in the active site of many hydrolytic enzymes. This serine readily accepts acetyl and other acyl groups around pH 5, and loses them at neutrality and rapidly at pH 5–6 in the presence of hydroxylamine (see later).

Acetic anhydride also reacts readily with available —SH groups, but these occur in only a few proteins. A great number of enzymes and other biologically active proteins are not inactivated by acetylation of most of

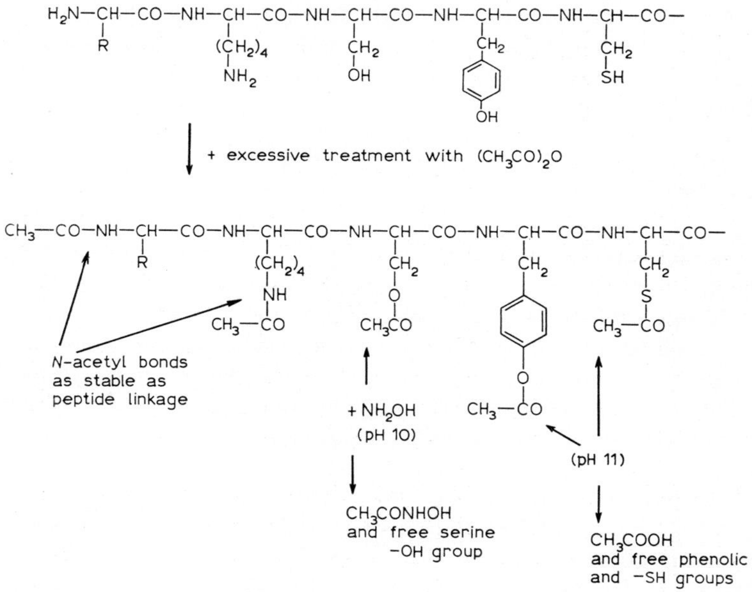

$$H_2N-CH-CO-NH-CH-CO-NH-CH-CO-NH-CH-CO-NH-CH-CO-$$

with side chains: R, $(CH_2)_4$ NH_2, CH_2 OH, CH_2–(phenol)OH, CH_2 SH

+ excessive treatment with $(CH_3CO)_2O$

$$CH_3-CO-NH-CH-CO-NH-CH-CO-NH-CH-CO-NH-CH-CO-NH-CH-CO-$$

with side chains: R, $(CH_2)_4$ NH CH_3-CO, CH_2 O CH_3CO, CH_2–(phenol)O CH_3-CO, CH_2 S CH_3-CO

N-acetyl bonds as stable as peptide linkage

+ NH_2OH (pH 10)

(pH 11)

$CH_3CONHOH$ and free serine —OH group

CH_3COOH and free phenolic and —SH groups

XXIII

their amino groups. Trypsin is markedly stabilized by acylation with acetic anhydride and a variety of higher aliphatic anhydrides, but most dramatically by succinic anhydride[41]. In contrast, and for now well understood reasons acetylation of trypsinogen, the precursor of trypsin, renders the molecule non-activable (see later).

Aromatic acyl groups also are frequently introduced into proteins. Inactivation produced by these reactions is often difficult to interpret, partly owing to the lesser specificity of the reagents, and partly owing to the danger of denaturation resulting from the size and hydrophobic nature of the introduced group.

A selective modification of only the α-amino groups of the chain ends would often be desirable. Acetylation attacks the α-amino group more rapidly than the ε-amino groups, but selective acetylation of the former groups has not been achieved. A careful study of the amino groups of

References p. 105

chymotrypsinogen has led Chervenka and Wilcox[42] to the conclusion that the well-known addition reaction of *carbon disulfide* (Formula XXIV a),

$$\text{Prot.--}NH_2 + S{=}C{=}S \longrightarrow \text{Prot.-}-NH-\overset{\displaystyle \nearrow S}{C}-SH \qquad \text{(XXIVa)}$$

with amino groups could be made specific for the α-amino residue if performed at pH 6.9 and stopped when one mole of CS_2 had become bound.

A frequently employed modification of amino groups represents the addition of *O*-methyl isourea, which transforms them to guanidine groups[43] (Formula XXIV b).

$$\text{Prot.--}NH_2 + CH_3-O-C\underset{\displaystyle \diagdown NH}{\overset{\displaystyle \diagup NH_2}{}} \longrightarrow \text{Prot.--}NH-C\underset{\displaystyle \diagdown NH}{\overset{\displaystyle \diagup NH_2}{}} + CH_3OH$$

$$\text{(XXIVb)}$$

This *guanidination* requires long reaction periods at or above pH 10 to go to completion, but a recently proposed alternate reagent (1-guanyl-3,5-dimethyl pyrazole nitrate) is reported to act more rapidly[44] and at a lower pH. Guanidination and acetylation act in various ways in complementary manner. For guanidination increases the basic nature of the lysine group which acetylation abolishes; and guanidination proceeds preferentially and at times almost selectively with the ε-amino groups, while acetylation favors the α-amino groups.

Of all amino reactions, only the carbon disulfide reaction is readily reversible. Guanidination has the particular advantage that it lends itself to good analytical evaluation. For the homoarginine residue formed through the reaction can easily be measured by the Sakaguchi reaction (see p. 76) either before or after hydrolysis; moreover, amino acid analysis reveals the quantitative relationship between the lysine lost and the homoarginine formed.

Other reactions which have frequently been used and affect the amino groups are deamination with nitrous acid and formaldehyde treatment. Both have previously been mentioned because of their analytical application, but their lack of specificity makes them less useful for selective modifications than those described above.

(ii) Esterification and alkylation

No ideal reagent is available for the selective *esterification* of *carboxyl groups*. Oddly enough, no search has been made for a reagent which would preferentially combine with the most reactive carboxyl groups, and it is quite possible that epoxides in acid solution (Formula XXV)

$$R\text{--}COOH + CH_2-CH_2 \longrightarrow R\text{--}CO\text{--}OCH_2\text{--}CH_2OH \qquad \text{(XXV)}$$
$$\diagdown O \diagup$$

or diazoacetamide (Formula XXVI)

$$R—COOH + N\text{----}CH—CONH_2 \longrightarrow R—CO—OCH_2CONH_2 + N_2 \quad (XXVI)$$
$$\underset{\diagdown N \diagup}{}$$

may selectively esterify those groups[35]. As with the amino groups, interest has focused on extensive or complete esterification without side reactions. The best reagent for that purpose appears to be, as previously mentioned, methanol[31] containing a little HCl, but many proteins are very susceptible to denaturation by organic solvents. This is not the case with insulin which can easily and safely be esterified by this procedure, and de-esterified by treatment with mild alkali[35] (Formula XXVII).

$$\text{Prot.}—COOH + CH_3OH \underset{OH^-}{\overset{H^+}{\rightleftharpoons}} \text{Prot.}—CO—OCH_3 + H_2O \quad (XXVII)$$

Serum albumin shows only beginning signs of denaturation if the reaction is performed at low temperatures. Certain other proteins may well be more stable than the albumins.

Many esterifying agents are in more general terms *alkylating agents*. The diazo compounds have some preference for carboxyl groups (Formula XXVI), the epoxides and mustard gas type reagents may tend to alkylate carboxyl groups in acid solution and nitrogeneous and sulfur compounds in alkaline solution (Formula XXVIII a), and the alkylsulfates and halides preferentially attack the nitrogen and sulfur compounds (XXVIII b)

(a) $\text{Prot.} \underset{\diagdown SH}{\overset{\diagup COOH}{-NH_2}} + CH_2 \underset{\diagdown CH_2 \diagup}{\text{----}} S^+ \text{---} CH_2—CH_2Cl \longrightarrow \text{Prot.} \underset{\diagdown S—CH_2CH_2SCH_2CH_2Cl}{\overset{\diagup CO—O—CH_2CH_2SCH_2CH_2Cl*}{-NH—CH_2CH_2SCH_2CH_2Cl}}$

Mustard gas
(β,β'-dichloroethylsulfide)

(b) $\text{Prot.} \underset{\diagdown SH}{\overset{\diagup NH_2}{}} + (CH_3O)_2SO_2 \longrightarrow \text{Prot.} \underset{\diagdown S—CH_3}{\overset{\diagup NH—CH_3}{}} + CH_3OSO_3^-$

Dimethyl sulfate

(XXVIII)

We have previously mentioned the ease of alkylation of —SH groups by iodoacetic acid, and many alkyl halides react similarly. However, most proteins have no —SH groups, and the question is therefore of interest as to what other groups of the protein might become alkylated by a given reagent. We have discussed the affinity of FDNB for amino, imidazole, and phenolic groups. This seems too non-specific to be of interest for the present

---

* The second chlorine reacts in similar fashion, thus crosslinking the protein, or it is hydrolyzed off, leaving an —OH group.

purposes; yet it was shown that at pH 10 the reactivity of one of the two histidines of chymotrypsin exceeded all other affinities for the reagent sufficiently so that in small amounts it acted specifically on this group.

An even more interesting illustration of the fact that one can teach an old dog new tricks is the recent careful investigation of the alkylating activity of *iodoacetic acid*[45]. For it was found that aside from the alkylation of any available —SH groups (which is by far the fastest reaction at or above pH 7), this reagent alkylated the methionine sulfur in acid solution, the histidine imidazole group around neutrality, and the lysine amino groups at or above pH 9 (Formula XXIX). It was further found that in

XXIX

the specific protein under study, ribonuclease, only one of the 2 histidines reacted, and this occurred at the unusually low pH of 5.5, and not at pH 7. In contrast, the methionine reaction was repressed in this protein. Denaturation, however, made each of the groups react "normally", *i.e.* the methionine over a wide range of pH, both imidazole groups at pH 7. The imidazole group which in the native protein reacted abnormally with iodoacetate and which was found by a different research team[46] to become alkylated also quite readily upon treatment with bromoacetate, was apparently located in the active site of this enzyme, since the substitution of a single imidazole group caused inactivation.

Thus we see how careful investigations of the effect of a well-known reagent can reveal quite novel behavior with a particular protein. The fact that methionine has not previously been mentioned as a modifiable group is probably due to the difficulty of detecting and analyzing for S-alkyl-methionines, which is due to the instability of these alkyl sulfonium salts[45].

It illustrates the important general fact that the description of protein reactions is only as complete as the available analytical tools, as well as the thoroughness and the know-how of the investigator, permit.

(iii) Iodination and photo-oxidation

Another reagent of great versatility is *iodine*. It may be noted parenthetically that the words versatility and lack of specificity have very similar connotations. Only one term seems to carry the seal of approval which the other lacks. Versatility may best be interpreted in this connection as the ability of a reagent to combine with a variety of groups while proving to act selectively on one group in a given protein under carefully controlled conditions.

The two classical effects of iodine are the oxidation of available —SH to —S—S— groups, and the *ortho* substitution of available phenolic groups to di-iodotyrosine. Actually most proteins lack the former and their tyrosine groups frequently react quite sluggishly. Instead the primary target in the iodination of lysozyme is histidine, resulting in the partly reversible substitution on a nitrogen of the single imidazole group which is probably associated with the active site[47]. In TMV, on the other hand, the first reaction is the oxidation substitution of the single masked —SH to a sulfenyl iodide (—SI) group which is sufficiently stable to persist only because of the unusually "masked state" of the original —SH group deeply embedded in the virus particle[48]. In other proteins, —SI groups may be formed only as unstable intermediates. Iodine is also known to add to the methionine sulfur, and to oxidize the indole ring, and specific cases where these reactions represent the inactivating event are unknown probably only because of analytical limitations pertaining to the reaction products.

Another selective oxidation method makes use of visible light activated by dyes such as methylene blue (photo-oxidation). Of the various oxidizable groups of a protein (imidazole, phenol, indole and the sulfur containing residues) those imidazole groups appear selectively oxidizable which seem to be part of the active sites of several enzymes and of unusual reactivity also in other regards[49].

3. Structural analysis of proteins

(a) End group analysis and stepwise degradation of proteins and peptides

(i) Chemical methods

The nature of the end groups of proteins might be regarded as one important parameter which, in conjunction with analytical and physico-chemical properties, serves to define a given protein. The determination

References p. 105

of the end group is not always easy, nor are the results always reliable and unambiguous, but this situation also applies to other characteristic parameters of proteins.

Under favorable circumstances, end group analyses of proteins serve the following purposes: (1) they can give information concerning the number of different peptide chains and their molecular weights; (2) they can supply an indication of the homogeneity of the protein, or a means of detecting the nature or the amount of a contaminant; and (3) they represent the initial step of a complete structural analysis of the protein (see later).

The methods of end group analysis are in part chemical, and in part enzymatic. The main chemical method for the analysis of N-terminal groups is the reaction with FDNB, which was previously discussed. With rare exceptions (*e.g.*, ACTH) the results have proven qualitatively reliable. However, owing to the lability of the DNP-amino acids and the need for corrections, the magnitude of which is not easily determined, the quantitative evaluation of the data is sometimes difficult. The isolation of DNP-peptides may supply evidence concerning the nature of one or two additional residues along the peptide chain.

The PTC-method, also previously discussed, serves to complement or confirm the end group characterization of proteins and peptides. This method, furthermore, permits the stepwise degradation, and thus is the method of choice for the determination of sequences. However, the cumulative effect of side reactions, largely due to the acid required for cyclization of the thiohydantoins, limit its applicability. Under favorable circumstances about 8 residues can be sequentially released and identified, but it appears doubtful whether the method will be adaptable to the elucidation of much longer sequences. The combined use of several methods, and attack of a peptide from both ends appears to give the best promise of success.

The preferred chemical method for C-terminal analysis is by hydrazinolysis. It consists in heating the dry protein dissolved in dry hydrazine to $100°$ for 6 h, which leads to the hydrazinolytic disruption of all peptide bonds (Formula XXX).

$$R' \quad \overset{\displaystyle CONH_2}{\underset{\displaystyle CH_2}{|}} \quad R'' \quad \overset{\displaystyle COOH}{\underset{\displaystyle CH_2}{|}} \quad R'''$$

$$-NH-CH-CO-NH-CH-CO-NH-CH-CO-NH-CH-CO-NH-CH-COOH \; + \; NH_2-NH_2$$

$$R' \quad \overset{\displaystyle CONHNH_2}{\underset{\displaystyle CH_2}{|}} \quad R''$$

$$\longrightarrow \quad H_2N-CH-CONHNH_2, \; H_2N-CH-CONHNH_2, \; H_2N-CH-CONHNH_2,$$

$$\overset{\displaystyle COOH}{\underset{\displaystyle CH_2}{|}} \quad R'''$$

$$(XXX) \qquad H_2N-CH-CONHNH_2, \; H_2N-CH-COOH$$

Only the C-terminal residue yields a free amino acid, which can by various means be separated from the hydrazides of all other amino acids, identified, and estimated[50,51]. The limited stability of certain amino acids under the reaction condition introduces the need for high correction factors; cystine and tryptophan are decomposed almost quantitatively and C-terminal asparagine and glutamine present problems of separation. Clear-cut positive results obtained with hydrazinolysis showing a stoichiometric amount of one or two amino acids are usually correct, but doubtful or negative results do not represent evidence for the absence of C-terminal groups. This is to a varying degree true for all end group methods.

Many other chemical methods for the determination of N- or C- terminal groups have been proposed and have found occasional applications. However, none has found as much acceptance as those mentioned.

(ii) Enzymatic methods

A group of enzymes has been found to attack proteins or peptides only from one end or the other, splitting off the terminal residues one at a time. Carboxypeptidase A from pancreas is the best known of these enzymes. It does not readily split off glycine, nor the basic amino acids (arginine, lysine) and rarely releases proline or an amino acid bound to proline. Nevertheless this enzyme has proven very useful. Many proteins are attacked in a clear-cut fashion, with release of only one or a few residues in clearly sequential order[51].

Carboxypeptidase B (also from the pancreas, and previously called protaminase) specifically releases only basic amino acids from the C-terminus and in general seems to complement the action[52] of carboxypeptidase A. Aminopeptidase (from spleen) attacks proteins from the other end[53,54]. Neither of these latter enzymes have been applied as successfully or as frequently to intact proteins as has carboxypeptidase A; both have proven most useful for the sequential analysis of peptides.

In principle the use of such enzymes coupled with careful analyses for the relative rate of liberation of each amino acid should supply the sequence of any protein or peptide. In fact (as with the chemical methods for sequence analysis previously discussed), this is only rarely as straight-forward as one might hope, largely owing to the great differences in the affinity of the enzymes for different R-groups. Thus proline, glycine and others are either slowly or not at all released, while leucine, valine, phenylalanine and others may be released so rapidly that they may seem to appear simultaneously.

One particular disadvantage of the enzymatic methods lies in the difficulties of interpretation of the results obtained with multi-chain proteins. Thus when carboxypeptidase treatment of aldolase released 3 moles of tyrosine, it appeared impossible to decide whether these came from one,

two, or three chains. Through the use of ^{18}O-containing water it was proven
that each tyrosine was terminal and thus aldolase is a 3-chain protein[55].
This may represent an important advance in methodology. However, no
conclusive interpretation is possible if from more than one chain more than
one residue is split off.

Another difficulty in the interpretation of carboxypeptidase data is
illustrated by human serum albumin[56]. For it was shown that the sequence
–Ala–Ala–Ala–Gly–Leu yielded an amino acid release pattern in which the
alanine at all time periods exceeded the glycine, thus suggesting a different
sequence. Yet the results are readily understandable on the basis of the
different rates of release of glycine and alanine by the enzyme.

It must also be stressed that many proteins are unpredictably refractory
to the enzymes, possibly owing to their secondary and tertiary structure.
Thus, negative results have no evidential significance. It appears that proteins
must first be degraded to more manageable and predictable units before
their complete structure can be elucidated[54].

(b) Specific splitting of peptide chains and disulfide bonds

The principles and methods pertaining to the molecular weight of proteins
represents the topic of a later chapter. It will there be shown that many
proteins occur as aggregate or complex molecules composed of several
peptide chains which are held together only by secondary valences (Fig. 1A).

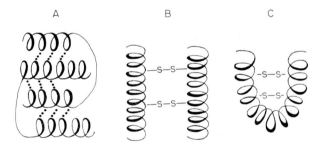

Fig. 1. Schematic presentation of three protein structural principles. (A) Two-chain
protein held together only by secondary valences. (B) Two-chain protein held together
by interchain disulfide bonds. (C) One-chain protein crosslinked by intrachain disulfide bonds.

This is usually concluded from the fact that they can be degraded by agents
which would not attack any known primary chemical bond, such as solutions
of urea, detergents, or guanidinium halides at neutrality and in the cold.
Often but not always is biological activity lost when such subunits are

separated. In certain instances, disaggregation and loss of biological function are reversible processes.

The structural integrity and the biological activity of another class of proteins is lost upon treatment with reagents which break their disulfide bonds. Extensive or complete disulfide breakage usually requires simultaneous action by one of the above disaggregating agents. Complete disulfide bond rupture may or may not be associated with a decrease in molecular weight. If the molecular weight is decreased upon complete oxidative or reductive cleavage of the —S—S— bonds, this is regarded as evidence that the protein molecule consists of 2 or more peptide chains; if not then a single-chain structure is indicated (Fig. 1 B,C). The methods for cleavage of the disulfide bonds of proteins have been previously discussed.

Finally, the effect of gradual and controlled peptide bond breakage on the biological and physicochemical properties of a protein can be studied. Such studies may indicate that removal of a single amino acid residue from the end of the chain causes inactivation; as the other extreme case, they may show that complete hydrolysis to amino acids does not cause inactivation, which would signify that the biologically active agent is not a protein, nor even a peptide, but a single amino acid, as is the case for thyroxin. This question of how much of a given protein is required for maintenance of its biological activity will be discussed in another chapter. Here we wish to discuss only those peptide bond-splitting reactions which are of importance for the structural elucidation of proteins. As discussed above, long peptide chains must be degraded into smaller units if their amino acid sequence is to be determined.

Random splitting by partial acid hydrolysis gives a very great number of peptides and is therefore applicable only to relatively short peptide chains. To illustrate this, the numerous peptides obtainable by random splitting from an octapeptide composed of only 4 amino acids (A, B, C, D) are listed below:

A—B—C—D—D—C—B—A ⟶ AB, BC, CD, DD, DC, CB, BA

ABC, BCD, CDD, DDC, DCB, CBA

ABCD, BCDD, CDDC, DDCB, DCBA

ABCDD, BCDDC, CDDCB, DDCBA

ABCDDC, BCDDCB, CDDCBA

ABCDDCB, BCDDCBA

Specific agents which split only at certain sites are of obvious advantage in this type of work. For instance an agent which would split only on the right of the residue C in the above scheme would yield only ABC, DDC, and BA. If another agent splitting next to B were available, then this would yield only AB, CDDCB and A. The isolation and analysis of these 6 products would supply all the information needed to arrive at the original sequence.

Indications have been obtained that seryl bonds are particularly labile under certain conditions of strong acid treatment in the cold[57]. This is mediated by the acyl shift reaction previously described (Formula II). Furthermore some aspartic acid residues are released from certain proteins near pH 2.5 at 100°. Neither of these reactions, however, has proven of sufficient general specificity for the intended purpose. Treatment of proteins with N-bromosuccinimide has been found to lead beyond the primary oxidation of the indole (and some tyrosine) groups to a cleavage of the adjacent peptide bonds[58]. This reaction has found some use in protein structural work, even though side reactions and low yields suggest caution in the interpretation of the data.

Enzymes represent the most useful tools for the non-random splitting of proteins and one enzyme in particular, namely trypsin, acts very specifically on all proteins, and now plays a key role in protein structural analysis. Trypsin splits only the lysyl and arginyl bonds of proteins and peptides, thus transforming a protein into a mixture of peptides, all but one of which, the originally C-terminal fragment, have C-terminal arginine or lysine[59]. The number of peptides corresponds approximately to the number of lysine and arginine residues (plus one) though occasionally fewer peptides are formed owing to enzyme resistance of a particular bond. The usefulness of trypsin for specific splitting has led to a search for means of artificially introducing additional trypsin-susceptible sites in proteins, one example of which, the result of the alkylation of cysteine residues with 1-bromo-2-ethylamine[60] is illustrated in Formula XXXI c.

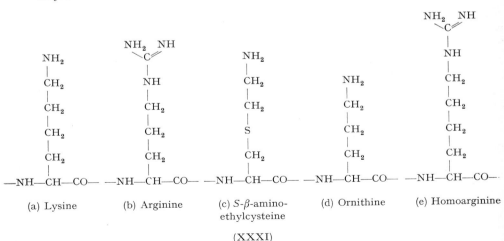

(a) Lysine   (b) Arginine   (c) S-β-amino-ethylcysteine   (d) Ornithine   (e) Homoarginine

(XXXI)

A comparison of the R chain length of this product with that of arginine, lysine, ornithine and the homoarginine resulting from guanidination of lysine is illustrative of the specificity of trypsin which will split peptide bonds next to the first three but not the last two of these R-groups (XXXI). Dinitrophenylation or acetylation of the lysine groups also abolishes their affinity for the trypsin, in this case by depressing or abolishing their basicity. Thus after any of these modifications, trypsin specifically cleaves only next to arginyl residues.

Other proteolytic enzymes are less selective. Chymotrypsin preferentially attacks tyrosyl, phenylalanyl, tryptophanyl and leucyl bonds, but occasionally (about 1 out of 4 splits) others. Certain bacterial proteases (e.g. subtilisin) show yet lower specificities, although under carefully controlled conditions they may attack native proteins in only one or two specific sites. Such cases of limited and specific proteolysis are of considerable interest, and will be discussed in detail in other chapters. Pepsin appears quite non-specific, often attacking the same bonds as chymotrypsin, and often others. It would seem as if the action of some of those enzymes were determined by factors not related to the R-group, but possibly to the steric nature of the site.

None of these enzymes, however, act in random fashion, for each tends to split the same bond in each molecule and thus they supply useful tools for specific purposes, particularly when applied to peptides obtained with trypsin.

After the partial degradation of a protein or peptide, the important and difficult task remains of separating the fragments cleanly one from the other. This is often as complex as the isolation and separation of pure proteins from a crude tissue extract. Similar methods are generally used, although the lower average molecular weight of the peptide mixture somewhat influences the choice of method. Ion exchange resins of low crosslinkage (e.g. Dowex 50, or Dowex 1 X-2) have often proven of advantage, as well as countercurrent distribution between buffered or acid aqueous phases and a butanol. Differential dialysis and dextran gel (Sephadex) columns cause separation according to molecular weight. Electrophoresis on paper or starch gels, and paper chromatography finally represent the simplest and most generally applicable methods for purification and particularly for the detection of the presence or absence of impurities. Examples for the use of most of these methods will be given in a later section.

We have now surveyed the techniques used for the structural analysis of proteins. To summarize we will outline a suggested procedure. End group analysis on the protein is first used to ascertain the number and the length of the peptide chains. Any disulfide bonds are disrupted, preferably by reduction, and any different chains separated chromatographically, monitoring these manipulations with end group analysis. The isolated chains are then subjected to trypsin digestion. The resulting mixture of peptides is resolved into its components by chromatographic and other techniques. Each peptide is analyzed for amino acid composition and N-terminal residues. The summation of the amino acids in the peptides should account for all amino acids in the original protein or peptide chain. The bigger peptides are further degraded by other enzymes. All split products are finally subjected to chemical and enzymatic methods of stepwise degradation to ascertain their amino acid sequence. Since all peptides obtained with trypsin terminate in arginine or lysine and are thus resistant to carboxypeptidase A, they must be treated with carboxypeptidase B or a mixture of the enzymes for C-terminal degradation.

Finally it must be stressed that each protein or peptide represents a separate problem. The efficacy of the various tools must be tested at every step, and the most favorable selected. Specific examples for their application, and the resulting complete sequential elucidation of two selected proteins will represent the subject of the next section.

(c) Sequential analysis of proteins

Insulin was the first protein the structure of which was elucidated[59]. The fact that it consists of two chains held together by disulfide bonds, and that all the pioneering development of methods and circumventing of pitfalls was part of the course of this work makes this an epoch-making piece of research. Subsequent elucidations of other hormones did not have to contend with multiple chains, but in the case of the ACTH's, with a somewhat longer peptide chain. The chemistry of these hormones will be described in other chapters. We will here choose as a primary example the elucidation of the structure of the enzyme *ribonuclease*, because the careful and critical study of the various techniques required for a protein of its size makes this also a classical achievement[61-63]. Ribonuclease consists of a peptide chain of 124 residues, 3 times longer than any previously tackled. Another protein, yet bigger (158 residues), the complete structure of which has recently been established is that of the tobacco mosaic virus, which we will also refer to occasionally. Several other proteins of biological interest (hemoglobin, trypsin, chymotrypsin, papain, lysozyme, cytochrome *c*, etc.) are under active study. The procedures used with all these proteins are principally similar to those used with insulin and ribonuclease with variations according to the taste of the investigator and the special nature of the problem.

The first question is always the number of chains making up the protein under study. End group analyses had indicated one N-terminal lysine and one C-terminal valine per mole of ribonuclease. Four crosslinking cystine residues were present, but their oxidation did not alter the molecular weight, thus supporting the belief that the disulfide bonds formed intrachain di-sulfide bridges between different parts of a single-chain molecule (Fig. 1 C).

Obviously, the possibility that the crosslinking disulfide bridges hold tryptic peptides together considerably complicates the analysis, and it is for this reason that not only interchain but also intrachain disulfide bonds are usually broken, be it by oxidation or reduction and alkylation, before sequential analysis is initiated. The fact that ribonuclease like insulin lacks tryptophan made the oxidative procedure acceptable. Methionine was oxidized to the sulfone but no other untoward effects were noted.

$$
\begin{array}{cc}
\mid & \\
CO & O \\
\mid & \parallel \\
CH-CH_2-CH_2-\overset{\displaystyle \parallel}{\underset{\displaystyle \parallel}{S}}-CH_3 \\
\mid & \parallel \\
NH & O \\
\mid &
\end{array}
$$

Digestion of the oxidized protein by trypsin yielded a mixture of 13 peptides, two fewer than expected, because of the failure of the enzyme to split a Lys–Pro bond and to release the N-terminal lysine residue. This mixture of peptides was resolved into its components primarily by ion exchange chromatography.

Chymotryptic and peptic digests were also prepared from the oxidized protein and fractionated. Peptides which appeared to be pure from their behavior under various fractionating conditions were analyzed for end groups and amino acid composition. Simple straightforward stoichiometric relationships of such analyses supplied further evidence for homogeneity. The summation of the components of all tryptic peptides equalled the composition of the original protein.

The next step, the sequential analysis, was obviously quite easy for di-peptides and tripeptides, but became progressively more difficult with the bigger peptides of up to about 20 residues, which were therefore subjected to digestion by another enzyme. Phenylisothiocyanate and carboxypeptidase were the methods which were most frequently successful in establishing sequences. Many sequences were confirmed by the use of several methods. Finally the sequential arrangement of the peptides had to be determined, and this was possible by trial-and-error alignment of the tryptic peptides with those chymotryptic and peptic peptides which contained arginine and lysine.

The resultant sequence of 124 residues lacked one important feature of the original protein, the disulfide bonds, since each cystine had been trans-formed into two cysteic acid residues. Sanger's earlier work on insulin had demonstrated the great tendency for disulfide exchange in proteins and had established conditions which favored and which forestalled such exchanges (Formula XXI). To avoid disulfide exchanges Hirs *et al.* resorted to pepsin digestion at pH 2 as a primary means of degradation of the native not oxidized ribonuclease. The authors were in this manner able to obtain cystine peptides, the component amino acids of which enabled them to locate the 4 disulfide bonds in the chain. The complete structure of ribonuclease is represented in Fig. 2.

The work on the *TMV protein* proceeded along similar lines[64-66]. This protein also consists of a single chain, but this fact was difficult to establish because the N-terminal group was acetylated and thus unreactive to all amino reagents[67]. The acetyl end group appears to be a feature of many if not all plant virus proteins (as well as at least one pituitary hormone, α-MSH). The C-terminal amino acid, threonine, was remarkably susceptible to carboxypeptidase action, and the preceding residues, alanine and proline, completely resistant, a good illustration of the specificity requirements of the enzyme. The protein lacks disulfide crosslinks, but carries one masked cysteine residue. Oxidation was therefore not necessary. Tryptic digestion yielded 12 of the expected 14 peptides (one Arg–Arg sequence was split between the two residues, the resultant N-terminal arginine being resistant; a Lys–Pro bond was again resistant). Fractionation of the peptides was performed by countercurrent distribution or column chromatography. Most of the peptides had to be refractionated by a different procedure before they were sufficiently pure for further study. *N*-bromosuccinimide was used on

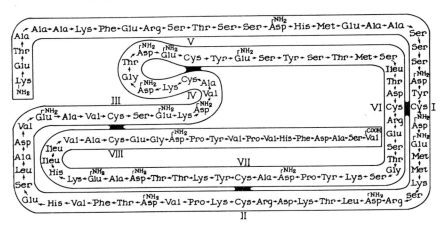

Fig. 2. The primary structure of ribonuclease. (Courtesy of Dr. S. Moore.) The schematic presentation shows the sequential arrangement of the 124 amino acid residues and 4 disulfide bonds of bovine pancreatic ribonuclease, as proposed by the Rockefeller Institute group[61,62]. Minor revisions have been made in the N-terminal part of the molecule.

the whole protein and on tryptophan-containing peptides to obtain specific splits and identify the adjacent residue[58]. Both aminopeptidase and the carboxypeptidases A and B were extensively used, as well as the chemical methods. Most of the sequence of the 158 residues has been independently determined in two laboratories and can be regarded as final; certain parts, however, are less well established. This is particularly true of the *N*-acetylated terminal peptide which is 41 residues long, the longest trypsin-resistant peptide yet studied and lacking a terminal amino group.

It is of great importance in this type of work that as many sequences as possible be determined by more than one technique, since all procedures are subject to error and misinterpretation. An added danger is that of trans-peptidization (or peptide bond interchanges) which may lead to the appearance of new peptide sequences in the course of the analytical work. This is fortunately a rare occurrence since all peptides isolated in significant yield are usually consistent with a unique sequential arrangement*.

We must again reiterate that amino acid sequences are only part of the story of protein structure. There remains the complex question of the nature of the folding which transforms a thread-like molecule into a 3-dimensional object of definite shape and function. In the case of the TMV protein we begin to glimpse a few disconnected facts concerning the steric arrangement of the chain to form a long egg-shaped molecule, and we know a good bit more about the geometry and the bonds that make 2200 such molecules aggregate in the form of a helix and thus produce a rod-like virus particle (Fig. 3). In regard to ribonuclease a very important discovery has recently been announced which may represent the beginning of an understanding of the forces that shape protein molecules[68]. Ribonuclease, upon reduction of its —S—S— bonds which were then stabilized in the "open" form by alkylation, showed all the physicochemical properties expected for a stretched out long chain molecule and was enzymatically inactive. If, on the other hand, the —SH groups were not alkylated, but allowed to reoxidize slowly, then the original disulfide bridges were re-established and an active enzyme was formed which showed in all regards the same behavior as the original folded molecule. Similar observations have been made with several other proteins.[69].

---

* It would have been regarded as fantastic to suggest in 1945 that we would know the structure of proteins of molecular weights of nearly 20,000 in such detail in 1960. While the impact of radio communication or air travel on our lives may be much greater, this writer certainly derives an enormous intellectual elation out of the rapid advance of man's knowledge concerning the world he lives in, be it in the direction of outer space or of the fine structure of matter, or of the stuff he is made of and what makes him tick. Whether later technological developments of these discoveries lead to atomic energy or H-bombs, space travel or space wars, and cures for diseases, or new biological warfare agents, the primary discovery represents a gain in knowledge, uncontaminated by profit or mayhem.

References p. 105

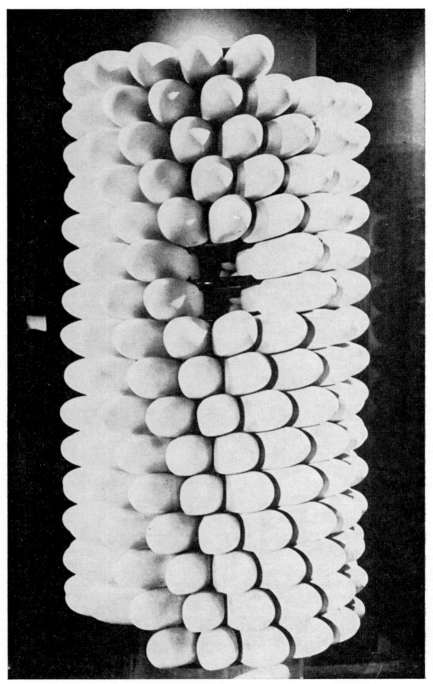

Fig. 3. For legend see p. 99.

Such a tendency of proteins to refold to a unique conformation may in some as yet incomprehensible way be a function of the amino acid sequence as such. It seems at first sight more probable that it is the product of extensive disulfide exchange. The conditions are ideal for such exchange since the reaction mixture consists of more or less open chains carrying many reactive disulfide and a gradually decreasing number of sulfhydryl groups. If one assumes that the original (and final) structure is the one of greatest thermodynamic stability, then it is easy to visualize a continuous trial-and-error formation and random exchange of disulfide bonds leading slowly but surely to this most stable state. The only aspect of this presumed mechanism for protein folding, which is intellectually unsatisfying, is the fact that it requires separate explanations for the folding of the many proteins which lack disulfide bridges and of which the TMV protein is one example. Evidence has been presented that also this protein can after denaturation, re-form its native conformation[70]. If the protein was really completely denatured, this finding would strongly support the concept that secondary and tertiary structure may actually be a function and consequence of the amino acid sequence.

4. Chemical mechanisms of protein function

We may now proceed from the fact that the primary structure of several bio-active proteins is known or will soon be known and that their secondary and tertiary folding, possibly determined by the primary structure, is in the early stages of elucidation. Does such knowledge explain the biocatalytic effects of proteins? The proteins and peptides which have at first been elucidated were all hormones, substances which act only on intact cells or tissues; the complexity of these biological effects is such that no positive answer to that question would be anticipated. The action of most enzymes is conceptually much closer to simple chemical reactions. To take as an example a hydrolytic enzyme: the substrate is bound, a bond is hydrolyzed, the products are released. Although no enzyme is known at present for which the mechanism of this sequence of events is completely clarified, evidence is accumulating at a sufficient rate to give one confidence that this will soon be achieved. In the case of ribonuclease, for instance, we know from the bromoacetate work[46] that the histidine residue nearest the C-terminus (119) is functionally important, as is also the presence of the

---

Fig. 3. Model of TMV structure. The model shows the arrangement of the TMV protein to form the virus rod. The white bodies represent the protein subunits, each consisting of one peptide chain of 17,500 mol. wt. (158 amino acid residues). These are held together only by secondary valences, but readily and spontaneously enter into the helically stacked aggregate. The black tube revealed by the removal of a few protein units represents the RNA, both in position and dimensions. Its presence stabilizes the aggregate, but is not required for its formation.

N-terminal 20-residue peptide[71] (the evidence for this will be discussed in
a later chapter); we also know that most amino groups are unimportant,
but that modification of the least reactive one causes loss of enzymatic
activity[72].

A somewhat clearer picture emerges with a group of enzymes which split
certain peptide bonds and/or certain specific esters. To this group belong
the important enzymes trypsin, chymotrypsin, cholinesterase, etc. All
these enzymes seem to contain a serine residue of unusual reactivity towards
acyl or phosphoryl compounds. This reactivity appears to be dependent upon
the native configuration of the protein and on the proximity of an imidazole
residue which actually is not nearby on the peptide chain, possibly even on
another chain, but brought into juxtaposition to the active serine through
the tertiary folding of these proteins[73]. Simple imidazoles catalyze many
hydrolytic reactions, but none of these approach the rate of the enzymatic
ones. The first result of the enzymatic action appears to be the transfer of
the acid group from its "base" to the active serine (Reaction A, Formula
XXXII a). Depending on the nature of the esterifying group it will be released at varying rates (Reaction B). If the rate is fast, we say the enzyme
acts; if the rate is negligible or slow, we say the enzyme is more or less
inhibited, since the blocking of the serine by that acid group prevents it
from accepting other acyl groups of typical substrates. The reaction of

XXXII

chymotrypsin with p-nitrophenyl acetate (Formula XXXIIa) is one example
of such limited inhibition that has been thoroughly studied. The trapping
of the enzyme by the most firmly bound inhibitor-substrate, diisopropyl-

phosphofluoridate[74], has been the breakthrough discovery which has gradually led to a better understanding of this than any other enzyme action[35, 73,74] (Formula XXXII b).

The firm binding of the poisoning phosphate group to the particular serine and the use of a ^{32}P-labelled reagent has made it possible to identify the peptide sequence around that serine. Amazingly, it was found to be the same for several related enzymes, and quite similar even for other types of enzymes, all of which have almost nothing in common except what counts in this context: the reaction mechanisms[54] (Table IV). Thus here we have

TABLE IV

SEQUENCES AROUND THE "ACTIVE SERINE" OF VARIOUS ENZYMES [a]

Enzyme	Sequence
Chymotrypsin	Gly–Asp–*Ser*–Gly–Glu–Ala or Gly–Asp–*Ser*–Gly–Gly–Pro–Leu
Trypsin	–Asp(NH$_2$)–Ser–CyS–Glu–Gly–Gly–Asp–*Ser*–Gly–Pro–Val–CyS–Ser–Gly–Lys–
Elastase (pancreas)	Gly–Asp–*Ser*–Gly
Pseudocholinesterase	Phe–Gly–Glu–*Ser*–Ala–Gly–
Thrombin	Gly–Asp–*Ser*–Gly

[a] Most of the data reviewed by Hill *et al*.[54], Boyer[86], and Hartley[87].

evidence showing that the primary structure and amino acid sequence of a protein directly contributes to its enzymatic function. It must be kept in mind, however, that all function stops when the native tertiary structure is disturbed.

In another important aspect our understanding of enzyme function has made great advances in recent years through the application of the methods of protein chemistry. It has long been known that many enzymes occur naturally in an inactive or precursor form and require a special process for their activation. Such mechanisms of shielding the cutting edges of the biochemical knives are of obvious advantage to the organism. The prime examples are again the pancreatic proteases trypsin, chymotrypsin, and pepsin, components of the blood-clotting system and others. In the case of trypsin where activation is autocatalytic, it has now been shown that this is due to the existence in the native inactive precursor protein, trypsinogen, of a single lysyl bond which is highly sensitive to trypsin. The result of its splitting by trypsin is the release of a small acidic peptide (Val–Asp–Asp–Asp–Asp–Lys). This release in turn favors the rearrangement of the rest of the molecule, which is now trypsin, into a new possibly more helical configuration. The rearrangement probably leads to a juxtaposition of the "active serine" with the catalytic histidine, and thus the creation of the active site[73,75].

In the case of chymotrypsinogen, trypsin is also the activating agent. It again acts on a single typical bond (–Arg–Ileu–) and this opening of a chain appears to be all that is required for the activation of chymotrypsin. The enzyme then tends to autodigest itself in a stepwise and limited fashion by typical chymotrypsin action to other forms, several of which retain full enzymatic activity[76,77]. The principle that limited proteolysis uncovers or shapes the functional site of an active protein appears to be frequently employed in biological processes. It would appear possible that the next few years may witness the complete elucidation of the mechanisms of activation and of enzymatic action not only for trypsin but for a variety of enzymes.

5. Genetic aspects of protein structure

A few years ago the idea was still widespread that proteins represented mixtures of molecules, differing randomly one from the other by a few amino acids. The structural elucidation of many proteins has not revealed a single instance which would support such a concept. Yet we now know that corresponding proteins from different species may differ from one another in minor detail, even though sharing most of their properties. This was first demonstrated by Sanger when he found that the insulins isolated from various species differed from one another by one or two amino acids[18]. Another interesting series of comparative peptide analyses by Tuppy[78] has shown that the peptide segment of cytochrome c which carries the red heme prosthetic group is very nearly the same for related and unrelated

TABLE V

SPECIES VARIATIONS IN PORPHYRIN-CARRYING PEPTIDE[78]
OF CYTOCHROME c[a]

Species	Sequence
Beef	–Val–GluNH$_2$–Lys–CyS–Ala–GluNH$_2$–CyS–His–Thr–Val–Glu–Lys–
Horse	–Lys–CyS–Ala–GluNH$_2$–CyS–His–Thr–Val–Glu–Lys–
Pig	–Lys–CyS–Ala–GluNH$_2$–CyS–His–Thr–Val–Glu–Lys–
Chicken	–Val–GluNH$_2$–Lys–CyS–*Ser*–GluNH$_2$–CyS–His–Thr–Val–Glu–
Salmon	–Val–GluNH$_2$–Lys–CyS–Ala–GluNH$_2$–CyS–His–Thr–Val–Glu–
Silk moth	–Val–GluNH$_2$–*Arg*–CyS–Ala–GluNH$_2$–CyS–His–Thr–Val–Glu–
Yeast	–*Arg*–CyS–*Glu–Leu* . . . CyS–His–Thr–Val–Glu–

[a] The porphyrin is bound by thioether linkage to the two cystein residues.

species, but that some variations at definite sites do occur in certain species (Table V).

Another important discovery is that hemoglobin differs not only from species to species within certain limits, but that certain heritable diseases in man can be attributed to a change in a single peptide sequence of this hemoglobin[79]. Thus sickle cell hemoglobin and another abnormal hemoglobin (C) carry a valine, and a lysine respectively, in lieu of the glutamic acid of normal hemoglobin (A) in seventh position from the N-terminus of one of the two chain types (the β-chain). While it has long been established that all species characteristics are under genetic control, the direct genetic determination of matters of fine structure, such as the replacement of one amino acid in one particular protein had not previously been demonstrated. The discovery that an exchange of one out of 300 amino acids in hemoglobin actually was the cause of a gross phenotypic effect, namely a disease in man, beautifully illustrated the role and the consequence of the genetic determination of primary protein structure. At present, amino acid sequential analyses are usually performed for the dual purpose of unravelling the biologically functional mechanism, and of determining the range and location of genetic variation in the family of proteins under investigation.

Simple viruses consist of a genetically active nucleic acid wrapped into a protein for the purposes of protection during transport from one host to another (Fig. 3). The functional properties of the protein are thus the relatively simple ones of forming a stable well-fitting coat for the nucleic acid[80]. It is therefore not surprising that many virus mutants show minor variations in their coat protein[81]. However, such mutations which would tend to decrease the stability of the protein coat would be expected to represent an evolutionary disadvantage, and thus to have lesser survival value. If we now consider the amino acid sequence of TMV protein, it is interesting to note that all natural strains of this virus that were studied have the same enzyme-resistant ends, an acetyl-seryl group on the amino end, and a proline near the carboxyl end. This is so even in those strains which show marked differences in the rest of their amino acid composition and sequence from the common strain. The fact that the common (or wild-type) strain has seemingly remained unchanged over 25 years of chemical observation in laboratories all over the world, even though mutants can be detected whenever searched for, indicates that this is a very stable form. It is now possible to evoke mutants by chemical modification of the viral nucleic acid, and it is of interest to note that many such mutants show heritable alterations in their protein. One such mutant obtained from TMV showed an exchange of 3 amino acid residues, one of which involved the proline near the C-terminus[82]. This was exchanged for leucine, and the virus protein was thus rendered susceptible to extensive degradation by carboxypeptidase.

It appears probable that the advances in protein chemistry which now enable us to locate the results of many mutational events will contribute greatly to a solution of one of the most important problems of biology, the nature of the genetic code carried by the nucleic acids, and its transmittal into phenotypic expression.

REFERENCES

1 E. FISCHER, *Ber.*, 39 (1906) 530.
2 E. BRAND, LEO J. SAIDEL, W. H. GOLDWATER, B. KASSELL AND F. J. RYAN, *J. Am. Chem. Soc.*, 67 (1945) 1524.
3 V. DU VIGNEAUD, *Harvey Lectures*, 50 (1956) 1.
4 G. L. MECHANIC AND M. LEVY, *J. Am. Chem. Soc.*, 81 (1959) 1889.
5 G. IVANOVICS AND G. H. BRUCKNER, *Naturwissenschaften*, 25 (1937) 250.
6 H. FRAENKEL-CONRAT in J. M. LUCK (Ed.), *Ann. Rev. Biochem.*, 25 (1956) 291.
7 P. M. GALLOP, S. SEIFTER AND E. MEILMAN, *Nature*, 183 (1959) 1659.
8 A. GOTTSCHALK AND D. H. SIMMONDS, *Biochim. Biophys. Acta*, 42 (1960) 141.
9 G. PERLMANN, *Advances in Protein Chem.*, 10 (1955) 1.
10 R. CONSDEN, A. H. GORDON, A. J. P. MARTIN AND R. L. M. SYNGE, *Biochem. J.*, 41 (1947) 596.
11 S. MOORE, D. H. SPACKMAN AND W. H. STEIN, *Anal. Chem.*, 30 (1958) 1185.
12 D. H. SPACKMAN, W. H. STEIN AND S. MOORE, *Anal. Chem.*, 30 (1958) 1190.
13 A. L. LEVY AND D. CHUNG, *Anal. Chem.*, 25 (1953) 396.
14 A. L. LEVY, *Nature*, 174 (1954) 216.
15 H. FRAENKEL-CONRAT, J. I. HARRIS AND A. L. LEVY in D. GLICK (Ed.), *Methods of Biochemical Analysis*, Vol. II, Interscience, New York, 1955, p. 359.
16 G. R. TRISTRAM in H. NEURATH AND K. BAILEY (Eds.), *The Proteins*, Vol. IA, Academic Press, New York, 1953, p. 181.
17 E. E. SNELL, *Advances in Protein Chem.*, 2 (1946) 75.
18 J. T. EDSALL AND J. WYMAN, *Biophysical Chemistry*, Vol. I, Academic Press, New York, 1958, p. 72.
19 S. W. FOX AND J. F. FOSTER, *Introduction to Protein Chemistry*, John Wiley, New York, 1957.
20 J. W. MEHL, E. PACOVSKA AND R. J. WINZLER, *J. Biol. Chem.*, 177 (1949) 13.
21 O. H. LOWRY, N. J. ROSEBROUGH, A. L. FARR AND R. J. RANDALL, *J. Biol. Chem.*, 193 (1951) 265.
22 H. N. RYDON AND P. W. G. SMITH, *Nature*, 169 (1952) 922.
23 S. MOORE AND W. H. STEIN, *J. Biol. Chem.*, 176 (1948) 367.
24 H. FRAENKEL-CONRAT in S. P. COLOWICK AND N. O. KAPLAN (Eds.), *Methods in Enzymology*, Vol. IV, Academic Press, New York, 1957, p. 247.
25 D. D. VAN SLYKE, D. A. MAC FADYEN AND P. B. HAMILTON, *J. Biol. Chem.*, 141 (1941) 671.
26 F. SANGER, *Biochem. J.*, 39 (1945) 507.
27 R. R. PORTER, *Biochem. J.*, 46 (1950) 304.
28 H. S. OLCOTT AND H. FRAENKEL-CONRAT, *Chem. Rev.*, 41 (1947) 151.
29 P. EDMAN, *Acta Chem. Scand.*, 4 (1953) 283.
30 S. P. L. SØRENSEN, *Biochem. Z.*, 7 (1908) 45.
31 H. FRAENKEL-CONRAT AND H. S. OLCOTT, *J. Biol. Chem.*, 161 (1945) 259.
32 A. C. CHIBNALL and M. W. REES, *Biochem. J.*, 68 (1958) 105.
33 H. ROSENBERG, A. H. ENNOR AND J. F. MORRISON, *Biochem. J.*, 63 (1956) 153.
34 H. FRAENKEL-CONRAT AND B. SINGER, *Arch. Biochem. Biophys.*, 65 (1956) 296.
35 H. FRAENKEL-CONRAT in P. D. BOYER, H. LARDY AND K. MYRBÄCK (Eds.), *The Enzymes*, Vol. I, Academic Press, New York, 1959, p. 589.
36 H. S. OLCOTT in D. M. GREENBERG (Ed.), *Amino Acids and Proteins*, Charles C. Thomas, Springfield, Ill., 1951, p. 56.
37 P. D. BOYER in P. D. BOYER, H. LARDY AND K. MYRBÄCK (Eds.), *The Enzymes*, Vol. I, Academic Press, New York, 1959, p. 511.
38 R. CECIL AND T. R. McPHEE, *Advances in Protein Chem.*, 14 (1959) 256.
39 E. V. JENSEN, *Science*, 130 (1959) 1319.
40 H. FRAENKEL-CONRAT, A. MOHAMMAD, E. D. DUCAY AND D. K. MECHAM, *J. Am. Chem. Soc.*, 73 (1951) 625.
41 L. TERMINIELLO, M. BIER AND F. F. NORD, *Arch. Biochem. Biophys.*, 73 (1958) 171.
42 C. H. CHERVENKA AND P. E. WILCOX, *J. Biol. Chem.*, 222 (1956) 621.
43 W. L. HUGHES JR., H. A. SAROFF AND A. L. CARNEY, *J. Am. Chem. Soc.*, 71 (1949) 2476.

[44] A. F. S. A. HABEEB, *Biochim. Biophys. Acta*, 34 (1959) 294.
[45] H. G. GUNDLACH, W. H. STEIN AND S. MOORE, *J. Biol. Chem.*, 234 (1959) 1754.
[46] W. D. STEIN AND E. A. BARNARD, *J. Mol. Biol.*, 1 (1960) 339, 350.
[47] H. FRAENKEL-CONRAT, *Arch. Biochem.*, 27 (1950) 109.
[48] H. FRAENKEL-CONRAT, *J. Biol. Chem.*, 217 (1955) 373.
[49] L. WEIL, A. R. BUCHERT AND J. MAHLER, *Arch. Biochem. and Biophys.*, 40 (1952) 245.
[50] S. AKABORI, K. OHNO, T. IKENAKA, Y. OKADA, H. HANASUFA, I. HARUNA, A. TSUGITA, K. SUGAE AND T. MATSUSHIMA, *Bull. Chem. Soc. Japan*, 29 (1956) 507.
[51] C. I. NIU AND H. FRAENKEL-CONRAT, *J. Am. Chem. Soc.*, 77 (1955) 5882.
[52] J. E. FOLK AND J. A. GLADNER, *J. Biol. Chem.*, 231 (1957) 379.
[53] R. L. HILL AND E. L. SMITH, *J. Biol. Chem.*, 228 (1957) 577.
[54] R. L. HILL, J. R. KIMMEL AND E. L. SMITH, *Ann. Rev. Biochem.*, 28 (1960) 97.
[55] A. KOWALSKI AND P. D. BOYER, *J. Biol. Chem.*, 235 (1960) 604.
[56] T. IKENAKA, *J. Am. Chem. Soc.*, 82 (1960) 3180.
[57] P. DESNUELLE in H. NEURATH AND K. BAILEY (Eds.), *The Proteins*, Vol. IA, Academic Press, New York, 1953, p. 87.
[58] L. K. RAMACHANDRAN AND B. WITKOP, *J. Am. Chem. Soc.*, 81 (1959) 4028.
[59] F. SANGER in E. D. GREEN (Ed.), *Currents in Biochemical Research*, Interscience, New York, 1956, p. 434.
[60] H. LINDLEY, *Nature*, 178 (1956) 647.
[61] C. H. W. HIRS, S. MOORE AND W. H. STEIN, *J. Biol. Chem.*, 235 (1960) 633.
[62] H. SPACKMAN, W. H. STEIN AND S. MOORE, *J. Biol. Chem.*, 235 (1960) 649.
[63] C. H. W. HIRS, *J. Biol. Chem.*, 235 (1960) 625.
[64] D. T. GISH, L. K. RAMACHANDRAN AND W. M. STANLEY, *Arch. Biochem. Biophys.*, 78 (1958) 433.
[65] F. A. ANDERER, H. UHLIG, E. WEBER AND G. SCHRAMM, *Nature*, 186 (1960) 922.
[66] A. TSUGITA, D. T. GISH, J. YOUNG, C. A. KNIGHT, W. M. STANLEY AND H. FRAENKEL-CONRAT, *Proc. Natl. Acad. Sci. U.S.*, 46 (1960) 1463.
[67] K. NARITA, *Biochim. Biophys. Acta*, 28 (1958) 184.
[68] F. H. WHITE JR., *J. Biol. Chem.*, 235 (1960) 383.
[69] T. ISEMURA, T. TAKAGI, Y. MAEDA AND K. IMAI, *Biochem. Biophys. Research Communs.*, 5 (1961) 373.
[70] F. A. ANDERER, *Z. Naturforsch.*, 14b (1959) 642.
[71] F. M. RICHARDS AND P. J. VITHAYATHIL, *J. Biol. Chem.*, 234 (1959) 1459.
[72] W. A. KLEE AND F. M. RICHARDS, *J. Biol. Chem.*, 229 (1957) 489.
[73] H. NEURATH in C. B. ANFINSEN, M. L. ANSON, K. BAILEY AND J. T. EDSALL (Eds.), *Advances in Protein Chemistry*, Vol. 12, Academic Press, New York, 1957, p. 319.
[74] A. K. BALLS AND E. F. JENSEN in F. F. NORD AND C. H. WERKMEN (Eds.), *Advances in Enzymology*, Vol. 13, Interscience, New York, 1952, p. 321.
[75] L. W. CUNNINGHAM JR., *Science*, 125 (1957) 1145.
[76] M. ROVERY, M. POILROUX, A. YOSHIDA AND P. DESNUELLE, *Biochim. Biophys. Acta*, 23 (1957) 608.
[77] H. NEURATH AND G. H. DIXON, *Federation Proc.*, 16 (1957) 791.
[78] H. TUPPY in A. NEUBERGER (Ed.), *Symposium on Protein Structure*, John Wiley and Sons, New York, 1958, p. 66.
[79] J. A. HUNT AND V. M. INGRAM, *Nature*, 184 (1959) 640.
[80] H. FRAENKEL-CONRAT AND L. K. RAMACHANDRAN, in C. B. ANFINSEN, M. L. ANSON, K. BAILEY AND J. T. EDSALL (Eds.), *Advances in Protein Chemistry*, Vol. 14, Academic Press, New York, 1959, p. 175.
[81] C. A. KNIGHT in F. M. BURNET AND W. M. STANLEY (Eds.), *The Viruses*, Vol. II, Academic Press, New York, 1959, p. 127.
[82] A. TSUGITA AND H. FRAENKEL-CONRAT, *Proc. Natl. Acad. Sci. U.S.*, 46 (1960) 636.
[83] H. G. WITTMANN AND G. BRAUNITZER, *Virology*, 9 (1959) 726.
[84] L. K. RAMACHANDRAN, *Virology*, 5 (1958) 244.
[85] H. FRAENKEL-CONRAT AND B. SINGER, *Biochim. Biophys. Acta*, 24 (1957) 540.
[86] P. D. BOYER, *Ann. Rev. Biochem.*, 29 (1960) 15.
[87] B. S. HARTLEY, *Ann. Rev. Biochem.*, 29 (1960) 45.

Chapter III

Acid-Base Properties and Electrophoresis of Proteins

RODES TRAUTMAN

Plum Island Animal Disease Laboratory,
Animal Disease and Parasite Research Division, Agricultural Research Service,
U.S. Department of Agriculture, Greenport, Long Island, N.Y. (U.S.A.)

1. Introduction

Acid–base equilibria and electrophoresis are special topics in the science of solutions. Both phenomena involve the complex behavior of ions—molecules in solution that have gained or lost one or more electrons. In addition to reactions with electrons, ions may combine with neutral molecules or with other ions in three ways, characterized by the decreasing strength of the bonds. First, the combination is of such strength that the bonds are not easily broken. Secondly, the bond is weak enough to permit an equilibrium exchange between the bound and unbound forms (as in the acid–base interaction of proteins with hydrogen ions). Thirdly, the interaction is between each ion and the distribution, called the ionic atmosphere, of positive and negative ions just balancing its own charge. Not only is each ion part of another's atmosphere but it is in continual motion.

The freedom of ions to move in a solution, exemplified by the thermal and Brownian motions, can be used by applying an external direct current electrical field. The resulting systematic relative motion of charged particles with respect to the solvent is called electrophoresis, and can effect separations of ions with different electrical properties. When proteins are undergoing electrophoresis, there is generally also a flow of the solvent because the container walls are charged. This electroosmosis, as well as electrophoresis, is a special topic of electrokinetics, the study of motion subject to the laws of static and dynamic electricity and hydrodynamics.

In Section 2, the acid–base reaction is considered in some detail as it is the major determinant of the charge on a protein. Preliminary to that, the physical chemistry of the dissociation of a weak acid is presented, for it is required in understanding the buffer solutions essential in electrophoretic studies. A classification of methods, given in Section 3, focuses attention on the basic manner in which the electrophoretic migration is used without specifying the apparatus. Selected theories are briefly covered in Section 4 to illustrate the method of approach. This section can be omitted if only the details are desired of the most widely used application—zone electrophoresis in a supporting medium (Section 5). Similarly, the interpretation in Section 6 of common schlieren patterns in moving boundary electrophoresis can be understood without reading Section 4.

More emphasis is placed here on concepts and methods than on specific applications, and personal assessment of the relative importance of various topics in biochemistry is perhaps reflected in the space allocations. Fortunately, two excellent treatises are available which should be consulted for details and specific applications through 1957: *Biophysical Chemistry* by Edsall and Wyman[1] and *Electrophoresis*, edited by Bier[2]. An additional treatise by Audubert and DeMende[3] on theory and selected applications through 1954 has been recently translated*.

2. Acid–base properties

(a) *Ionic strength and pH*

To understand reactions of proteins with protons, *i.e.*, hydrogen ions H^+, it is necessary to describe some useful terms. The first of these is the ionic strength, $\Gamma/2$, of a solution which is computed from

$$\Gamma/2 \equiv \tfrac{1}{2} \sum c_j z_j^2 \tag{1}$$

where c_j is the molar concentration of ions with a charge per ion (valence) of z_j. Many non-specific effects of salts are more easily described in terms of ionic strength than in terms of molarity. There is no instrument that measures ionic strength of a solution. However, the electrical conductivity for a given salt is proportional to the ionic strength.

The second important term is the pH of a solution, defined as

$$pH \equiv -\log c_{H^+} \tag{2}$$

where c_{H^+} is the concentration of hydrogen ions in moles/l. In more rigorous considerations the effective concentration or activity must be used. The

---

* This chapter was submitted in March, 1961. The references 54–58 may be helpful (added in proof).

pH is easily determined in all solutions of biochemical interest with a pH meter after calibration with standard solutions. Fundamental to the pH meter are the two electrodes. The "glass electrode" is merely a thin glass tube containing dilute HCl and an electrode reversible to Cl⁻. The "calomel electrode" is a porous glass tube containing saturated KCl and a calomel–mercury electrode. The dc voltage produced is amplified and measured on a scale reading from 0–14 with 7 being neutrality at 25°.

(b) Titration

The Brønsted formulation of acids and bases defines an acid as a substance, of any initial charge, that can dissociate a proton. The remaining portion of the substance will have one less positive charge and is called the (conjugate) base. This can be shown symbolically as

$$B^iH^+ \rightleftharpoons B^i + H^+ \tag{3}$$

where BH is the acid, B the base and i can be any charge, positive or negative. The equilibrium constant of this reaction is called the acid dissociation constant K_a

$$K_a = \frac{[B^i]\,[H^+]}{[B^iH^+]} \tag{4}$$

where the square brackets around capital letters are used to represent molar concentrations of these substances, as in conventional treatments.

A clerical simplification used in applying eqn. (3) to aqueous solutions ignores the fact that a proton leaving a protein or acid molecule attaches itself to a water molecule forming the hydronium ion H_3O^+. Thus the rigorous dissociation of water

$$H_2O + H_2O \rightleftharpoons H_3O^+ + OH^- \tag{5}$$

will be written

$$H_2O \rightleftharpoons H^+ + OH^- \tag{6}$$

with equilibrium constant, in water

$$K_a = \frac{[H^+]\,[OH^-]}{[H_2O]} = \frac{[H^+]\,[OH^-]}{55.5} \equiv \frac{K_w}{55.5} \tag{7a}$$

where $K_w = 10^{-14.00}$ at 25°. In analogy with eqn. (2), pOH is defined as $-\log c_{OH^-}$ and eqn. (7a) can be written

$$pH + pOH = pK_w \tag{7b}$$

The dissociation of weak acids or proteins may be studied by taking advantage of the fact that a strong acid dissociates its H^+ completely in aqueous solution supplying a known amount of protons. The method, known as titration, is to place a precise amount of the deionized* substance (say protein) in each of a series of tubes, then add various determined amounts of strong acid (or alkali) and the proper amount of salt solution (*e.g.* KCl) to give the same total volume and ionic strength. To determine c_{H^+} the pH is measured after careful mixing at a known temperature. For special studies a rapid flow apparatus as used by Steinhardt and Zaiser[4] permits measurements within 3 sec after mixing. This was important in studying the dissociation of hemoglobin in the acid region.

The mean number $\bar{h}$ of protons per protein molecule** dissociated may be computed from the normality c_a of the strong acid, c_{H^+} calculated from the measured pH using eqn. (2), and the molar concentration of protein c_p as

$$\bar{h} = (c_{H^+} - c_a)/c_p \tag{8a}$$

or, similarly, if strong alkali of normal concentration c_b is used

$$\bar{h} = (c_b - c_{OH^-})/c_p \tag{8b}$$

where c_{OH^-} can be calculated from the pH using eqn. (7b).

A plot of $\bar{h}$ *vs.* pH is known as a titration curve, several examples of which are shown in Fig. 1. The explanation of the simple sigmoidal shape of Figs. 1b or 1d may be developed as follows. Rearrange eqn. (4) and take the log of both sides to give

$$pH = pK_a + \log \left\{ [B^i]/[B^iH^+] \right\} \tag{9a}$$

$$pH = pK_a + \log [\alpha/(1 - \alpha)] \tag{9b}$$

where α, the fraction of molecules that are in the conjugate base form, is defined by

$$\alpha \equiv [B^i]/\left\{ [B^iH^+] + [B^i] \right\} \tag{10a}$$

$$1 - \alpha = [B^iH^+]/\left\{ [B^iH^+] + [B^i] \right\} \tag{10b}$$

For this univalent acid or base, $\bar{h}$ is equal to α since the number of protons dissociated is equal to the number of conjugate base molecules formed.

---

* Three methods have been used with proteins: (*i*) recrystallization followed by dialysis, (*ii*) electrodialysis and (*iii*) passage through a mixed-bed ion exchange resin.
** If the molecular weight is known, otherwise, per unit weight of protein present.

Hence, eqn. (9b) yields

$$pH = pK_a + \log [\bar{h}/(1 - \bar{h})] \tag{11}$$

This is the required equation for the sigmoid curves. For some purposes it may be more convenient to plot pH against $\{ \log [B^i H^+] - \log [B^i] \}$ to give "linear" titration curves[5].

The simplest model for protein titration is a polyvalent acid of n identical

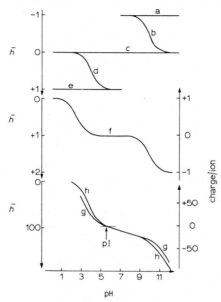

Fig. 1. Titration curves. Ordinate $\bar{h}$ is the number of protons dissociated per ion; (a) strong univalent base; (b) weak univalent base, $pK_a = 10$; (c) H_2O; (d) weak univalent acid, $pK_a = 4$; (e) strong univalent acid; (f) simple amino acid such as glycine; (g) simple protein, low ionic strength ($\Gamma/2 = 0.01$); (h) simple protein, high ionic strength ($\Gamma/2 = 0.15$) (data for bovine serum albumin after Tanford *et al.*[7]).

groups so far apart that they ionize independently. Thus, α represents the fraction of all groups that have dissociated a proton, and $\bar{h}$, per mole of these groups, will still equal α. But expressed per mole of protein

$$\bar{h} = n\alpha \tag{12}$$

and eqn. (9b) becomes for this special case[6]

$$pH = pK_a + \log [\bar{h}/(n - \bar{h})] \tag{13}$$

which is still a simple sigmoid curve of height n instead of unity. Going one

References p. 146

step further, considerable success has been achieved in resolving the titration curve of a protein, such as Fig. 1g, into a sum of m sigmoid curves[7]. Each has a $(pK_a)_i$ equal to the pH at each inflection point and n_i equal to the separation between the asymptotes of each sigmoid curve. By studying the changes with temperature[1], the functional groups can be identified and the number of amino acids corresponding to each n_i decided.

The next several sections will consider standard topics of acid–base reactions as deductions from the titration curves for simple substances and proteins.

(c) Buffer

The steepest portion of the titration curve is called the buffering region, since the pH changes much less with the addition of strong acid or alkali than it does at a given pH along the asymptotic limbs. The buffering action is the result of the added H^+ combining with the conjugate base and thus becoming unavailable to change the pH; conversely, some of the added alkali is neutralized by free H^+ which is partially replenished by dissociation of some of the acid form. A buffer solution contains at least one such substance, present in both acid and conjugate base forms, which resists attempted pH changes. Buffers are of fundamental importance in life processes, for even a change of a few tenths of a pH unit can mean the difference between life and death. They are also extremely important in biochemical studies since the physical and chemical behavior of proteins depend markedly on the pH. The calculation of the ionic strength and pH of any of the standard buffers[1,2] used in electrophoretic studies is done with eqns. (1) and (9a).

The buffering capacity β of a solution, defined as the number of moles/l of strong alkali required to change the pH by one unit, is as important as the pH in biochemical applications. Buffers from charged acids have a smaller buffering capacity than those from uncharged ones at the same ionic strength, and the addition of neutral salt increases the ionic strength, without changing β or the pH, except slightly[8].

By differentiation of eqn. (8a)

$$\beta \equiv - \, dc_a/dpH = 2.303 \, c_{H^+} + c \, d\bar{h}/dpH \tag{14a}$$

or, similarly, from eqn. (8b)

$$\beta \equiv dc_b/dpH = 2.303 \, c_{OH^-} + c \, d\bar{h}/dpH \tag{14b}$$

where c is the total molar concentration of both forms of the buffering substance. In practical buffer solutions, the terms in c_{H^+} or c_{OH^-} are negligible and the buffering capacity is approximately proportional to the slope of the titration curve

$$\beta = c \, d\bar{h}/dpH \tag{15}$$

For sigmoid curves of the polyvalent acid type, an analytical expression can be obtained from eqns. (13) and (15) as

$$\beta = 2.303 \, \bar{h} \, (1 - \bar{h}/n)c = 2.303 \, \alpha(1 - \alpha)cn \tag{16}$$

which has a maximum value for $\alpha = \frac{1}{2}$ occurring at pH = pK_a. The buffering capacity of a 10% (100 g/l) albumin solution in H_2O can be calculated from the titration curve of Fig. 1g, the molecular weight, and eqn. (15) as $\beta = [100/(6.8 \cdot 10^4)] \, 8 = 0.012$ where the slope near neutrality was taken as 8. This is equal to the buffering capacity of a $\Gamma/2 = 0.01$ univalent, uncharged acid buffer at pH = pK_a (0.02 M in buffering substance).

(d) Ampholyte

The titration curve provides information about the changes but not the absolute value of the charge on the substance. An amphoteric substance or ampholyte is one whose net charge is positive, zero or negative according to the pH. The isoelectric point, pI, is the pH at which the net charge is zero. This is usually determined from electrophoretic measurements as the pH of no migration. However, the ampholyte may bind[6] ions other than H^+, especially buffer anions, and there will be a dependence of pI on the previous history of the protein and the nature and concentration of the buffer. The isoionic point is the pH at which there is no net charge when all bound ions other than H^+ are removed from the substance, and hence is a special isoelectric point. At the isoionic point there must be other ions in the solution to give electroneutrality, if p$I \neq 7$, but under experimental conditions these ions may often be bound. However, if the concentration of protein is high enough the pH of deionized protein will be very close to the isoionic point. Following a calculation by Edsall and Wyman[1], the pH of salt-free albumin at $10^{-4} M$ (ca. 0.7 g/100 ml) was about 5. The charge of the solvent calculated from the concentration of H^+ minus the concentration of OH^- ions was 10^{-5}. Hence the average negative charge per molecule of albumin was only $-10^{-5}/10^{-4} = -0.1$ out of 90 possible[7]. This point can be located on the titration curve and the ordinate $\bar{h}$ scale converted thereby to net charge, as is given on the right hand side of Fig. 1g. The higher the protein concentration used and the steeper the titration curve, the closer will the pH of deionized protein correspond to pI.

The simplest ampholyte is glycine, as in Fig. 1f. Here it has been shown

References p. 146

that the buffering region around pH 2 is due to the dissociation of the α-carboxyl group and that around pH 10 to the α-amino group. Most of the amino acid chains of proteins are formed through the α-peptide linkage making these groups unavailable for buffering; hence the strong buffering regions must be due mainly to functional groups in the residues of the more complicated amino acids. A few terminal α-carboxyl and α-amino groups of the polypeptide chains as well as of some amino acids not held in position by α-peptide bonds may also contribute to the titration.

In the neighborhood of the isoelectric point the ampholyte is electrically neutral because the number of positive charges on the molecule equals the number of negative charges somewhere else on the molecule. Such a molecule is called a zwitterion or dipolar ion which, compared to the uncharged form of the molecule, has high melting point, high electric moment, high positive dielectric increment, high solubility in H_2O, characteristic spectroscopic frequencies and the amphoteric acid–base behavior just discussed. Because of the exhibition of these properties, it is concluded that the dipolar ion form of amino acids and proteins is favored over the completely uncharged form[1].

(e) Charge heterogeneity[9,10]

If each molecule of protein has a total of n different sites that may yield protons in the titration, then the number of ways that $\bar{h}$ of these may be distributed is $n!/\bar{h}!(n - \bar{h})!$. For hemoglobin at the isoelectric point, this is in the order of 10^{50}. Because of the wide separation of the pK's of the various groups, most of this large number of possibilities are of low probability. In fact, Cohn and Edsall[10] compute that the isoelectric condition for hemoglobin obtains when 12 of 33 imidazole groups of the histidine residues have lost a proton. The number of ways to get isoelectric hemoglobin is then reduced to $33!/(12!)(21!) = 3.5 \cdot 10^8$. At present, this still enormous number of protein ions of the same charge are all considered to have a reasonable chance of existence and not only are they in rapid equilibrium with each other, but with forms of greater or lesser net charge. Linderstrøm-Lang and Nielsen[9] showed that the variance of the distribution of these ions with different net charges can be obtained from the slope of the titration curve at any pH according to

$$\sigma^2 = (1/2.303)\, d\bar{h}/dpH \tag{17}$$

where σ is the standard deviation. For albumin at pI, from Fig. 1g, $d\bar{h}/dpH = 8$, giving $\sigma = 1.9$. Using a table of the normal distribution, the proportion of molecules that have a charge between -0.5 and $+0.5$ with this σ is 21%. Hence only 21% of the albumin molecules are isoelectric at any one moment. Similarly, 18% have a net charge between $+0.5$ and $+1.5$.

The importance of charge heterogeneity should not be minimized, for it may well be that certain reactions proceed through one of the least probable forms. In contrast, the heterogeneity can be used to treat the protein molecules as though the ionizable groups are randomly distributed and resolve the titration curve into m polyvalent acids previously mentioned. However, this ignores both slight deviations in sigmoid shape and the change in the titration curve with ionic strength shown in Fig. 1g as a general clockwise rotation about the isoelectric point. Both of these subtleties are explained by considering the mutual electrostatic interaction between charges on a single protein and their interaction with the charges of the solvent. The usual equation fits the data by overestimating the real charge–charge interaction because of the assumption of randomly distributed ionizable groups on a rigid sphere to the same extent that it underestimates it by the use of the bulk dielectric constant of water[9]. This equation is

$$\mathrm{pH} = \mathrm{p}K_i + \log\left[\bar{h}_i/(n_i - \bar{h}_i)\right] - 0.868\,w(z^0 - \bar{h}) \qquad (18)$$

where $(z^0 - \bar{h})$ is the net charge at any pH, n_i and $\mathrm{p}K_i$ are the parameters of the component simple dissociation curves of eqn. (13) and w is a constant throughout the entire pH range but is dependent on the ionic strength and the radius of the protein. Tanford, Swanson and Shore[7] experimentally determined w for albumin and found that it was constant, except at low pH where it decreased. The interpretation that this change corresponded to a swelling of some 20-fold in volume has been confirmed by viscosity studies[11].

3. Classification of electrophoretic methods

It is natural that terms should arise encompassing not only the purpose, type, and method of assay but also aspects of the equipment itself, such as filter paper electrophoresis or immunoelectrophoresis. These are somewhat unsatisfactory for a general classification. Define type as the basic way the phenomenon of electrical migration can be exploited, and assay as the method used to reveal the distribution in the direction of the field of some substance or substances. These will be considered before the various purposes for performing the electrophoresis. This classification scheme of type–assay–purpose may help the new user select the proper instrument for the problem at hand—something that is frequently not done.

Before the classification is given, some general comments should be made about "mobility"[12]. If the displacement, time, and solvent movement are known, the velocity of a substance can be computed. Of even more value is the mobility, defined as the systematic relative velocity per unit field strength. This mobility is independent of the time or current (except at enormous field strengths), but it does not always have to be computed. Serum proteins have been so widely studied that special terminology has been more useful than reporting their mobility in quantitative units such as 10^{-5} cm^2/(volt sec). Components with mobility less than that of albumin are given Greek letters prefixed to the term "globulin" and the faster components are called pre-albumin. As greater resolution is obtained with newer techniques, these names will lose some of their aura of finality. They have served well and, in honor, will undoubtedly be carried along as generic terms. It should be emphasized that terminology introduced for the components revealed by one phenomenon should not be employed for another unless it is shown experimentally that the same group of molecules is included. Thus, membership in any one of the following is not a necessary and sufficient condition for membership in another: γ-globulin, antibody, third saturated ammonium sulfate precipitate, 7S, or Cohn fraction III-1.

(a) Type

There are six types: (i) redistribution at electrodes, (ii) individual particle, (iii) moving boundary, (iv) moving zone, (v) isoelectric, and (vi) continuous flow. In all, there is the required systematic relative motion of the solute of interest with respect to the solvent, but the experimental set-up to use the phenomenon is different.

(i) The redistribution at electrodes type

The "redistribution at electrodes" type, attributed to Hittorf, involves the changes in concentration in the neighborhood of the electrodes because of the electrical transport of the various ions at different rates in opposite directions[12]. It is sometimes called the "analytical method" because analytical chemistry has been used to measure the changes, but other methods of assay, such as radioactive counting, are also possible. This method is rarely used at present.

(ii) The individual particle type

The most widely used application of the individual particle type (Fig. 2A) is the microscope method[3, 13] in which a light microscope is focused at a given level in the cell. The velocity of a particle is then computed from the time $(t - t_0)$ required for it to move a given distance on the reticule. The particles must be identifiable in the microscope; therefore, the method has been limited to viruses, bacteria, and cells. Electroosmotic solvent flow is a major complication and care must be taken in experimental arrangements so that particles are observed only at levels where this is zero (see Section 4). Miniaturization and use of 10 c/sec alternating current have recently been reported[14].

(iii) The moving boundary type

The moving boundary type (Fig. 2B) was developed to "see" particles too small for direct microscopic observation by following the movement of a boundary between the solution and a solvent devoid of the substance of

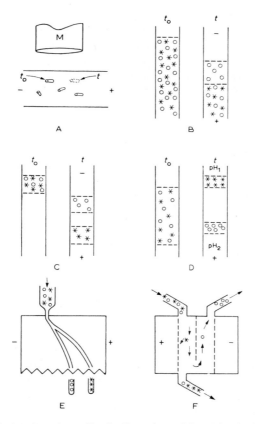

Fig. 2. Types of electrophoresis. t_o distribution of particles at beginning; t distribution after electric field has been applied; circles represent a component with slower mobility and higher pI than component marked with asterisks. (A) Individual particle type, M microscope. (B) Moving boundary type, dashed line indicates boundary position between two solutions. (C) Moving zone type, zones move with the mobility of their particles, anticonvection stabilization is required. (D) Isoelectric type in a pH gradient, particles move to their isoelectric point and then the zones remain stable with time, anticonvection stabilization is required. (E) Continuous flow of hanging curtain subtype, solvent flow from top to bottom of vertical migration unit is superimposed on migration of moving zone type, fractions are recovered from drip points at lower edge. (F) Continuous flow of forced flow subtype, convection is superimposed on solution flow due to migration of horizontal moving boundary type, output contains a relative enrichment of particles.

interest[12, 15, 16]. The solution, containing unknown species of ions in addition to the background electrolyte, is layered beneath a solvent of the same background electrolyte, as shown in Fig. 2B at t_0. With the passage of current, all the ions move. The ones marked in the figure are not replaced by ones above the initial boundary; hence, there is a moving boundary characterized by the disappearance of one constituent across it, as shown at time t. Evidently the initial boundary must be made gravitationally stable, and the system so chosen that all the moving boundaries which develop have no density inversions. In an actual case, there are phenomena, *e.g.*, diffusion, electroosmosis, and thermal convection, affecting the distribution, and the boundary does not remain "infinitely sharp". Even so, a "true boundary position" can be defined such that its movement is characteristic of the particles ahead of the boundary region. Mathematically, this is the location of the first moment of the concentration gradient curve of the disappearing species[12] for a uniform field in a cell with a uniform cross section. The theory has been extended for any geometry in such a manner that it is applicable both to electrophoresis and ultracentrifugation and so that other mathematical properties of the concentration distribution can be employed, depending upon the means of measurement[17].

Most moving boundary experiments have been conducted in free solution in the "Tiselius" apparatus, which is comparatively elaborate and contains complex optical systems using such properties of solutions as the index of refraction or specific absorption to yield precise registration of the boundary regions. These patterns are so common that their interpretation will be considered in Section 6.

(iv) The moving zone type

The moving zone type, shown in Fig. 2C, completely revitalized electrophoresis more vigorously than moving boundary methods had done when observations were limited to following individual particles. Advantageously, a complete separation of components can be achieved concurrently with the displacement needed to determine the velocity of the substance. Evidently, there will be an inverted density difference at the lower edge of the initial zone (Fig. 2C, t_0) because the protein molecules, being more dense, increase the solution density over that of the solvent. Three methods have been used to avoid the convection and will be described briefly as subtypes.

Consider first the *density gradient*[12,18] subtype. If the protein zone is in a vertical density gradient of an uncharged solute, then any increase in solution density, even when protein migrates into solvent, can be made less than that of the solvent immediately below, and the zone would be stable. However, even with such a density gradient, made with sucrose for example, there is a dramatic complication called droplet sedimentation—the raining of small drops of solution out of the lower boundary of the protein zone[19,20]. The diffusion of the sucrose into the protein zone, which is faster than the protein diffuses out, results in local regions with an inverted density gradient producing the droplet sedimentation. It can be avoided if the solvent density is decreased (by decreasing sucrose concentration) as the protein concentration is increased in proceeding from below into the initial zone. Svensson and Valmet[21] have developed a simple apparatus to introduce the initial sample in this manner and have advanced the theory for the stability of moving zones.

In a small tube, the resistance to fluid flow increases inversely as the fourth power of the radius and the use of either a small capillary tube or the interstices of a porous medium should also enable the zone method to work. The former can be called the *rotating horizontal capillary* subtype and has required coating of the tube with methyl cellulose to avoid the otherwise disastrous effects of electroosmosis on the zone[22]. The latter is known as zone electrophoresis in a *supporting medium* and is by far the most widely used subtype of electrophoresis at present[23-25]. The complications from the supporting medium are at least "geometrical"—*i.e.*, occupying space and providing a tortuous channel for migration—and at most, those of interaction—*i.e.*, reaction with the solute to retard or completely prevent the migration. The details of moving zone electrophoresis in a supporting medium will be considered in Section 5 because of its importance.

(v) The isoelectric type

The isoelectric type differs from the moving zone type in that the separation and width of the final zones become independent of the time. The substances migrate in a pH gradient to the place where they have no net charge[12,18,26]. If this is performed in free solution, there must also be a density gradient for stabilization (Fig. 2D). The low migration velocity of the serum proteins is the main limitation, but decreased solubility at the isoelectric point and the instability of the pH gradient over long periods of time are others. The isoelectric zone type has not been met with the enthusiasm that the analogous isodensity type has in ultracentrifugation.

(vi) The continuous flow type

The continuous flow techniques have essentially unlimited capacity to separate materials on a truly large scale. Some of the equipment has been perfected to such an extent that many investigators use it for small quantities even when only the mobility of an active fraction is to be determined. Such an application should be discouraged. One subtype (Fig. 2E) is basically the moving zone type superimposed with solvent flow roughly at right angles to the electric field and termed *continuous zone* electrophoresis. This is sometimes called hanging curtain electrophoresis[27] but is not restricted to vertical filter paper arrangements[28]. The sample and solvent flow separately into the filter paper curtain at the top, and fractions are collected from drip-points at the bottom. In a second subtype (Fig. 2F), called *forced flow* electrophoresis[18], free solution in a horizontal field is superimposed with convection that is partitioned by suitably arranged incomplete vertical membranes. A more descriptive name would be continuous moving boundary electrophoresis. The sharpness of resolution in the two outputs depends upon the rate of flow, the electric field, the type of microporous membrane, and the number of recyclings performed or number of units in cascade.

(b) Assay

Evidence for the movement and separation of substances during and/or at the completion of electrophoresis is provided by the assay. The assay should be highly reproducible and sufficiently sensitive to micro amounts of materials. This is because the substances of interest are often scarce and must contribute only negligibly to the conductivity of the solutions for precise measurements. Quantitative methods from chemistry, biology and physics have been employed successfully. But, regardless of its discipline, any assay may be considered from two points of view which are pertinent in electrophoretic applications: specificity and location of use. These will now be discussed separately.

The assay can be completely non-specific, detecting any and all solutes, or it can range to one highly specific for only a single substance. In many cases, a biological assay defines the particle of interest and electrophoresis is merely one of many phenomena used to characterize the active agent—the name for the material detected by a highly specific bio-assay.

The location of use of the assay may be point-by-point in place in the migration unit, in which case it must not change the relative positions of the components and often can be applied during the migration. Alternatively, it may be applied on fractions removed from the migration unit. Here the resolution depends on the thickness of the fractions compared with the total distance migrated and any disturbances inherent in the fractionation system.

For purposes of illustration, some examples are listed under the four possible combinations of specificity and location just given. These show the intermingling of type, assay, and equipment into the terminology. It should be emphasized that practically all assay methods may be used with any of the six basic types of electrophoresis and frequently several assay procedures are applied to the same separation.

(i) Non-specific, in place

(a) Schlieren, interferometric or absorption optical analysis of the Tiselius apparatus; (b) dye applied to starch gel electrophoresis.

(ii) Specific, in place

(a) Antigen–antibody reaction in agar gel of immunoelectrophoresis; (b) radioactivity measured along a filter paper electrophoresis strip.

(iii) Non-specific, on fractions

Index of refraction or optical density measurements on fractions removed from macro cell of free electrophoresis.

(iv) Specific, on fractions

(a) Chemical analysis for a particular substance from drip-points of hanging curtain electrophoresis; (b) infectivity titration or hormone assay on samples eluted from starch block electrophoresis segments.

(c) Purpose

The interests a biochemist might have in or the purposes he might have for applying electrophoresis can now be stated in terms of the general discussion of mobility, types and assays given above.

When a *single active agent* is of interest there are four purposes: (i) to determine its mobility; (ii) to determine its amount; (iii) to isolate it from substances of different mobility; and (iv) to characterize its electrophoretic homogeneity and reactions with itself and other ions.

When *multiple substances* are of interest there are three purposes: (i) to display all the mobility classes in a solution; (ii) to determine their relative concentration; and (iii) to determine the extent of interactions between components. A clinical study means the survey of multicomponent displays over a vast number of samples obtained in various conditions. Such an investigation often yields explanations of anomalous patterns; but it forces standardization in instrumentation not required with a detailed investigation of only a few samples. Clinical studies of moving boundary patterns and then, in a wider series, of moving zone patterns of sera have been unrewarding in relation to the amount of research time expended. The explanation is simply that there can be no clinical correlation if single molecular species are not observed[16]. The resolution of immunoelectrophoresis and starch-gel electrophoresis (to be described in Section 5) into twenty or more components as compared with the classical five has enabled some encouraging results of genetic significance.

References p. 146

When *instrumentation* is of interest there are five purposes: (*i*) to develop techniques for greater mobility resolution; (*ii*) to increase sensitivity; (*iii*) to reduce anomalies and artifacts; (*iv*) to advance the theory for a specific instrument; and (*v*) to advance the theory of transport processes, in general, and electrophoresis, in particular.

Whereas any of the types of electrophoresis or methods of assay can be used to meet most, if not all, of these purposes, it is evident that certain ones may be more suitable than others. The terms "analytical" and "preparative" have not been used since any transport process which displays components in an "analytical" manner can be made to yield fractions. Conversely, zone methods are inherently "preparative" with their yield depending only on the size of the migration unit, yet are frequently used merely to display components "analytically".

(*d*) *Limitation*

Of the many limitations of electrophoresis the following may be cited:

Theoretical studies have been applied to oversimplified model systems and hence fundamental ionic parameters, such as the charge, cannot be calculated, in general, for an actual situation.

The duration of experiments is usually long—most runs extending over hours. This gives stability problems with the buffer, the agent and the equipment. However, micromethods to reduce both the quantity and the time required are being continually developed.

Separation in this transport process is not without the simultaneous occurrence of other major phenomena. These are: (*i*) electroosmosis—the solvent is not stationary; (*ii*) diffusion—concentration profiles do not remain steep; (*iii*) thermal effects—dissipation of the heat produced by the electric current results in temperature gradients with not only consequent variation of the mobility (*ca.* $-3\%/°C$) but also solution density variations causing thermal convection; and (*iv*) shift in equilibria—whereas covalent and strong ionic bonds or association complexes are not broken by the field itself, changes in relative concentration result in changes in chemical equilibria and hence extreme complexity in the overall interacting system.

4. Theory of electrokinetics

(*a*) *Electrical conduction*

In a metal a difference of potential causes electrons to move from one atom to another—the movement of negative charges constituting the entire electrical current. In an electrolytic conductor[29,30], the electrons do not move separately but rather entire ions migrate, positive ones to the cathode and negative ones to the anode. The electric current is thus made up of charges moving in opposite directions. The energy increase observed experimentally with a calorimeter has been shown to be equal to the amount calculated from the voltage and current in the external circuit. Thus the ions act as agents in transferring the energy from the voltage source to the solution in terms of heat, and do not undergo continual acceleration. The existence of a terminal velocity, obtained practically instantaneously[3,14], means that the driving force is balanced by a retarding force. If the particle is small enough and the ionic atmosphere diffuse enough, the particle can be considered an isolated charged sphere whose motion under an electrical field is opposed by a purely viscous drag. The force producing migration is qe, where q is the charge on the particle and e is the field strength (force per unit charge) of the external field. The force of the viscous resistance from Stoke's law is $6\pi\eta\,rv$ where r is the radius of the sphere and v is its velocity through the solution of viscosity η. Equating these forces gives

$$u \equiv v/e = q/(6\,\pi\eta r) \tag{19}$$

where u is the mobility. This equation implies that the particle size (and analogously, its shape) has an influence on its mobility. However, a closer inspection of the ionic atmosphere reveals that the diffuse double layer[3,30,31] of both positive and negative charges (which statistically averages out to be equal and opposite to the particle's charge) may, instead, have dimensions comparable with that of the particle. The shifting of members of each other's ionic atmosphere under the impressed field results in a retarding force, which complicates the hydrodynamic friction experienced by moving uncharged particles or the model chosen to develop eqn. (19). In the extreme in which the thickness of the double layer is very small in comparison with the particle size, the mobility becomes independent of the size and shape of the particles. Curiously, the applicable expression can be obtained from eqn. (19) by changing the 6 to 4 and converting to the potential of the surface, ζ, determined as though the particle were at rest in an infinite medium. For a sphere $\zeta = q/(\varepsilon r)$ where ε is the dielectric constant. With this substitution and the conversion on the numerical factor, eqn. (19) becomes the Smoluchowski equation

$$u = \varepsilon\zeta/(4\,\pi\eta) \tag{20}$$

When particles aggregate, or coat quartz filaments of various shapes, the ζ potential would not be expected to change, and the mobility might be expected to remain constant. Experimentally, the mobility of protein coated particles was found independent of size and shape[13,32], the mobility of subunits of tobacco mosaic virus rods were identical to that of the whole virus[33], and the mobility of deoxynucleic acid was independent of concentration even though the solution viscosity was varied over 6-fold[34].

Theoretical developments have been along two main lines: molecular and macroscopic. The former concerns ionic parameters such as charge density, ζ potential and details of the double layer, whereas the latter concerns the overall behavior in the apparatus. Some examples will perhaps provide a deeper understanding of the phenomenon of electrokinetics and may stimulate a fresh attack, which will solve some of the problems.

(b) Electrical and hydraulic quantities

Starting with macroscopic considerations, some general deductions about an electrolytic solution may be listed. First, Faraday's law that 96,500 coulombs of electricity produces a chemical change of 1 gram-equivalent at the electrodes implies that in an electrolytic solution current is composed only of the movement of ions. Second, the acceleration of ions may be neglected. Third, the freedom of motion of ions means that in a macroscopic element of volume there will be electroneutrality, *i.e.*, no net charge. And fourth, wherever there is a pressure difference, the laws of hydrodynamics are applicable to the bulk solution flow. These apply whether experiments are performed in straight channels or in porous media[24]. The electrical variables are the impressed voltage difference E across the (container) length L and the current I through the total cross sectional area A. The hydrodynamic variables are the applied pressure difference P and the efflux fluid volume per unit time V. In theoretical studies, it is convenient to reduce the measured values according to the dimensions of the conductor to

$$e \equiv E/L \tag{21}$$

the voltage gradient or (macroscopic) field strength,

$$i \equiv I/A \tag{22}$$

the (macroscopic) current density,

$$p \equiv P/L \tag{23}$$

the (macroscopic) pressure gradient, and

$$v \equiv V/A \tag{24}$$

the (macroscopic) efflux fluid velocity.

Ohm's law states that for a solid, electrolytic or porous medium the current will be proportional to the impressed voltage difference if (*i*) high conductivity fluid is employed (to reduce electrokinetic effects, to be described), (*ii*) the frequency of alternating current used is between 0.5 and 50 kilocycles, and (*iii*) the diameter of the largest circle inscribed in the cross section is greater than 25 times the largest diameter of the grains of porous media. The ratio of E to I is called the resistance R. Ohm's law can be written for the container volume AL as

$$i/e = (L/A) \, (1/R) = [L^2/(AL)] \, (1/R) \equiv \kappa \tag{25}$$

where κ, defined hereby, is the specific conductivity because it depends on the nature of the conductor and not its dimensions.

The power delivered by the power supply is the product of E and I, and is frequently referred to as the Joule heat produced. Expressed per unit volume of the migration unit, it is $EI/(AL) = ei$.

These electrical quantities also apply for direct current in the migration unit. But the overall measurements are complicated by polarization from reaction products at the electrodes. The conductivity is altered giving a different (usually greater) voltage drop between the electrode and the undisturbed solution even at constant current. The reaction products should be prevented from entering the migration unit by proper construction of the electrode vessels to include baffles and sufficient volume.

There is an analogy between hydraulic and electrical quantities[24]. However, in strict contrast, fluid flow through a pipe depends on the shape as well as the size. For (*i*) a high conductivity fluid (to reduce electrokinetic effects) and (*ii*) low velocities (to have laminar rather than turbulent flow), Darcy's law states that the efflux volume per unit time V will be proportional to the applied pressure difference P. Using the reduced variables p and v Darcy's law can be written to define the permeability K as

$$K \equiv \eta(v/P) \tag{26}$$

where η, the coefficient of viscosity of the fluid, is the "specific" part of K depending on the fluid, and thus corresponds to κ. It should be noted that both i/e and v/p vary because of changes in viscosity with temperature (*ca.* $-3\%/°C$ for water) even though η is not explicit in Ohm's law. K, on the other hand, is necessary to further take into account the size and shape of the cross section and does not have a counterpart in Ohm's law. An attempt to separate a general size factor from K by using the square of the hydraulic radius has not succeeded since the remaining portion is still shape dependent, as seen below. This hydraulic radius m is defined as

$$m \equiv \text{fluid volume/wetted area exclusive of ends} \tag{27}$$

It is unfortunate that twice this quantity was not called a "radius" since for a cylinder $m = \pi r^2 L/(2\pi r L) = r/2$. With eqn. (27) Darcy's law can be written

$$v = (K/\eta)p \equiv \{ (2m)^2/[8(k/2)] \} p/\eta \tag{28}$$

defining a new constant $k/2$, which empirically has been found to vary from 0.6 for an eccentric core in a cylinder to 1.5 for a slit. Applied to a cylinder $(2m = r, k/2 = 1)$, eqn. (28) is Poiseuille's law.

Ohm's and Darcy's laws are also applicable to the porous medium case where the solid provides support against convection and divides the current and fluid flow into a myriad of interconnected paths. Now, for both fluid and current flow in porous media i and v are independent of the shape or size of the total cross section. However, if expressed in terms of the viscosity η_o and conductivity κ_o of the pore fluid (in bulk), they do depend upon how much of the total volume is solid and how the solid is dispersed to leave the tortuous channels.

First, it is important to consider the entire volume of support rather than just the solid in swelling systems; hence the support content S is operationally defined as

$$S \equiv 1 - (\text{displaceable volume/total volume}) \tag{29}$$

This correction factor was not enough to account for the measured conductivities in the electrical case (with $0.1\ M$ KCl in insulating media and no pressure head). Thus a structure coefficient T can be defined to make up the difference so that Ohm's law, eqn. (25), can be written

$$i/e = \kappa \equiv [(1 - S)/(1 + T)]\kappa_o \tag{30}$$

or

$$T \equiv [\kappa_o(1 - S)\ (e/i)] - 1 \tag{31}$$

There is adequate theoretical and experimental justification to believe that the $1 + T$ so defined does represent the statistical average of all the possible current paths in the form of the square of the ratio of its length to the container length. Note that S and T have been defined so that they approach zero as the ratio of solid to fluid is reduced to zero. $(1 - S)$ is frequently called porosity and $(1 + T)$ tortuosity.

Secondly, it would be anticipated that the factors S and T should also apply to fluid flow through the maze of interconnected channels in a porous medium. Using these factors, Darcy's law, eqn. (28), can be written

$$\frac{v}{p} = \frac{K}{\eta} \equiv \frac{(1 - S)}{(1 + T)} \frac{m^2}{k_o \eta_o} \tag{32}$$

defining k_o, the Kozeny constant, as the factor left over to make the equation fit the data. The value of $k_o/2$ is not constant, but depends on the grain shape. For packed spheres, it is 1.65 and goes as high as 4 for randomly packed cubes. This further shows the difference between electrical and hydraulic flow, but does not invalidate the factors of $1 - S$ and $1 + T$ for porous media. If a value of k_o is assumed for a given porous medium then the wetted area inside can be computed from eqn. (27) after m is calculated from the pressure and efflux from Darcy's law, eqn. (32).

(c) Electrophoretic mobility

Ohm's law and the deduction from Faraday's law that current is carried only by moving ions permits the conductivity of an electrolytic solution to be written as the sum of the products of concentration times the velocity for all the ionic species present. This idea can be formulated in many ways. The following develops the formulae for mobility in free solution as well as in porous medium[24].

Let v_j^0 be the free solution velocity of ion species j in a field of strength e^0. Then the mobility u_j^0, a signed quantity defined as the velocity per unit field strength, is

$$u_j^0 = v_j^0/e^0 = v_j^0 \kappa_o/i_o \tag{33}$$

using eqn. (25). Now let c_j^0 be the molar concentration, z_j the valence and F be 96.5 coulombs/gram-equivalent (i.e., 10^{-3} faradays), then

$$i_o = F \sum c_j^0 z_j v_j^0 \tag{34}$$

since it can only be made up of moving ions. By combining eqns. (33) and (34), the conductivity κ_o can be expressed as

$$\kappa_o = i_o/e_o = F \sum c_j^0 u_j^0 z_j \tag{35}$$

In a porous medium having a voltage E impressed across a length L, κ can be written in the same form as eqn. (35) using apparent values, denoted by the superscript a

$$\kappa = F \sum c_j^a u_j^a z_j = \kappa_o(1 - S)/(1 + T) \tag{36}$$

where the right hand side comes from eqn. (30). Using the definition of support content (eqn. (29)), the apparent concentration c_j^a is related to the concentration c_j^0 in the pore fluid as

$$c_j^a = c_j^0(1 - S) \tag{37}$$

The apparent mobility is computed directly from the gross displacement and the apparent field strength E/L as

$$u_j^a = D_j L/(Et) \tag{38}$$

where D_j is the distance an ion of species j moves relative to solvent in the time t. Substituting eqns. (35), (37) and (38) in (36) yields

$$\sum c_j^0 z_j u_j^0 = \sum c_j^0 z_j \left[\frac{D_j L}{Et} (1 + T) \right] \tag{39}$$

From this it is evident that the free solution mobility of each ion is

$$u_j^0 = [D_j L/(Et)] (1 + T) \tag{40}$$

which has been derived in other ways[24].

This equation is used when the voltage gradient and the displacement of the particle itself, or a zone of the particles, can be measured. Conversion to forms involving the current are complicated in porous media by surface conductivity, as well as non-insulating properties of the supporting medium.

For the moving boundary method in free solution similar relationships of current to ion concentration and velocity are written for the homogeneous phases on either side of a boundary. The law of conservation of mass is applied to develop the moving boundary equation. The solution and deductions from the set of such equations are well reviewed by Longsworth[12]. Here it is appropriate to show only the modification of eqn. (33) commonly used when the voltage across the migration unit cannot be measured because of the geometry of the apparatus. Let d be the displacement of the particle relative to the container in the time t. Then eqn. (33) can be written

$$u = (d/t)\kappa/i = [(Ad)/(It)]\kappa = v'\kappa \tag{41}$$

where v' has the dimensions of cm³/coulomb. These units make little sense when applied to an individual particle, but are convenient for a boundary movement. The units of mobility are generally one of three: cm/sec/volt/cm, μ/sec/volt/cm, or 10^{-5} cm²/(volt sec).

(d) Electroosmosis in open and closed cells

The latest approach in transport theory is the controversial thermodynamics of irreversible processes. This has given perhaps a better phenomenological description of the interplay of electric and hydrodynamic phenomena, but remains barren of mechanistic description at the individual particle level, and hence may be only complementary to classical dynamics.

For fluid interspersed in a general solid support subjected to both an impressed dc voltage gradient e and applied pressure gradient p the general phenomenological description is[35, 36]

$$i = \lambda_{11}e + \lambda_e p$$

$$v = \lambda_e e + \lambda_{22}p \tag{42}$$

where the λ's are coefficients with special names. Unfortunately neither the "conductance" λ_{11} nor the "permeability" λ_{22} are equal to the ordinary conductivity $\kappa = \kappa_0 \, (1 - S)/(1 + T)$ of eqn. (30) or permeability $K/\eta = (m^2/k_0\eta_0) \, (1 - S)/(1 + T)$ of eqn. (32) measured in the absence of all electrokinetic effects. Their respective differences are called surface conductivity and electroviscosity and need not be discussed further since the term of interest here is λ_e, the electropermeability[36].

After Bikerman[37], consider an open system consisting of a flat slit with no impressed pressure difference in which the velocity w_z of the fluid depends only on the distance from the faces located at $z = \pm a$. The charge on these faces caused by adsorption of negative groups from the solvent is indicated in Fig. 3A. The field strength at any point is made up of a component normal to the face because the charge distribution is a function of z and a component e parallel to the face because of the external field. Let the component normal to the face be expressed as a derivative of a potential function ψ. By Poisson's law, the net charge density ρ_z is

$$\rho_z = \varepsilon'(\mathrm{d}^2\psi/\mathrm{d}z^2)/(4\pi) \tag{43}$$

where ε' is the dielectric constant of the actual pore fluid. The external field exerts a net force on the charges in a volume element $\mathrm{d}x \, \mathrm{d}y \, \mathrm{d}z$ equal to

$$f_e = e\rho_z(\mathrm{d}x \, \mathrm{d}y \, \mathrm{d}z) \tag{44}$$

The coursing of opposite charges through this element results in no acceleration of the charges; hence, the driving force on them is equal and opposite to the force exerted by the water molecules. But the water does not accelerate either so there is a balancing viscous drag f_v on the volume element caused by neighboring water molecules moving at a different velocity. This is expressed hydrodynamically as

$$f_v = [\eta'(\mathrm{d}^2w_z/\mathrm{d}z^2)\mathrm{d}z] \, (\mathrm{d}x \, \mathrm{d}y) \tag{45}$$

where η' is the coefficient of viscosity of the actual pore fluid. Equating (44) and (45) yields

$$\frac{d^2 w_z}{dz^2} = \frac{\varepsilon' e}{4\pi\eta'} \frac{d^2 \psi}{dz^2} \tag{46}$$

Neither the potential distribution ψ nor the velocity w_z is thus explicitly given, but it can be shown that the constants of integration are such that the potential will decrease from its value at the wall to the place where the net charge is zero, whereas the velocity will increase from its no-slip value of zero at the wall to a maximum, also where the net charge is zero. Letting w_{eo} be this velocity and ζ the potential difference, eqn. (46) gives

$$\frac{w_{eo}}{e} = \frac{\varepsilon'}{4\pi\eta'} \cdot \zeta \tag{47}$$

This is, of course, related to the Smoluchowski eqn. (20), using w_{eo}/e as the electroosmotic mobility.

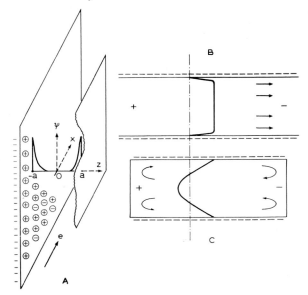

Fig. 3. Electroosmosis. (A) Open slit of separation $2a$ along z axis, external field strength e along x axis; each wall has a fixed negative charge adsorbed from the solution; positive ions of higher concentration next to the wall decrease steadily through the double layer to the electroneutrality concentration in center of cell; Ψ is the electrostatic potential due to the charge distribution. (B) Plug solvent velocity profile in an open system, due to H_2O dragged by the net concentration of positive ions in double layer moving toward cathode. (C) Parabolic solvent velocity profile in a closed system; net flow is zero due to circulation.

Now the change in the velocity w_z takes place at either wall in the double layer, which is only of molecular dimensions, hence the water velocity is constant and equal to w_{eo} at each point across the slit. Such a velocity profile, shown in Fig. 3B, is generally referred to as plug flow[37] and occurs even if the hydrodynamic equation is invalid within molecular dimensions or if the ζ potential refers to some level in the double layer rather than the wall itself. In a porous medium there will be a superposition of these profiles in the interconnected maze of capillaries and, analogously to eqn. (36), the efflux resulting from all the $(w_{eo})_j$ contributions will be [24]

$$\sum (w_{eo})_j/e = v/e = [\varepsilon'\zeta/(4\pi\eta')] (1 - S)/(1 + T) = \lambda_e \qquad (48)$$

where v/e has been set equal to λ_e from the second eqn. (42) for this special case of $p = 0$. Eqn. (48) permits conversion of λ_e, in mobility units, to ζ, in voltage units, provided the constants are known.

In a completely closed system[37], as in Fig. 3C, there can no longer be plug flow since fluid must be returned in the same channel. Assuming that the dimensions across the slit are large compared with the thickness of the double layer, the velocity w_{eo} appears essentially at the walls. It is then only a hydrodynamic problem to obtain the velocity distribution across a slit which has a net flow of zero. The pressure head that develops supplies the force for the return flow, which, on an element of volume, is $p \, dx \, dy \, dz$. Setting this equal to f_v of eqn. (45), integrating, and evaluating the constants as well as the pressure gradient p which develops[13] yields

$$w_z = (w_{eo}/2) (3z^2/a^2 - 1) \qquad (49)$$

This is the parabolic distribution shown in Fig. 3C. Note that the maximum return velocity, at the center, is $-w_{eo}/2$, independent of the size a of the channel and that $w_z = 0$ at the level $z = \pm a\sqrt{3}$.

The electroosmotic flow of neutral fluid with either a "plug" or parabolic distribution cannot be ignored even when the primary interest is the electrophoretic velocity of particles with respect to solvent. In the individual particle method, the data are recorded only for those particles located at the levels where the solvent flow is zero[13]. In the moving boundary method, the density difference across the boundary gives it a horizontal stability that averages out the distribution of solvent velocity[38]. It is incorrect to say, then, that there is no electroosmosis, and evidence of the required turn-around can be seen as an erosion of the boundaries. In the moving zone method in porous media, the interconnected maze of capillaries averages out all the profiles and leaves just one net electroosmotic fluid flow contributed by the buffer, which is superimposed on the electrophoretic velocity of the solute zones. The effect of a different electroosmotic velocity inside solute zones is one of the several neglected aspects of electroosmosis[39].

Another consequence of these profile considerations is the explanation for the fact that enormous pressures are required to force fluid through some gels, but a very small voltage can cause considerable flow. In the former, a hydrodynamic flow is required with its parabolic profile and consequent high resistance because of viscosity. In the latter, a plug type flow has minimal velocity gradients and hence little viscous resistance. Further, a zone displaced by hydrodynamic flow is broadened much more than one displaced by electroosmosis[40].

(e) Interacting systems

It was formerly thought that particles in rapid equilibrium would always reveal only a single broad boundary[41] since any one particle would statistically take on all forms, as with the various charged species of a protein at a given pH described in Section 2. Recently, Gilbert and Jenkins[42] realized that, in systems in which the equilibrium was concentration dependent, once a particle took a form with slower speed and fell behind it would have no way of converting to a faster form and catching up. They have classified many theoretical types of boundary patterns that might develop for systems in rapid equilibrium. For this they used the fact that the separation of two boundaries because of mobility differences is proportional to the time, whereas the diffusion broadening of each boundary, which tends to obscure the resolution, is proportional to the square root of the time[43]. Hence in normalized boundary patterns, converted to have the same separation, the effect of diffusion becomes less and less as the time is increased.

Gilbert and Jenkins have also stimulated investigation into the effect of interactions in the moving zone type of electrophoresis. For example, Bethune and Kegeles[44] have applied the mathematics of countercurrent distribution to the interacting system $A + B \rightleftharpoons C$ in which diffusion of the zones is permitted but only rapid reaction rates have thus far been considered. Extensive application[12, 15] of these recent theories of interacting systems, both in electrophoresis and ultracentrifugation experiments, are certain to follow when more subunit studies of proteins and viruses are made, and as antigen–antibody reactions are exploited.

5. Zone electrophoresis procedure

The basic moving zone type is described in Section 3; here, some typical details of operation are given. The factors for selecting a specific instrument are: the purpose of the electrophoresis, the volume of solution, the availability of equipment, and the experience of the investigator. Two moving zone techniques can be singled out as fundamental to the researcher. The first is block-electrophoresis[24]. It is the simplest, most versatile method for separating proteins according to their free-solution mobilities, giving, simultaneously in each run, fractions either for display of their presence or for use in further studies. It should be used to determine the mobility of a new active agent. The second is high resolution molecular-sieving-electrophoresis[45], which has revealed the greatest number of components of any method so far devised. It should be used in critical tests for electrophoretic homogeneity or in clinical studies. The two methods are complementary, and both are simple and inexpensive. As will be seen, they differ mainly in the supporting medium used.

(a) Properties of supporting media

Each of the following is of itself a desirable property, but, evidently, not all can be realized in the same medium[24].

(i) *Ease of handling*: Fibrous materials such as string or paper make the most rugged media, next are gels and swelling granular materials and, finally, the least rugged are non-swelling granular materials because of their tendency to flow under slight pressure ("melt").

(ii) *Absence of undesirable reactions with the solute*: The most common reaction of non-inert media is a chromatographic type of binding that gives tailing—the trail of material left behind a moving zone. Alternatively, the medium may give up substances that react with the solute. Or, the medium may swell and permit solutes of low molecular weight ($< 30,000$) to enter, which interferes with their migration. On the other hand, such entry can be advantageous when large molecules are being studied because a degree of dialysis is effected on introducing the crude sample.

(iii) *Absence of contaminants which interfere with the assay*: Starch, e.g., is not suitable if carbohydrate analyses are to be made.

(iv) *Absence of undesirable reactions with the buffer*: The net positive charge left in the buffer when the medium selectively adsorbs negative buffer constituents results in fluid flow toward the cathode. This electroosmosis is commonly thought undesirable; actually, it does not broaden zones much and frequently can be used to displace low mobility zones from the site of application, or "elute" fractions after electrophoretic separation. The pH and ionic strength changes resulting from ionic exchange can be eliminated by rinsing the medium with buffer before use.

(v) *Ease of fractionation*: Either the medium must be capable of direct staining, or the solute must be easily eluted. The most direct approach uses rubber sponges that can be simply squeezed.

(*vi*) *Presence of desirable reactions with the solute*: Advantage can be taken of non-inert media with special properties that will enhance the separation. Simultaneous chromatography has not been rewarding but molecular sieving in gels has been (to be described).

(*b*) *Block electrophoresis* (*general utility*)

(*i*) *Directions for granular starch-block*[24]

Fig. 4 illustrates the general set-up which includes an adjustable dc power supply capable of delivering 50 mA at 500 V (a constant current supply is preferable to a constant voltage one), glass plate, polyethylene sheeting, plastic or wood strips $1\frac{1}{2}$ cm high, 5 cm wide and 60 cm long, electrode

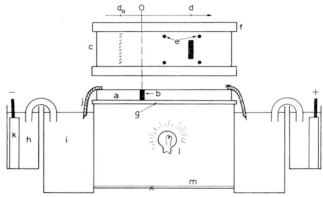

Fig. 4. Block electrophoresis by moving zone method. (a) Side view of starch block at time t_o; (b) initial zone; (c) top view of starch block after time t; (d) distance from origin to migrated zone; d_o distance from origin to substance with zero mobility (moved by solvent flow); (e) reference marker substances along each border; (f) strip used in molding block; (g) glass support; (h), (i) two chamber electrode vessel; (j) connecting bridge to block; (k) electrode; (l) lamp; (m) connecting tube to equalize levels in electrode vessels.

vessels, carbon electrodes, granular starch, barbital buffer pH 8.6, $\Gamma/2$ 0.1, coarse sintered glass funnels: one 500 ml size and several 15 ml size.

Mix the buffer and starch to give a slurry, rinse with two volumes of buffer in the large sintered glass funnel on a suction flask, add enough buffer to be able to pour into the mold. This mold is made by laying the plastic sheeting across the plastic strips 10 cm apart on the glass plate and closing the ends with thick wads of filter paper. Let stand until the filter paper has drawn off enough buffer to give a firm 1 cm thick slab. Dilute 2 ml of serum with an equal volume of buffer; dialysis is not necessary. Cut an 8 cm transverse slit in the block at about 1/3 the distance between ends, moving the spatula so as to form a V-groove without removing any starch. Apply

4 ml of the sample with a thin tipped pipette. Regulation of the moisture content of the block before insertion of the sample can be done by moistening with buffer or drying with a towel so that the sample spreads evenly giving, in this case, a zone $8 \times 1.5 \times 1$ cm^3. Press back the starch with the spatula to close the slit. Prepare a solution of *ca.* 10 mg/ml each of hemoglobin and albumin colored with bromphenol blue. Use 0.2 ml of this solution at each border in a separate V-groove to provide reference markers.

Thoroughly dry the block with a towel and fold down the sheeting, eliminating air in a spreading operation, which starts at the origin. With experience the proper moisture content of the block will be obtained before starting. Remove filter paper and place glass and block on lips of the electrode vessels, Fig. 4i, in a cold room (for serum all the preliminaries can be done at room temperature). Apply pieces of cloth toweling, or thick filter paper strips, rinsed in buffer to make the connecting bridges between the electrode vessels and a 2 cm strip across each end of the block which was left un-covered. Cover the toweling with small pieces of sheeting without concern for air pockets. Open connecting tubing between electrode vessels. Inspect block with transmitted light from below for any gross anomalies in applying the sample. Connect electrodes and apply power, selecting a voltage just below that which causes slight warming (to the hand) of the glass plate: *ca.* 10 V/cm. No significant increase in current should occur during an over-night run at constant voltage; conversely no decrease in voltage with a constant current supply. During the separation, the positions of the markers and probably the (yellow) albumin of the serum can be seen by transmitted light. There should be no significant difference between the two sides.

For termination, turn off power supply, remove towel bridges and im-mediately place dry filter paper pads at the ends. Using transmitted light, inspect for variations in zones either from top to bottom or transversely. These indicate non-uniform field strength due to excessive heating or an uneven block. Mark positions of interest and remove glass plate with block for fractionation (room temperature for serum). The medium should appear relatively dry before sectioning. Pack transverse segments into the small sintered glass funnels, add buffer equal in volume to the starch and apply suction. Alternate methods for recovery of the sample include (*a*) adding buffer to segment, mixing, centrifuging and decanting supernatant, or (*b*) centrifuging segment in special perforated inserts, collecting "super-natant" below in centrifuge tube. Determine the protein content of starting sample and each fraction. The starch is generally not salvaged.

(*ii*) *Typical pattern*

The histogram representation of a serum run[46] shown in Fig. 5 emphasizes that the measured concentration is for a finite width segment; hence, the resolution depends not only on the migration distance but also on the ratio of segment width to starting zone width. For a complete distribution curve, this ratio should be close to unity. In preparing a sample of electrophoretically pure albumin, *e.g.*, the ratio could be 5–10. The lower portion of Fig. 5

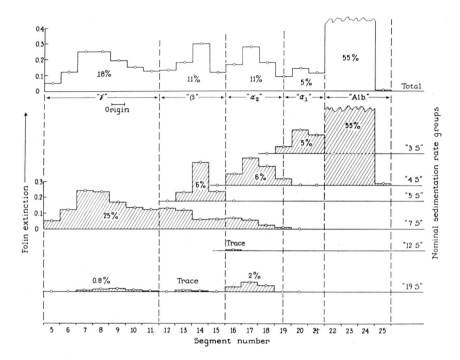

Fig. 5. Zone electrophoresis of normal lipid-free human serum in starch block with protein and ultracentrifugal assay. Upper histogram: Protein analysis by Folin extinction on supernatant of diluted segments cut from the block; initial dimensions: 70 cm long (between electrode vessels), 22 cm wide and 1.3 cm thick; 10 ml sample at "origin" extended 1.3 cm in direction of current. Lower shaded histogram: Schlieren optical analysis of velocity ultrafiltration patterns on eluates from each segment concentrated by ultracentrifugation; different groups indicated at the right in terms of their nominal sedimentation rate in Svedbergs at 20°; sum of shaded ordinates for each segment equals ordinate of electrophoretic histogram; percentages are relative amounts of each component between dotted lines. (Reprinted from Wallenius *et al.*[46] with permission of the editors of *J. Biol. Chem.*).

shows the results of ultracentrifugal analysis of the electrophoretic fractions. This is shown here to illustrate two assays applied to the same separation and to emphasize that behavior in an electric field does not necessarily parallel behavior in a centrifugal field.

(*iii*) *Calculations*

Imagine a neutral substance present in the initial zone with no electrophoretic mobility. It will be moved from the site of application by electroosmotic flow or conceivably by hydraulic flow, as would be the case if the connecting tube had not been left open and a pressure head were present initially or developed during the run. Define its hypothetical location as the zero mobility zone, at a distance d_0 measured with respect to the container from the starting position, as in Fig. 4. This can be computed from eqn. (40) if written separately for each marker and solved simultaneously to give

$$d_o = (d_s - d_f u_s/u_f)/(1 - u_s/u_f) \qquad (50)$$

where d_s and d_f are the displacements from the starting position of the slower and faster markers having free solution mobilities u_s and u_f, respectively, and for which $D_s = d_s - d_o$ and $D_f = d_f - d_o$ are the displacements from the zero mobility zone. The determination of the reference mobilities u_s and u_f can be done on the block itself by using a zero mobility marker (dextran) or by moving boundary electrophoresis in a Tiselius apparatus.

The mobility u of an unknown that moves a distance d from the site of application is

$$u = u_f(d - d_o)/(d_f - d_o) \qquad (51)$$

also from eqn. (40). An expression for u involving displacements of both markers can be obtained by eliminating d_o with eqn. (50) to give

$$\frac{u}{u_f} = \frac{d - d_s + (d_f - d)u_s/u_f}{d_f - d_s} \qquad (52)$$

Absolute determination of the mobility requires knowledge of T and d_o in eqn. (40). For example, nominally for starch (swelling) $S = 0.7$ (wetness 0.5) and $T = 0.5$. Values for other media can be estimated from the figure in ref.24. There is no point to this calculation if d_o was obtained from reference markers. The voltage gradient must be measured with a vacuum tube voltmeter using two probes in the starch since there is a variable voltage drop from the electrodes to the block. Computation of the field strength from the current and the conductivity is not reliable because of the leakage currents in the connecting tube, in the swollen (conducting) grains, and in the double layer. Note that the current should be held constant during the run but that the voltage on the block should be measured for calculations involving field strength.

The classical nomenclature of α,β,γ-globulin shown in Fig. 5 is usually assigned by inspection of the pattern for its minima but, with isolated fractions or patterns with obviously anomalous minima, a predetermined schedule can be used. In barbital buffer pH 8.6 the hemoglobin marker can be considered β and serum albumin (yellow) has a slightly smaller displacement from the zero mobility zone than does the bromophenol blue dyed albumin marker. The relative composition of the various components is merely the relative areas of the histogram. The total recovery should be calculated taking into account the initial and final volumes together with the concentrations.

(iv) Limitation and modification

The success of the separation depends to a certain extent on the technique and experience of the investigator. Differences in results from various laboratories also reflect differences in the packing of the porous medium, which influences S and T. Complete recovery is rarely possible because of losses in the elution and adherence to the top and bottom sheeting. The swelling of the starch grains, which makes the medium easy to handle, is a limitation for small molecules because of penetration. The elution of starch unavoidably carries along fragments that interfere with carbohydrate analyses. The last two limitations are removed by using polyvinyl chloride resin (high electroosmotic flow) or a co-polymer of this with polyvinyl acetate[47] (low electroosmotic flow) in place of the starch.

Broad blocks can be used for larger quantities or to accommodate many samples simultaneously. The thickness should not exceed $1\frac{1}{2}$ cm but the width can be increased at least to 60 cm giving a block capable of separating 30 ml of serum, used undiluted in this case. Other geometrical shapes can be employed in the migration unit such as a horizontal half-cylindrical trough or a vertical column. Circular cross-sections increase tremendously the temperature gradients, frequently giving cone-shaped zones[40]. In the column procedures the fractionation and elution are combined, which destroys some of the resolution obtained by the field. However, since a greater choice of supporting media would be possible in a packed column with possibilities of re-use, developments may be expected that will make such a modification compete with the basic block geometry described above.

(v) Extensive variations

Paper electrophoresis[23,27] can be considered a specific form of moving zone electrophoresis of the block type. The thinness of the strips limits the quantity but enables high field strengths, easy application of the initial sample, and a staining assay followed by mechanized photodensitometric scanning with output connected directly to computers[48]. Closed systems are possible but difficult; instead, the fibrous nature of the paper has permitted open systems with the paper merely draped over a supporting rod in an inverted-V position. Non-linear separation takes place because the solvent velocity varies along the strip due to evaporation, which also changes the ionic strength. Computations of mobility are nearly impossible, but standardized procedures for relative analyses have been extensively used. Other fibrous materials have been substituted for cellulose papers to obviate their undesirable property of adsorbing so many materials of biochemical interest.

(vi) Immunoelectrophoresis

Immunoelectrophoresis[24,49] is a variation using low concentration gels and a direct double diffusion antigen–antibody assay, illustrated in Fig. 6. The block is made of 2.0% agar in the buffer, poured hot into a mold. The sample is mixed with unsolidified gel prior to insertion into a rectangular slit. The gel is covered during electrophoresis by a closed atmosphere, mineral oil, polyethylene sheeting, or a spray of polyvinyl chloride in methylene chloride. After electrophoresis, a trough is cut lengthwise alongside the migration path and filled with antiserum. The double diffusion leads to

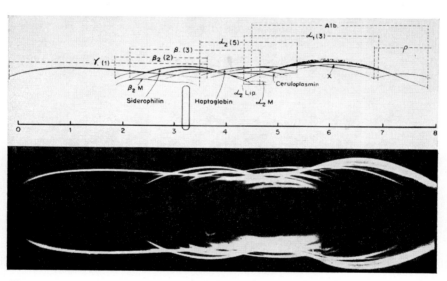

Fig. 6. Zone electrophoresis of normal human serum in agar block with antigen–antibody assay (immunoelectrophoresis). Lower photograph: Electrophoresis in agar gel performed first along center strip between white precipitin bands; horse antiserum to whole normal serum placed in parallel troughs on either side. Upper diagram: Scale drawing of precipitin lines with identification; numbers in parentheses give number of lines found in each mobility group; ϱ pre-albumin; $\varkappa$ two mucoproteins: α_1 acid-glycoprotein and orosomucoid; oval near 3 represents the origin. (Reprinted from Cooper[49] with permission of Academic Press.)

precipitin lines where antigen from the electrophoretic zones meets specific antibody. Changes during the 2–3 week development of the final pattern can be recorded directly on photographic paper exposed with transmitted light. A modification has been developed[50] that uses a microscope slide to support the gel. Not only are the initial quantities diminished, but the time required for complete analysis is shortened considerably.

Note the enormous number of components that are revealed in the illustration of this technique shown in Fig. 6. The electrophoretic separation is equivalent to that of Fig. 5, the difference is in the specific assay. This demonstrates, as does the centrifugal assay of the lower portion of Fig. 5, that there are multiple species in each classical electrophoretic fraction.

(c) Molecular-sieving electrophoresis (high resolution)

(i) Directions for starch-gel[45]

Materials required include an adjustable dc power supply, plastic troughs, electrode vessels, carbon electrodes, hydrolyzed starch*, pH 8.5 borate buffer, slicing razor and dye solutions. Physically the set-up is the same as in Fig. 4, except that the plastic trough replaces the glass plate.

Dissolve the prehydrolyzed starch in warm buffer to about 15 % (w/v), pour into trough and place under slight vacuum to remove air bubbles as it gels. Cut a slot in the gel, add dry granular starch and apply sample with pipette. Pour a layer of mineral oil or liquid petroleum jelly to cover the gel. Connect electrode vessels with paper or towel bridges. Use room temperature (see limitations) and 6–10 V/cm allowing free circulation of air. A copper plate in contact with the plastic trough, but insulated from the electrode vessel fluid, facilitates heat transfer.

After turning off power supply, remove jelly by slicing in a steady motion with the razor guided by the edges of the tray. Peel out the gel and place in a similar tray with sides only half as high. Slice length-wise to yield two replicates, the inner surfaces of which contain zones of the sharpest resolution. Patterns are revealed by staining, and then rinsing to remove the background stain. The gel can be made transparent by boiling for 30 sec in 10 % acetic acid[51].

(ii) Typical pattern

A result for normal human serum is shown in Fig. 7. The right hand vertical strip shows the large number of bands that are obtained. Since this is a high resolution technique, it is preferable that the sample be

---

* Since trial-and-error methods are necessary to prepare suitably hydrolyzed starch, it is preferable to start with prepared starch available from Connaught Medical Research Laboratories, University of Toronto, Canada.

electrophoretically pure in the classical sense. This is conveniently done by performing moving zone paper electrophoresis first and simply inserting the strip in a slit in the gel. The resulting distribution is shown in Fig. 7 as the large "two-dimensional" diagram.

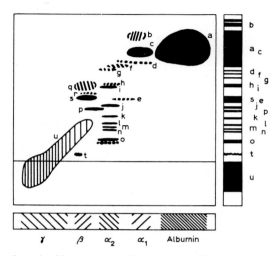

Fig. 7. Zone electrophoresis of human serum in starch gel with staining assay (molecular-sieving-electrophoresis). Right hand vertical rectangle: Diagram of bands revealed with amido-black stain after separation from initial zone located at upper edge of component u; anode at top. Lower rectangle: Diagram of filter paper electrophoresis, used as starting sample in slit along heavy horizontal line in square above; classical nomenclature of components; anode at right. Central square: Broad gel block with origin along heavy horizontal line; anode at top; filter paper strip used without prior staining. Some of the 20-odd zones have been identified: the pre-albumin b is oroso-mucoid; h, j, k, l, m, n, are haptoglobins which show heredity variations; i may be ceruloplasmin; o the 19S α_2-glycoprotein; s transferrin C which shows hereditary variations; t high molecular weight lipoprotein. The 19S γ_1-globulin is probably held back at the site of application and is generally not distinguished from the broad γ-globulin band u. (Reprinted from Smithies[45] with permission of Academic Press.)

(iii) *Limitation and variation*

The reasons for the increased resolution shown by the components off the diagonal line in Fig. 7 are (*a*) sharpening of the initial zone occurs as the proteins are slowed on entry into the gel, (*b*) the weak borate buffer produces specific effects by complexing with components such as carbohydrate proteins, and (*c*) the high concentration of gel produces a network of pores comparable with the dimensions of the serum proteins to give a molecular sieving effect depending upon size and shape. The sieving effect is much more temperature sensitive than usual viscosity changes of solvent would indicate and is the main reason for operating at room temperature. The introduction of synthetic gels of desired pore size at various temperatures, such as acrylamide gel[52], should extend this high resolution technique not only to smaller molecules but also to viruses. Variations of the field strength along the gel are due to the changes in conductivity contributed by the proteins themselves and their complexes with the extremely weak borate buffer. Slight changes in the buffer can lead to predictable sharpening of either the leading or trailing edge of the albumin zone.

Recently, a vertical arrangement[45] has been used which gives more uniform zones throughout a cross section. Recovery of the fractions for analysis or other purposes has been by (a) freezing and squeezing and (b) overlaying segments with buffer followed by migration out by electrophoresis. Elution by electroosmotic flow is anticipated, which would take advantage of the plug flow profile in Fig. 3B. Hydrostatic flow through the gels is practically impossible because of the high pressures required. Note that for this same reason the molecular sieving effects of this gel cannot be realized at present by non-electrical methods but other gels are available[40].

6. Moving boundary interpretation

(a) Optical pattern

The moving boundary type of electrophoresis has been described in general in Section 3. Here, schlieren optical patterns of the type frequently shown in the literature for solutions of biochemical interest[12] are considered in brief. The five fundamentals required to grasp their significance are (see Fig. 8):

(i) *Kind*: In the ascending pattern, marked either a or r, the boundaries

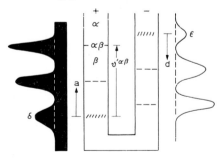

Fig. 8. Moving boundary electrophoresis with schlieren optical assay. U-tube contains a 2 component protein solution initially between levels marked with diagonal lines; left hand side is ascending pattern; right hand side is descending. Left hand pattern is example of knife edge schlieren diaphragm, right hand of phaseplate. δ and ε are salt boundaries; homogeneous phases between boundaries are assigned Greek letters; boundary $\alpha\beta$ has moved through a volume per unit charge passed of $v'^{\alpha\beta}$.

move out of the initial bulk solution; in the descending pattern, marked with *d*, they move into it.

(*ii*) *Starting position*: The direction of migration and initial boundary position are marked with a line and arrow labeled with *a* or *d*. The polarity is sometimes marked. The patterns may be printed in any orientation on the page. The boundary remaining at the starting position on the ascending side is called δ and is generally larger than that on the descending side, called ε.

(*iii*) *Base line*: The straight right hand limit of the black knife edge photograph shown on the left in Fig. 8 is not the base line which is shown for illustration as a straight connection between the boundary-free regions at either end of the pattern. A similar construction is shown for the phaseplate pattern on the right. Sometimes a matched solvent cell is used to give the base line optically on the photograph.

(*iv*) *Peak*: The pattern between two minima (valleys) is called a peak. The position of its maximum is taken as the location the boundary would have had if it had remained infinitely sharp.

(*v*) *Area*: The relative area under a peak is taken as the relative concentration of that component in the initial solution. Rayleigh interference optical patterns represent the concentration distribution whereas the schlieren pattern represents the concentration gradient. Generally, measurements are more precise on the interference patterns whereas visual interpretation is easier on the schlieren patterns.

(b) Analysis

Not only are there more peaks than unknown particles, but the ascending and descending patterns for the same initial solution are different (non-enantiography). This, of course, stimulated considerable instrumentation studies of a theoretical and practical nature with the following results[12, 15].

(*i*) On a gross level one extra, essentially stationary peak in each pattern (δ and ε) is to be expected and ignored in relative area calculations. Each is denoted a concentration boundary since all the components present on one side are also present on the other. In precise work, neither can be taken as a marker for zero mobility.

(*ii*) The mobility of a peak is equal to the mobility of the constituent on the solution side of the boundary region (in the homogeneous phase) and not characteristic of the particles in the boundary region or the next homogeneous phase from which the constituent has disappeared. For an asymmetrical peak, the position of the centroid rather than that of the maximum ordinate should be chosen as the boundary location. This deduction from the moving boundary equation for either strong or weak electrolytes can

References p. 146

be expressed as a formula for computation of the mobility u_p (cm²/volt sec) of a particle from eqn. (41).

$$u_p = v'_p \kappa_p \tag{53}$$

where v'_p is the volume from the zero mobility level swept out by the peak per total charge of electricity passed (cm³/coulomb) and κ_p is the conductivity of the homogeneous phase on the side containing the particle (ohm· cm⁻¹). As an approximation, κ_p is taken as the conductivity of the dialyzed protein solution at 0.0° and the mobility is considered to be for this temperature even though the run was performed close to the temperature of maximum density of the buffer.

(*iii*) Slight departures (*ca.* 20%) from enantiography are to be expected because of the differing compositions of the intervening phases. In particular, differences in conductivity and pH lead to differences in velocity, whereas differences in concentration give superimposed gradients either adding to or subtracting from the gradient due to the disappearing constituent. Shoulders on peaks represent incomplete resolution of components. Homogeneity should not be claimed from symmetry of a single peak unless it has migrated 5–10 times its average width.

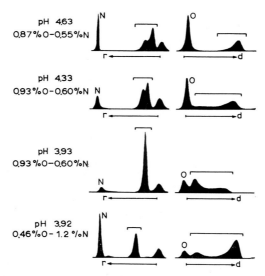

Fig. 9. Moving boundary electrophoresis with schlieren optical assay in interacting systems. Ascending (*r*) and descending (*d*) patterns for mixtures of ovomucoid (*O*) and yeast nucleic acid (*N*) in 0.1 *N* NaAc buffers; square bracket denotes reaction boundary which will never resolve into completely separated peaks. Note that the ascending and descending patterns are not mirror images of each other. (Reprinted from Longsworth[12] with permission of Academic Press.)

(*iv*) Marked departures from enantiography, such as illustrated in Fig. 9, indicate interactions of the solute components with each other or with the buffer. In the regions where reactions are taking place, "reaction boundaries" denoted by the square bracket, the pattern may show more than one maximum; if so, the intervening minima of the schlieren pattern will not return to the base line. The theory[42,44] is being developed rapidly and it should soon be possible to do more than just recognize that a given pattern reveals an interacting system.

(*v*) Departures from one-dimensional motion indicate convection. These are detected as differences in the schlieren pattern as a narrow vertical slit is moved across the cell, or by direct observation of the pattern obtained without the cylindrical lens but with manual elevation of a horizontal knife edge or phaseplate. Such boundary regions are conveniently denoted as non-planar[38]. They can be due to: (*a*) electroosmosis eroding boundaries of slight density stability as indicated in the theory section; (*b*) thermal convection caused by too high a current and identified by using alternating current of the same field strength; or (*c*) solution density inversions because of separation of particles with widely different particle density, *e.g.*, the β anomaly on the descending side in whole serum patterns due to lipoprotein[53].

(*vi*) The time dependence of patterns can be exploited by converting to distribution functions and extrapolating to infinite time[12,15,43]. The resulting separation and spread of the peaks represents true mobility differences uncomplicated by diffusion. In a special form of this technique, the current is reversed and any reversible boundary spreading is proof of heterogeneity.

REFERENCES

[1] J. T. EDSALL AND J. WYMAN, *Biophysical Chemistry*, Vol. I, Academic Press, New York, 1958.

[2] M. BIER (Ed.), *Electrophoresis: Theory, Methods, and Applications*, Academic Press, New York, 1959.

[3] R. AUDUBERT AND S. deMENDE, *The Principles of Electrophoresis*, translated by A. J. POMERANS, Hutchinson, London, 1959.

[4] J. STEINHARDT AND E. M. ZAISER, *J. Biol. Chem.*, 197 (1951) 190.

[5] N. R. JOSEPH, *Science*, 129 (1959) 1493.

[6] I. M. KLOTZ in H. NEURATH AND K. BAILEY (Eds.), *The Proteins*, Academic Press, New York, 1953, Chap. 8.

[7] C. TANFORD, S. A. SWANSON AND W. S. SHORE, *J. Am. Chem. Soc.*, 77 (1955) 6414.

[8] F. E. CRITCHFIELD AND J. B. JOHNSON, *Anal. Chem.*, 31 (1959) 570.

[9] K. LINDERSTRØM-LANG AND S. O. NIELSEN in M. BIER (Ed.), *Electrophoresis*, Academic Press, New York, 1959, Chap. 2.

[10] E. J. COHN AND J. T. EDSALL, *Proteins, Amino Acids and Peptides as Ions and Dipolar Ions*, Reinhold, New York, 1943.

[11] J. T. YANG AND J. F. FOSTER, *J. Am. Chem. Soc.*, 76 (1954) 1588.

[12] L. G. LONGSWORTH in M. BIER (Ed.), *Electrophoresis*, Academic Press, New York, 1959, Chaps. 3 and 4.

[13] C. C. BRINTON JR. AND M. A. LAUFFER in M. BIER (Ed.), *Electrophoresis*, Academic Press, New York, 1959, Chap. 10.

[14] L. D. SHER AND H. P. SCHWAN, *Alternating Current Microelectrophoresis*, abstracts Fifth Annual Meeting of The Biophysical Society (U.S.A.), St. Louis, 1961.

[15] R. A. BROWN AND S. N. TIMASHEFF in M. BIER (Ed.), *Electrophoresis*, Academic Press, New York, 1959, Chap. 8.

[16] D. H. MOORE in M. BIER (Ed.), *Electrophoresis*, Academic Press, New York, 1959, Chap. 9.

[17] R. TRAUTMAN AND S. S. BREESE JR., *J. Phys. Chem.*, 63 (1959) 1592.

[18] M. BIER in M. BIER (Ed.), *Electrophoresis*, Academic Press, New York, 1959, Chap. 7.

[19] M. K. BRAKKE, *Arch. Biochem. Biophys.*, 55 (1955) 175.

[20] N. G. ANDERSON, *Exptl. Cell Research*, 9 (1955) 446.

[21] H. SVENSSON AND E. VALMET, *Sci. Tools*, 6 (1959) 13.

[22] S. HJERTEN, *Arkiv Kemi*, 13 (1958) 151.

[23] CH. WUNDERLY in M. BIER (Ed.), *Electrophoresis*, Academic Press, New York, 1959, Chap. 5.

[24] H. G. KUNKEL AND R. TRAUTMAN in M. BIER (Ed.), *Electrophoresis*, Academic Press, New York, 1959, Chap. 6.

[25] T. WIELAND in M. BIER (Ed.), *Elektrophoresis*, Academic Press, New York, 1959, Chap. 11.

[26] A. KOLIN, *Proc. Natl. Acad. Sci. U.S.*, 41 (1955) 101.

[27] R. J. BLOCK, E. L. DURRUM AND G. ZWEIG, *A Manual of Paper Chromatography and Paper Electrophoresis*, 2nd ed., Academic Press, New York, 1958, p. 333.

[28] I. BRATTSTEN, *Arkiv Kemi*, 8 (1955) 347.

[29] H. B. BULL, *Physical Biochemistry*, 2nd ed., John Wiley, New York, 1951, p. 162.

[30] H. S. HARNED AND B. B. OWEN, *The Physical Chemistry of Electrolytic Solutions*, 2nd ed., Reinhold, New York, 1950.

[31] J. TH. G. OVERBEEK AND J. LIJKLEMA in M. BIER (Ed.), *Electrophoresis*, Academic Press, New York, 1959, Chap. 1.

[32] H. A. ABRAMSON, L. S. MOYER AND M. H. GORIN, *Electrophoresis of Proteins and the Chemistry of Cell Surfaces*, Reinhold, New York, 1942.

[33] W. F. HARRINGTON AND H. K. SCHACHMAN, *Arch. Biochem. Biophys.*, 65 (1956) 278.

[34] J. M. CREETH, D. O. JORDAN AND J. M. GULLAND, *J. Chem. Soc.*, (1949) 1406.

[35] P. MAZUR AND J. TH. G. OVERBEEK, *Rec. trav. chim.*, 70 (1951) 83.

[36] P. B. LORENZ, *J. Phys. Chem.*, 56 (1952) 775.

[37] J. J. BIKERMAN, *Surface Chemistry, Theory and Applications*, 2nd ed., Academic Press, New York, 1958, p. 412.

[38] R. TRAUTMAN AND J. W. GOFMAN, *J. Phys. Chem.*, 56 (1952) 464.

[39] R. D. MILLER, *Science*, 122 (1955) 373.

[40] J. PORATH, *Biochim. Biophys. Acta*, 22 (1956) 151; 39 (1960) 193.

[41] A. TISELIUS, *Nova Acta Regiae Soc. Sci. Upsaliensis*, IV, 7 (1930) 1.

[42] G. A. GILBERT AND R. C. LL. JENKINS, *Proc. Roy. Soc. (London), A*, 253 (1959) 420.

[43] L. J. GOSTING, *J. Am. Chem. Soc.*, 74 (1952) 1548.

[44] J. L. BETHUNE AND G. KEGELES, *J. Phys. Chem.*, 65 (1961) 1761.

[45] O. SMITHIES, *Advances in Protein Chem.*, 14 (1959) 65.

[46] G. WALLENIUS, R. TRAUTMAN, H. G. KUNKEL AND E. C. FRANKLIN, *J. Biol. Chem.*, 225 (1957) 253.

[47] H. J. MÜLLER-EBERHARD, *Scand. J. Clin. Lab. Invest.*, 12 (1960) 33.

[48] M. D. POULIK AND L. PINTERIC, *Nature*, 176 (1955) 1226.

[49] G. R. COOPER, in F. W. PUTNAM (Ed.), *The Plasma Proteins*, Vol. I, Academic Press, New York, 1960, Chap. 3.

[50] J. J. SCHEIDEGGER, *Intern. Arch. Allergy Appl. Immunol.*, 7 (1955) 103.

[51] S. D. VESSELINOVITCH, *Nature*, 182 (1958) 665.

[52] S. RAYMOND AND L. WEINTRAUB, *Science*, 130 (1959) 711.

[53] R. TRAUTMAN, *Arch. Biochem. Biophys.*, 53 (1954) 85.

[54] General: L. A. LEWIS in O. GLASSER (Ed.), *Medical Physics*, Vol. III, Year Book Publishers, Chicago, 1960, pp. 261–268.

[55] Detailed procedures: I. SMITH (Ed.), *Chromatographic and Electrophoretic Techniques*, Vol. II, *Zone Electrophoresis*, Heinemann, London, 1960.

[56] Special free solution techniques: A. KOLIN in O. GLASSER (Ed.), *Medical Physics*, Vol. III, Year Book Publishers, Chicago, 1960, pp. 268–282.

[57] Genetic differences with immunoelectrophoresis: J. HIRSCHFELD, *Sci. Tools*, 8 (1961) 17.

[58] Geometrical factors in porous media: J. C. GIDDINGS AND J. R. BOYACK, *J. Theoret. Biol.*, 2 (1962) 1.

Chapter IV

Reactions of Proteins; Denaturation

HAROLD A. SCHERAGA

Department of Chemistry, Cornell University, Ithaca, N.Y. (U.S.A.)

1. Introduction

Proteins undergo a variety of reactions. Among these may be listed:

(1) Dissociation of protons from side-chain groups (acid–base equilibrium),

(2) Binding of molecules and ions other than protons to the side-chain groups and also to the CO–NH peptide group of the backbone chains,

(3) Rupture of primary valence bonds, *e.g.* hydrolysis of peptide bonds of the backbone chains, and oxidation or reduction of disulfide bonds (cross-links between polypeptide chains),

(4) Association of protein molecules,

(5) Change of internal configuration of a protein molecule without rupturing primary valence bonds (denaturation),

(6) Chemical modification of the side-chain groups, *e.g.* esterification of carboxyl groups, acetylation of amino groups, reaction of amino groups with fluorodinitrobenzene, iodination of phenolic groups, etc.

These reactions involve the polar and non-polar side-chain groups and also the CO–NH peptide groups.

We shall adopt the point of view that the reactivity of any of these groups in a protein is identical with that in a low-molecular-weight model compound if the group is completely free in the protein and completely accessible to the solvent. For example, we shall assume that a side-chain glutamyl carboxyl group will dissociate protons with the same ease (*i.e.* have the same pK) as acetic acid *in the same solvent* if the glutamyl carboxyl group is free. We shall further assume that any departure from this *normal* reactivity arises from some kind of interaction which is present in the protein molecule but not in the corresponding model compound. Again referring to the example of the dissociation of protons from a side-chain glutamyl carboxyl group, we would account for an abnormal pK (*i.e.* one different from that of acetic acid) by any one or more of a variety of possible interactions. Thus, the pK would be abnormal if either the COOH or COO$^-$ forms could participate in a hydrogen bond with some other group in the protein molecule; or the pK would be abnormal if the carboxyl groups were imbedded in a non-polar portion of the molecule where the dielectric constant was different from that of the solvent; the presence of charged groups near the carboxyl group would give rise to an electrostatic interaction which would modify the pK; steric effects could also be involved. All of these kinds of interactions would affect not only the pK's of acid groups, but also the reactivity of the various groups in any of the other types of protein reactions listed above. In a more formal way, using the standard free energy change of a reaction for illustrative purposes, we may write

$$\Delta F^0_{obs} = \Delta F^0_{norm} + \Delta F^0_{interaction} \tag{1}$$

where ΔF^0_{obs} is the observed standard free energy change for any of the above types of reactions, in which a protein might be involved, ΔF^0_{norm} is the corresponding standard free energy change for the same reaction in an appropriate model compound, and $\Delta F^0_{interaction}$ is the standard free energy change arising from any of the interactions mentioned above. If $\Delta F^0_{interaction}$ is zero, then the particular reaction in the protein will be the same as that in the model compound. However, if $\Delta F^0_{interaction}$ is not zero, then the reaction in the protein will differ from that in the model compound. Since the reader is familiar with the various kinds of reactions in model compounds, we shall focus our attention here on $\Delta F^0_{interaction}$ in order to understand why ΔF^0_{obs} for a particular reaction in a protein may differ from ΔF^0_{norm} for the same reaction in a model compound. An understanding of the structural basis for $\Delta F^0_{interaction}$ will add to our knowledge of the internal configurations of proteins.

In paying attention to $\Delta F^0_{interaction}$ we shall concentrate on reaction types (1)–(5) since reaction type (6) chemical modification) has been covered extensively in Chapter II. Also, since acid–base properties were discussed in detail in Chapter III, we shall assume that the reader is familiar with this material when we discuss $\Delta F^0_{interaction}$ for proton dissociation equilibria.

2. Nature of interactions

Before discussing the nature of the interactions in a protein, and their contribution to $\Delta F^0_{interaction}$, it is worthwhile to assign the various parts of a protein molecule to three categories. For this purpose we shall use the classification of protein structures that has been proposed by Linderstrøm-Lang[1], who regarded the molecule as composed of a primary, a secondary, and a tertiary structure. The polypeptide chain, in which the amino acid residues are linked together by covalent peptide bonds, is regarded as the primary structure. The folding of the polypeptide chain (e.g., into a helix) is a manifestation of the secondary structure of the molecule, and the interactions which link helices together comprise the tertiary structure. Problems, such as the determination of the amino acid sequence or the hydrolysis of a peptide bond, concern the primary structure; denaturation, which involves the rupture of hydrogen bonds between peptide NH and CO groups and the breakdown of interactions between the side-chain groups (without the disturbance of the primary structure), is a manifestation of changes in the secondary and tertiary structure.

In the case of fibrous and globular proteins, two extreme configurations of the polypeptide chain (secondary structure) have been much discussed. These are the α-helix[2-4] and the random coil[5]. The α-helix involves hydrogen bonding interactions between peptide NH and CO groups, which are disrupted when the helix is converted to a random coil. A number of investigators[6-12] have treated the thermodynamics and statistical mechanics of the helix-to-random coil conversion. We shall cite here the approximate thermodynamic parameters deduced by Schellman[6], and shall later incorporate Schellman's treatment into a theory of protein denaturation (p. 174).

Schellman showed that ΔF^0_{unf}, the standard free energy required to unfold an α-helix of a given sense (e.g., left-handed) to a random coil, in the absence of side-chain interactions, is

$$\Delta F^0_{unf} = (n - 4)\Delta H^0_{res} - (n - 1)T\Delta S^0_{res} \qquad (2)$$

where n is the number of peptide units in the chain and ΔH^0_{res} and ΔS^0_{res} are the changes in enthalpy and entropy per residue, respectively, to unfold an infinitely long chain. Schellman estimated ΔH^0_{res} as 1.5 kcal/mole, on the basis of a consideration of the thermodynamic properties of aqueous urea solutions, and ΔS^0_{res} as 3–4 e.u., from a consideration of the configurational entropy of the random coil. He also indicated how numerical values of these parameters could be obtained from studies of reversible denaturation by urea. Measurements of this kind have recently been made[13,14] and confirm the values of ΔH^0_{res} and ΔS^0_{res} proposed by Schellman.

In addition to the above interactions in the secondary structure, a variety of interactions between side-chain groups (tertiary structure) are possible. These include: hydrophobic bonds, electrostatic interactions, hydrogen bonds, and steric effects. Kauzmann[15] has discussed these interactions in some detail. At present we know relatively little about hydrophobic bonds, although there is now much activity in this field, primarily from the point of view of trying to understand the thermodynamics of the solubility of hydrocarbons in water and the effect of the hydrocarbon on the water structure[15-19]. As for electrostatic interactions, these have been amenable to theoretical treatment, *e.g.*, by Tanford and Kirkwood[20] and by Peller[11]. Relatively little work has been done to develop a quantitative treatment of steric effects in proteins. On the other hand, considerable attention has been devoted recently to providing a quantitative theory for the magnitude of side-chain hydrogen-bonding interactions and their effect on protein reactions[21-32]. We shall, therefore, develop the subject matter of this chapter, by regarding $\Delta F^0_{\text{interaction}}$ to arise from side-chain hydrogen bonding. However, it cannot be emphasized too strongly that this is only one type of interaction; the others cited above could be just as or more important than hydrogen-bonding. It is only the present lack of knowledge about these other interactions which prevents us at this time from discussing them too. The current activity in the fields of hydrophobic bonding and electrostatic interactions should remedy this situation in the not-too-distant future.

Side-chain hydrogen bonding of several types can exist in proteins, depending on the nature and number of groups involved in the bond[21]. These bonds have been referred to as homologous and heterologous, respectively, depending on whether the groups are chemically identical or distinct. Also, single and double bonds are possible, as well as competitive and co-operative situations. Examples of these various types of hydrogen bonds have been given elsewhere[21].

The strength of any of these hydrogen bonds may be expressed in terms of an equilibrium constant[21]. For example, if a heterologous single hydrogen bond can be formed between an ith donor DH and a jth acceptor A, according to the reaction

$$DH + A \leftrightharpoons DH \dots A \qquad (3)$$

then the equilibrium constant, K_{ij}, for this reaction is

$$K_{ij} = \frac{P_{(DH \dots A)}}{P_{(DH,A)}} \qquad (4)$$

where $P_{(DH\dots A)}$ and $P_{(DH,A)}$ are the concentration fractions of the protein species which have the ijth hydrogen bond and those which do not have this bond, respectively. An example of such a bond would be a tyrosyl...carboxylate ion bond. Similar equations can be written for other types of hydrogen bonds.

References p. 182

Since K_{ij} is related to the standard free energy change, ΔF^0_{ij}, by the equation

$$\Delta F^0_{ij} = - RT \ln K_{ij} = \Delta H^0_{ij} - T\Delta S^0_{ij} \qquad (5)$$

K_{ij} can be determined from ΔH^0_{ij} and ΔS^0_{ij}. These have been evaluated[21] by regarding the side-chain groups to be attached to rigid structures (e.g., the helically-folded backbone) and constrained within limits to interact only with neighboring side-chain groups. When the groups are free, there is the possibility of torsional oscillation about the single bonds in the side-chains. These oscillational degrees of freedom are considered to be lost when two side-chain groups interact to form a hydrogen bond. On this basis the following estimates have been made[21]:

$$\Delta H^0_{ij} \sim -6 \text{ kcal/mole}$$

$$\Delta S^0_{ij} \sim -20 \text{ to } -30 \text{ e.u.}$$

$$\Delta F^0_{ij} \sim 0 \qquad (6)$$

$$K_{ij} \sim 1$$

This value of K_{ij} could be considerably augmented by electrostatic effects if both donor and acceptor are oppositely charged (e.g., in a histidyl...carboxylate ion hydrogen bond[14]).

The homologous double bond (acetic acid dimer-type bond between two side-chain carboxyl groups), characterized by an equilibrium constant K_{lm}, is a considerably stronger one than the heterologous single bond. The co-operative bond (e.g., a tyrosyl...carboxylate ion...tyrosyl interaction), characterized by an equilibrium constant K_{rs}, is of intermediate strength. The relative magnitudes of these equilibrium constants may be estimated[21] as:

$$K_{ij} \sim 1$$

$$K_{rs} \sim 10 \qquad (7)$$

$$K_{lm} \sim 100$$

These interactions are the basis for the origin of the term $\Delta F^0_{\text{interaction}}$ in eqn. (1). Therefore, the rest of this chapter will be devoted to a discussion of equations of the type of eqn. (1) for a variety of protein reactions. In the course of this discussion, some experimental evidence will be cited for the validity of the values assigned to the thermodynamic quantities in eqns. (6).

3. Interaction of proteins with small ions and molecules [21]

(a) Heterologous single bonds

Proteins can react with small ions and molecules[33]. As an example of such a reaction we shall consider the case where the small species is a proton. However, since acid–base equilibria have already been treated in Chapter III we shall focus attention on those aspects of the problem in which $\Delta F^0_{\text{interaction}}$ is of consequence. Thus, if a hydrogen bond exists between a donor DH and an acceptor A, the pK's for the dissociation of protons from DH and HA will be affected[21].

The effect of the hydrogen bond can be seen qualitatively by considering, as an example, the tyrosyl...glutamate bond. If no hydrogen bond existed, then the intrinsic pK's of the phenolic and carboxyl groups should be the same as those observed for low-molecular-weight model compounds in a given solvent. In many proteins it is actually observed that the intrinsic pK's for side-chain glutamyl and aspartyl residues are about the same as the pK for acetic acid; correspondingly the intrinsic pK of tyrosyl groups is about the same as that observed in tyrosyl peptides. This would indicate that these groups behave normally in the protein, i.e., they presumably are not involved in any side-chain interaction. However, there are many proteins in which the pK's are abnormal, i.e., they do not have the thermodynamic parameters for ionization which are observed in model compounds. Such abnormalities can arise in the following way if the tyrosyl and glutamate groups are hydrogen-bonded. In order to dissociate a proton from a hydrogen-bonded tyrosyl group, it will be more difficult than in a model compound, since the hydrogen bond must also be broken. This would have the effect of making the tyrosyl group appear as a weaker acid with an abnormally higher pK than is observed in model tyrosyl compounds. Indeed, many proteins have tyrosyl groups with abnormally high pK's. Other explanations could account for such abnormally high pK's. The point of the discussion here is to show how hydrogen bonding, as one of several possibilities, can lead to abnormally high pK's. Considering now the hydrogen-bonded glutamate groups, it can be seen that it will be easier to dissociate a proton from a carboxyl group when the conjugate base, i.e., the carboxylate ion, acts as a hydrogen-bond acceptor. Thus, in such cases, the carboxyl group will appear as a stronger acid with an abnormally lower pK than is observed in acetic acid. Many proteins do have side-chain carboxyl groups of abnormally low pK. Hydrogen bonding of the carboxylate ion could be one of the explanations for the abnormality.

These effects of hydrogen bonding on pK's can also be treated quantitatively[21]. Considering first the ionization of the ith tyrosyl group in a protein in which it can be hydrogen-bonded as a donor, DH, in a heterologous single bond to a jth acceptor, A, the following species can exist:

$$P_{(DH, A)}$$

$$P_{(DH \ldots A)} \tag{8}$$

$$P_{(D, A)}$$

The first two represent the non-hydrogen-bonded and hydrogen-bonded states, respectively, in which the donor has its proton, and were already introduced in eqn. (4). The third represents the state in which the donor group has lost its proton, and cannot function as a hydrogen-bond donor. Species in which the acceptor is in the form HA have not been introduced since the acceptor will be predominantly in the form of the conjugate base in the pH region where the donor ionizes. For example, carboxyl groups are in the form of carboxylate ions near pH 10, the region of ionization of tyrosyl donors. The symbols in (8) will be used to represent species and also concentration fractions. Since the sum of all the concentration fractions must be equal to unity, we may write

$$P_{(DH, A)} + P_{(DH \ldots A)} + P_{(D, A)} = 1 \tag{9}$$

If the hydrogen bond did not exist, the ionization constant K_1 for the ionization of the tyrosyl group at any pH would be defined as follows:

$$K_1 = \frac{P_{(D, A)} [H^+]}{P_{(DH, A)}} \tag{10}$$

where $[H^+]$ denotes the hydrogen ion activity. If the system is at the isoelectric point, where the average net charge Z is zero, then K_1 is equal to the intrinsic ionization constant K_1^0. However, when the pH departs from isoelectric, K_1 is no longer equal to K_1^0 but depends on Z and, therefore on pH.

$$K_1 = K_1^0 e^{2wZ} \tag{11}$$

where w is the electrostatic interaction factor. For a uniformly charged sphere[34], w is given by

$$w = \frac{N\varepsilon^2}{2DRT} \left[\frac{1}{b} - \frac{\kappa}{1 + \kappa a} \right] \tag{12}$$

where N, R and T have their usual meaning, D is the dielectric constant, ε is the electronic charge, κ is the inverse of the radius of the ionic atmosphere, and b and a are the hypothetical radii of the molecule and of exclusion, respectively.

If the hydrogen bond exists, then the observed ionization constant, K_{obs}, of the donor group will not be equal to K_1 but, instead, will equal to

$$K_{obs} = \frac{P_{(D, A)}\,[H^+]}{P_{(DH, A)} + P_{(DH \ldots A)}} \tag{13}$$

In order to evaluate K_{obs} we need to know the concentration fractions appearing in eqn. (13). These may be obtained from eqns. (4), (9) and (10) as follows. Let $P_{(DH,A)} = 1/y$ where y is some number (see below). Then, from eqn. (4), $P_{(DH\ldots A)} = K_{ij}/y$; and from eqn. (10), $P_{(D,A)} = K_1/[H^+]y$. The quantity y is determinable from eqn. (9) as $(1 + K_{ij} + K_1/[H^+])$. Substituting these quantities in eqn. (13), we obtain

$$K_{obs} = \frac{K_1}{1 + K_{ij}} \tag{14}$$

This is the result that was predicted qualitatively, i.e., $K_{obs} < K_1$ because of the presence of the hydrogen bond. The ratio K_1/K_{obs} is $(1 + K_{ij})$. Since $K_{ij} \sim 1$, this ratio is about 2.

A similar treatment can be presented for the ionization of the jth carboxyl group in a protein in which it can be hydrogen-bonded as a carboxylate ion acceptor, A, in a heterologous single bond to an ith donor, DH. In this case, the predominant species would be

$$P_{(DH, A)}$$

$$P_{(DH \ldots A)} \tag{15}$$

$$P_{(DH, HA)}$$

The first two species have already been discussed. The third represents the state in which the acceptor group has gained a proton, and cannot function as a hydrogen-bond acceptor. Species in which the donor is in the form D have not been introduced since the donor will be predominantly in the form DH in the pH region where the acceptor ionizes. For example, tyrosyl groups retain their protons near pH 4, the region of ionization of carboxyl groups. By analogy with eqn. (9), we have

$$P_{(DH, A)} + P_{(DH \ldots A)} + P_{(DH, HA)} = 1 \tag{16}$$

If the hydrogen bond did not exist, the ionization constant, K_2, for the ionization of the carboxyl group at any pH would be defined as follows.

$$K_2 = \frac{P_{(DH, A)} [H^+]}{P_{(DH, HA)}} \tag{17}$$

where

$$K_2 = K_2^0 e^{2wZ} \tag{18}$$

If the hydrogen bond exists, then the observed ionization constant of the acceptor group will not be equal to K_2 but, instead will be equal to

$$K_{obs} = \frac{[P_{(DH, A)} + P_{(DH \ldots A)}] [H^+]}{P_{(DH, HA)}} \tag{19}$$

The concentration fractions in eqn. (19) may be obtained from eqns. (4), (16) and (17) as follows. Let $P_{(DH,A)} = 1/y$. Then, from eqn. (4), $P_{(DH...A)} = K_{ij}/y$; and from eqn. (17), $P_{(DH,HA)} = [H^+]/K_2 y$. The quantity y is determinable from eqn. (16) as $(1 + K_{ij} + [H^+]/K_2)$. Substituting these quantities in eqn. (19), we obtain

$$K_{obs} = K_2(1 + K_{ij}) \tag{20}$$

Again, this is the result that was predicted qualitatively, i.e., $K_{obs} > K_2$ because of the presence of the hydrogen bond. The ratio K_{obs}/K_2 is $(1 + K_{ij})$, or approximately 2.

A more general treatment for the ionization of groups involved in heterologous single bonds may be found elsewhere[21].

From the calculated expressions for K_{obs} it is possible to obtain the corresponding thermodynamic functions for ionization. Considering the donor group, we obtain the following results from eqns. (10) and (11).

$$\Delta F_1^0 = - RT \ln K_1 = (\Delta F_1^0)^0 - 2 RTwZ \tag{21}$$

$$\Delta S_1^0 = - \left(\frac{\partial \Delta F_1^0}{\partial T}\right)_{P, [H^+]} = (\Delta S_1^0)^0 + 2R \left[\frac{\partial(TwZ)}{\partial T}\right]_{P, [H^+]} \tag{22}$$

$$\Delta H_1^0 = \Delta F_1^0 + T\Delta S_1^0 = (\Delta H_1^0)^0 + 2RT \left\{ - wZ + \left[\frac{\partial(TwZ)}{\partial T}\right]_{P, [H^+]} \right\} \tag{23}$$

Here the terms $(\Delta F_1^0)^0$, $(\Delta S_1^0)^0$, and $(\Delta H_1^0)^0$ are the standard free energy, entropy and enthalpy changes for ionization of a *non-hydrogen-bonded* donor group on the protein at a pH where the protein has zero net charge, while $\Delta F_1^0, \Delta S_1^0$, and ΔH_1^0 are the ionization parameters at any other pH under consideration. From eqn. (14) we obtain for the *hydrogen-bonded* donor group

$$\Delta F_{obs}^0 = \Delta F_1^0 + RT \ln (1 + K_{ij})$$

$$= \Delta F_1^0 - \frac{K_{ij}}{1 + K_{ij}} \Delta F_{ij}^0 - RT \left[\frac{K_{ij}}{1 + K_{ij}} \ln K_{ij} - \ln (1 + K_{ij}) \right] \tag{24}$$

$$\Delta H_{obs}^0 = \Delta H_1^0 - \frac{K_{ij}}{1 + K_{ij}} \Delta H_{ij}^0 \tag{25}$$

$$\Delta S_{obs}^0 = \Delta S_1^0 - R \ln (1 + K_{ij}) - \frac{K_{ij}}{1 + K_{ij}} \frac{\Delta H_{ij}^0}{T}$$

$$= \Delta S_1^0 - \frac{K_{ij}}{1 + K_{ij}} \Delta S_{ij}^0 + R \left[\frac{K_{ij}}{1 + K_{ij}} \ln K_{ij} - \ln (1 + K_{ij}) \right] \tag{26}$$

It should be noted that $(\Delta F_1^0 - \Delta F_{obs}^0)$, $(\Delta H_1^0 - \Delta H_{obs}^0)$, and $(\Delta S_1^0 - \Delta S_{obs}^0)$ are not equal to ΔF_{ij}^0, ΔH_{ij}^0, and ΔS_{ij}^0, respectively, *i.e.*, the free energy, enthalpy, and entropy changes associated with hydrogen bonding. This approximation would be valid only if $K_{ij} \gg 1$, as can be seen from eqns. (24)–(26). Also, it should be pointed out that ΔF_1^0 corresponds to ΔF_{norm}^0 of eqn. (1); similarly, $RT \ln (1 + K_{ij})$ corresponds to $\Delta F_{interaction}^0$.

It is of interest to discuss the physical significance of the various terms in eqns. (24)–(26). In eqn. (24), ΔF_{obs}^0 is composed of three terms. The first, ΔF_1^0, is simply the standard free energy of ionization which would be observed if there were no hydrogen bonding. The second is a product of two factors, namely, $-\Delta F_{ij}^0$, the standard free energy of rupture of a hydrogen bond, and the factor $K_{ij}/(1 + K_{ij})$, which is the fraction of the un-ionized molecules which have the ij^{th} hydrogen bond formed. If *every* molecule had the ij^{th} hydrogen bond, *i.e.*, $K_{ij} = \infty$, then the second term would be simply $-\Delta F_{ij}^0$. If K_{ij} were zero, then the second term in eqn. (24) would vanish. The third term is the negative of the free energy of mixing of the hydrogen-bonded and non-hydrogen-bonded species in the un-ionized form. This mixing term would vanish for $K_{ij} = 0$ and $K_{ij} = \infty$. If $K_{ij} = 1$ (and, therefore, $\Delta F_{ij}^0 = 0$), there is still a hydrogen bonding contribution of $RT \ln 2$ in eqn. (24), arising from the free energy of mixing. In eqn. (25), ΔH_{obs}^0 is composed of two terms. The first, ΔH_1^0, is the enthalpy of ionization in the absence of a hydrogen bond. The second is $-\Delta H_{ij}^0$, the enthalpy of rupture of a hydrogen bond, multiplied by $K_{ij}/(1 + K_{ij})$ to take account of the fact that every molecule does not have the ij^{th} hydrogen bond intact.

References p. 182

In eqn. (26), ΔS^0_{obs} is composed of three terms. The first, ΔS^0_1 is the entropy of ionization in the absence of a hydrogen bond. The second is composed of two factors, $-\Delta S^0_{ij}$, the entropy gained when the freedom of the torsional oscillational motion is restored upon hydrogen bond rupture, and again the factor $K_{ij}/(1 + K_{ij})$. Finally, the third term is the entropy of mixing, corresponding to the mixing term in eqn. (24).

Equations similar to eqns. (21)–(26) could be written for acceptor groups.

Having obtained expressions (eqns. (24)–(26)) for the thermodynamic parameters for the ionization of hydrogen-bonded donor groups, we are now in a position to obtain an experimental verification of the values deduced for the thermodynamic parameters for the formation of hydrogen bonds in eqns. (6). For this purpose we shall make use of data of Tanford et al.[35] for the ionization of tyrosyl groups in bovine serum albumin. In the protein ΔF^0_{obs} was found to be 14.1 kcal/mole, compared with the value $\Delta F^0_1 =$ 13.1 kcal/mole observed for model tyrosyl compounds, i.e., the tyrosyl groups in bovine serum albumin are abnormal in that they are weaker acids than would be expected. If these values are substituted into the first of eqns. (24), a value of 4 is obtained[24] for K_{ij}. This is in very good agreement with the calculation, $K_{ij} \sim 1$. It may also be noticed that the term $RT \ln (1 + K_{ij})$ has a value of 1 kcal/mole in this case. This gives some idea of the free energy required to rupture this hydrogen bond. In the case of the enthalpy, ΔH^0_{obs} was found to be 11.5 kcal/mole. This value is much higher than the heat of ionization, ΔH^0_1, of 6 kcal/mole observed for model tyrosyl compounds. If we substitute $\Delta H^0_1 = 6$ kcal/mole, $\Delta H^0_{ij} = -6$ kcal/ mole, and $K_{ij} = 4$ in eqn. (25), we compute a theoretical value of 11 kcal/ mole for ΔH^0_{obs}, which is in very good agreement with the experimental value of ΔH^0_{obs}. Finally, ΔS^0_{obs} for tyrosyl groups in bovine serum albumin was found to be -9 e.u., in contrast to the more negative value $\Delta S^0_1 = -26$ e.u. for model tyrosyl compounds. If we substitute $\Delta S^0_1 = -26$ e.u., $\Delta H^0_{ij} = -6$ kcal/mole, and $K_{ij} = 4$ in the first of eqn. (26), we compute a theoretical value of -10 e.u. for ΔS^0_{obs}, which is in very good agreement with the experimental value of ΔS^0_{obs}. These results are summarized in Table I.

TABLE I

THERMODYNAMIC PARAMETERS FOR TYROSYL IONIZATION
IN BOVINE SERUM ALBUMIN[24]

	Normal value (from model compounds)	Theoretical	Experimental
ΔH^0_{obs}, kcal/mole	6	11	11.5
ΔS^0_{obs}, e.u.	−26	−10	−9

From these results, it can be seen that the thermodynamic parameters for hydrogen bond formation, cited in eqns. (6), are reasonable ones. In addition, this simple model accounts for the abnormal ionization behavior of the tyrosyl groups in bovine serum albumin.

(b) Homologous single bonds

Turning now to homologous single hydrogen bonds, we shall use the histidyl... histidyl bond as an example. Considering an ij^{th} pair, the various species which can exist, and their concentration fractions, x, are shown in Table II,

TABLE II

HOMOLOGOUS SINGLE BONDS

Species	xy
NH, N	1
NH . . . N	K_{ij}
NH, HN	$[H^+]/K$
N, HN	1
N . . . HN	K_{ij}
N, N	$K/[H^+]$

$$y = 2 + 2\, K_{ij} + [H^+]/K + K[H^+]$$

where K is the ionization constant of a non-hydrogen-bonded histidyl group. Here we cannot neglect the species (N, HN) when speaking about the ionization of (NH, N) since the pK's of both partners are the same.

If we focus attention on a specific histidyl group in the ij^{th} pair, say the left-hand one, then the observed ionization constant is

$$K_{\text{obs}} = \frac{[H^+]\,[(N,\ HN) + (N \ldots HN) + (N,\ N)]}{[(NH,\ N) + (NH \ldots N) + (NH,\ HN)]} \qquad (27)$$

Substituting from Table II, we obtain

$$K_{\text{obs}} = [H^+] \left[\frac{1 + K_{ij} + K/[H^+]}{1 + K_{ij} + [H^+]/K} \right] \qquad (28)$$

In eqns. (14) and (20), the dependence of K_{obs} on $[H^+]$ entered implicitly through the dependence of K_1 and K_2 on Z, and therefore on $[H^+]$ (see eqns. (11) and (18)). This has been referred to as a "trivial" dependence[21] on pH. However, K_{obs} in eqn. (28) depends on $[H^+]$, not only because of the implicit dependence of K on $[H^+]$, but also because of the explicit appearance of $[H^+]$ in the equation. This explicit dependence of K_{obs} on $[H^+]$, due to hydrogen bonding, has been referred to by the term "non-trivial"[21]. No question of "insignificance" is to be attached to the term "trivial". We thus see that additional pH effects can arise in the case of homologous single bonds because of the existence of the hydrogen bond.

It is of interest to consider some limiting forms of eqn. (28). If $K_{ij} = 0$, then $K_{obs} = K$, and there is a "trivial" dependence of K_{obs} on pH, i.e., if the hydrogen bond did not exist, then the observed ionization constant would reduce to K, or $K^0 e^{2wZ}$, as of course it must. On the other hand, if the hydrogen bond is very strong (i.e., $K_{ij} = \infty$), then eqn. (28) reduces to $K_{obs} = [H^+]$. In other words, if the hydrogen bond is extremely strong, then half of the molecules will be ionized at all pH's, i.e., there will always be an equal number of donors and acceptors in order to form the infinitely strong hydrogen bond. At intermediate values of K_{ij} (e.g., $K_{ij} = 1$), there will be an intermediate dependence of K_{obs} on pH. In other words, at low pH both nitrogens possess a proton which is relatively easily ionized since its ionization would lead to the formation of an acceptor group for the NH...N hydrogen bond. In fact eqn. (20) is the low pH limit of the value of K_{obs}, showing that ionization is enhanced at low pH by hydrogen bonding. However, as the pH increases, ionization becomes more and more difficult and, as the pH becomes greater than pK, the constant K_{obs} is smaller than K, with eqn. (14) becoming the high pH limit, i.e., at high pH the presence of the hydrogen bond reduces the tendency of the donor group to lose its proton.

(c) Homologous double bonds

We shall consider next the homologous double bond of the carboxyl...carboxyl (or acetic acid dimer) type. Since the double bond is much stronger than a single bond, viz., $K_{lm} \sim 100$ whereas $K_{ij} \sim 1$ (see eqn. (7)), we can see the details of the effect of double bonds better by neglecting single bonds altogether in this case. In other words, we are assuming that if one of the hydrogen bonds in the strongly double bonded structure is ruptured,

$$C \overset{O \cdots HO}{\underset{OH \cdots O}{\Big\langle}} C$$

then the other one is too weak to hold the groups together, i.e., $K_{ij} = 0$ in this assumption. Therefore, we shall neglect structures of the type:

$$C \overset{O, \quad HO}{\underset{OH \cdots O}{\Big\langle}} C$$

Both participating carboxyl groups are assumed to have the same *non-hydrogen-bonded* ionization constant K.

The various species which can exist, and their concentration fractions, x, are shown in Table III.

TABLE III

HOMOLOGOUS DOUBLE BONDS

Species	xy
(A) C⟨O, HO⟩C ⟨OH, O⟩	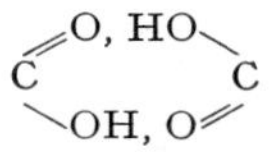 1
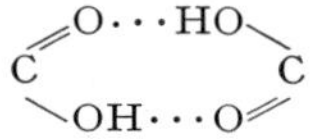 (B) C⟨O···HO⟩C ⟨OH···O⟩	K_{lm}
(C) C⟨O, O⟩ – C ⟨OH, O⟩	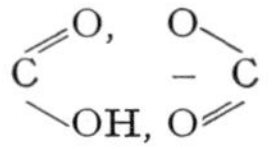 $K/[\mathrm{H^+}]$
(D) C⟨O, HO⟩ – C ⟨O, O⟩	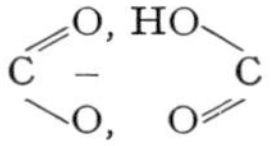 $K/[\mathrm{H^+}]$
(E) C⟨O, O⟩ – – C ⟨O, O⟩	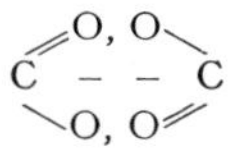 $(K/[\mathrm{H^+}])^2$

$$y = 1 + K_{lm} + 2K/[\mathrm{H^+}] + (K/[\mathrm{H^+}])^2$$

Considering the ionization of a specified carboxyl group, say the left-hand one, the observed ionization constant is

$$K_{\mathrm{obs}} = [\mathrm{H^+}] \frac{(x_\mathrm{D} + x_\mathrm{E})}{(x_\mathrm{A} + x_\mathrm{B} + x_\mathrm{C})} \tag{29}$$

Substituting from Table III, we obtain

$$K_{\mathrm{obs}} = K \frac{(1 + K/[\mathrm{H^+}])}{(1 + K_{lm} + K/[\mathrm{H^+}])} \tag{30}$$

with a sharp, non-trivial dependence on pH.

If K_{lm} (in addition to K_{ij}) were zero, then K_{obs} would be equal to K and we would have a trivial dependence on pH. If we can, for the moment, imagine a situation where there is no trivial dependence on pH, *i.e.* K independent of Z and pH, we would obtain an S-shaped curve for the dependence of pK_{obs} on pH. In such a case eqn. (30) approaches the limit

$$K_{obs} = \frac{K}{1 + K_{lm}} \qquad (31)$$

at low pH, since $K/[H^+] \ll 1$. In this region (pH $<$ 4) virtually all the carboxyl groups are present in the un-ionized, doubly bonded form, and the *double* bond has to be broken before a *specified* carboxyl group can ionize. Thus, it will be hard to ionize the carboxyl group and pK_{obs} will be high, around 6. As the pH is increased in the region where $K/[H^+] \sim K_{lm}$, the probability that the *other* carboxyl group is ionized increases. This correspondingly lowers the probability that the *specified* un-ionized carboxyl group is involved in a double hydrogen bond, and thus the value of K_{obs} increases; *i.e*, ionization becomes easier as the pH rises. At high pH $(K/[H^+] \gg K_{lm})$ virtually all double bonds are broken and the ionization constant K_{obs} closely approaches its high pH limit of simply K. Removing the imagined restriction that there is no trivial dependence on pH, we obtain the "real" situation, which is given by eqn. (30). At low pH the rate of change of pK_{obs} with pH is the same as that of pK with pH while, at high pH, pK_{obs} and pK approach each other asymptotically, the electrostatic effect predominating at the extreme pH ranges.

A plot of eqn. (30) as pK_{obs} *vs.* pH exhibits both a maximum and a minimum, the existence of which will be observed only if the trivial (*i.e.*, electrostatic) dependence is not too great. It can be shown[21] that K_{obs} of eqn. (30) will exhibit both a maximum and a minimum only if

$$\frac{2w}{2.303} \frac{dZ}{dpH} > \frac{1}{2\sqrt{1 + K_{lm}}} - \frac{1}{2} \qquad (32)$$

in the pH region of interest, *i.e.*, for $K/[H^+] \sim K_{lm}$.

The behavior of pK_{obs} of eqn. (30), in the intermediate range where it decreases with increasing pH, will lead to a phenomenon which may be referred to as an "ionization explosion". This would manifest itself as an abnormal steepening of a titration curve in the region in which the carboxyl groups ionize. Such steepening has been observed in the titration curves of several proteins, and a variety of explanations have been proposed to account for it.

In concluding this section, it may be mentioned that K_{ij} need not be neglected in treating the homologous double bond. The extension of the theory to take this into account is straightforward.

(d) Competition

As an example of competitive hydrogen bonding we may consider a situation in which an ionizable donor, DH, can compete for two *already ionized* acceptors, A. If the formation of a hydrogen bond between DH and either of the acceptor groups is K_{ij}, then the presence of two possible acceptor groups will make it even harder to ionize DH than if only one acceptor group were present. In such a case, K_{obs} is given by

$$K_{obs} = \frac{K_1}{1 + 2\,K_{ij}} \tag{33}$$

where K_1 is given by eqn. (11). This result obtains instead of eqn. (14). It should be noted that there is only the trivial dependence of K_{obs} on pH.

If one *ionizable* acceptor, HA, competes for two non-ionizable donors, DH, then there will be a stronger enhancement of the acidity of HA over that observed if only one donor were available. In such a case, K_{obs} for HA is given by

$$K_{obs} = K_2\,(1 + 2\,K_{ij}) \tag{34}$$

where K_2 is given by eqn. (18). This result obtains instead of eqn. (20). Here again there is only the trivial dependence of K_{obs} on pH.

However, hydrogen bonding may lead to a non-trivial pH dependence of K_{obs} in more complex competitive situations. We have such a situation in the last case considered if we focus attention on the ionization of a *specific* donor, and assume that the acceptor is already ionized. We shall also assume that K_1 and K_{ij} apply equally to both donors. Under these conditions the expression for K_{obs} is

$$K_{obs} = K_1 \left(\frac{1 + K_{ij} + K_1/[\mathrm{H^+}]}{1 + 2\,K_{ij} + (1 + K_{ij})\,K_1/[\mathrm{H^+}]} \right) \tag{35}$$

Here we obtain a non-trivial dependence of K_{obs} on pH. It can be seen from the model that the ionization of the given donor will become progressively more difficult as the pH rises. At low pH, eqn. (35) reduces to

$$K_{obs} = K_1 \left(\frac{1 + K_{ij}}{1 + 2\,K_{ij}} \right) \tag{36}$$

If $K_{ij} \gg 1$, this reduces to $K_1/2$. In other words, at low pH both donors possess a proton and either can form a hydrogen bond with the single acceptor, so that the acidity of the *given* donor is reduced by the statistical factor $1/2$. As the pH rises (and, therefore, the *other* donor will tend to be ionized), the *given* donor will become relatively more difficult to ionize since, being the only available donor, it will tend to be hydrogen bonded. In fact, if K_{ij} is large, ionization of the *other* donor will cause a comparatively

References p. 182

small loss in the amount of hydrogen bonding. The high pH limit is, of course, eqn. (14). If pK_1^0 is around 10 (*e.g.*, if the donors are tyrosyl groups) the maximum effect would be around pH 14, and thus go undetected in a titration curve, except for a numerical error in pK_{obs} of which the observer would be unaware.

Finally, we may consider the case of two donors, D_1H, and D_2H, competing for two already ionized acceptors A_1 and A_2, subject to a restriction that the first donor, D_1H, can be bonded only to the first acceptor, A_1, while the second donor, D_2H, can be bonded to either acceptor. This seems to be a sterically realistic possibility. For the ionization of these two donors we obtain

$$K_{obs}^{(1)} = K_1 \left(\frac{1 + 2 K_{ij} + K_1/[H^+]}{1 + 3 K_{ij} + K_{ij}^2 + (1 + K_{ij}) K_1/[H^+]} \right) \tag{37}$$

and

$$K_{obs}^{(2)} = K_1 \left(\frac{1 + K_{ij} + K_1/[H^+]}{1 + 3 K_{ij} + K_{ij}^2 + (1 + 2 K_{ij}) K_1/[H^+]} \right) \tag{38}$$

Both functions are non-trivially dependent on pH and both show qualitatively the same behavior as eqn. (35) of ionization becoming more difficult as the pH rises.

(e) Cooperative bonding

As an example of a cooperative hydrogen bond we shall consider the interaction between two tyrosyl groups with one carboxylate ion. The equilibrium constant for the formation of such a bond is K_{rs}. The expression for K_{obs} for the ionization of a specified donor is

$$K_{obs} = K_1 \left(\frac{1 + K_{ij} + K_1/[H^+]}{1 + 2 K_{ij} + K_{rs} + (1 + K_{ij}) K_1/[H^+]} \right) \tag{39}$$

For a cooperative bond $(K_{rs} \gg K_{ij})$ the ionization becomes easier as the pH increases, the low pH limit of eqn. (39) being

$$K_{obs} = K_1 \left(\frac{1 + K_{ij}}{1 + 2 K_{ij} + K_{rs}} \right) \tag{40}$$

and the high pH limit being given by eqn. (14). Since the ionization of the second donor group becomes much easier when the first group is ionized, cooperative hydrogen bonding would lead to an "ionization explosion" already discussed in the case of homologous double bonds of the carboxyl...

carboxyl type, with a similar non-trivial dependence of pK_{obs} on pH. This would lead to steepening of titration curves in the high pH region.

4. Limited proteolysis[23]

(a) Comparison of $(K_{pep})_{obs}$ and K_{pep}

Tertiary hydrogen bonds can play an important role in limited proteolysis[23] e.g., in the thrombin-fibrinogen reaction[25,30] or in the activation of zymogens[36]. If a peptide fragment is liberated from a protein by hydrolysis of a peptide bond, this reaction would be expected to go to completion on the basis of studies of equilibria in simple peptides[37], i.e., the hydrolysis constant, K_{pep}, for simple peptides is very large. However, if liberation of this fragment also involves the rupture of side-chain hydrogen bonds, then it may happen[23,30] that the observed hydrolysis constant $(K_{pep})_{obs}$ is significantly lower than K_{pep}, i.e., the hydrolytic reaction may not go to completion.

In order to see the effect of hydrogen bonding on $(K_{pep})_{obs}$ we must compute the concentration of protein molecules which have, and those which do not have, the stabilizing hydrogen bonds. Consider an ith donor and a jth acceptor, which can form the ij^{th} (heterologous single) hydrogen bond. If (P) represents the total concentration of non-hydrolyzed protein (i.e., those molecules both with and without side-chain hydrogen bonds), then the concentration of non-hydrolyzed protein, $(P_{HB})_{ij}$, which contains the ij^{th} hydrogen bond, is

$$(P_{HB})_{ij} = x_{ij}(P) \tag{41}$$

where

$$x_{ij} = \frac{K_{ij}}{1 + K_{ij} + K_1/[H^+] + [H^+]/K_2} \tag{42}$$

and is the concentration fraction of the non-hydrolyzed protein containing a hydrogen bond between the ith donor and j^{th} acceptor. In a pH region where the donors are in the form DH and the acceptors in the form A, and where no ionization occurs, eqn. (42) reduces to

$$x_{ij} = \frac{K_{ij}}{1 + K_{ij}} \tag{43}$$

The concentration of non-hydrolyzed protein which does not have the ij^{th} hydrogen bond intact, $(P_{NHB})_{ij}$, is

$$(P_{NHB})_{ij} = (1 - x_{ij})(P) \tag{44}$$

If the side-chain hydrogen bonds are independent of each other, e.g., heterologous, single bonds, then the concentration of the non-hydrolyzed protein (P_{NHB}), which contains no hydrogen bonds between the R groups of the peptide fragment liberated (A) and the protein core (C) will be given by the following expression

$$(P_{NHB}) = (P)\, \Pi\, (\mathbf{1} - x_{ij}) \qquad (45)$$

where the product is taken over all the possible hydrogen bonds between the protein core and the peptide fragment. The numerical value of (P_{NHB}) will be considerably smaller than that of (P), i.e., of all the non-hydrolyzed molecules, those which contain no hydrogen bonds between the core and the peptide fragment will be relatively few in number. Further, these species (with no side-chain hydrogen bonds) should have a hydrolysis constant, K_{pep}, which will be the same as that for a simple, non-hydrogen-bonded model compound. Therefore, we may write

$$K_{pep} = \frac{(C)\,(A)}{(P_{NHB})} \qquad (46)$$

where (C) and (A) are the concentrations of the protein core and peptide fragment, respectively. The *observed* hydrolysis constant for the protein will be given by the expression

$$(K_{pep})_{obs} = \frac{(C)\,(A)}{(P)} \qquad (47)$$

Combination of eqns. (45), (46) and (47) gives

$$(K_{pep})_{obs} = K_{pep}\, \Pi\, (\mathbf{1} - x_{ij}) \qquad (48)$$

Taking the expression for x_{ij} from eqn. (43) we obtain

$$(K_{pep})_{obs} = \frac{K_{pep}}{\Pi(\mathbf{1} + K_{ij})} \qquad (49)$$

Thus

$$(K_{pep})_{obs} < K_{pep} \qquad (50)$$

since K_{ij} is a positive quantity. The more side-chain hydrogen bonds which contribute to the denominator of eqn. (49), the smaller will be $(K_{pep})_{obs}$ compared to K_{pep}.

The thermodynamic parameters for the equilibrium are analogues of eqns. (24), (25) and (26).

$$(\varDelta F^0_{pep})_{obs} = \varDelta F^0_{pep} + RT\, \Sigma \ln\, (\mathbf{1} + K_{ij}) \qquad (51)$$

$$(\Delta H^0_{pep})_{obs} = \Delta H^0_{pep} - \Sigma \frac{K_i}{1 + K_{ij}} \Delta H^0_{ij} \tag{52}$$

$$(\Delta S^0_{pep})_{obs} = \Delta S^0_{pep} - R \Sigma \ln (1 + K_{ij}) - \frac{1}{T} \Sigma \frac{K_{ij}}{1 + K_{ij}} \Delta H^0_{ij} \tag{53}$$

where the summations are taken over all the side-chain hydrogen bonds. The term $RT \Sigma \ln (1 + K_{ij})$ is the free energy of stabilization, which makes $(K_{pep})_{obs}$ less than K_{pep} and thus prevents the hydrolysis of a peptide bond in a protein from proceeding as far to completion as it does in a model peptide. ΔF^0_{pep} corresponds to ΔF^0_{norm} of eqn. (1) and $RT \Sigma \ln (1 + K_{ij})$ to $\Delta F^0_{interaction}$.

(b) Magnitude of peptide bond stabilization

While the term $RT \Sigma \ln (1 + K_{ij})$ of eqn. (51) can make $(\Delta F^0_{pep})_{obs}$ greater than ΔF^0_{pep}, or $(K_{pep})_{obs}$ less than K_{pep}, the following practical problem arises. Since K_{pep} is a fairly large number[37] $(K_{pep})_{obs}$ must be significantly smaller in order that it be possible to distinguish a "strong" from a "weak" peptide bond. This can be illustrated by rewriting eqn. (47) in the form

$$(K_{pep})_{obs} = \frac{\alpha^2 (P)_0}{1 - \alpha} \tag{54}$$

where $\alpha = (C)/(P)_0 = (A)/(P)_0$, and $(P)_0$ is the initial molar concentration of the protein. If $(K_{pep})_{obs}$ were equal to K_{pep}, e.g., to 2 (ref. 37) then α would be indistinguishable from unity for values of $(P)_0$ less than 0.1 M. Since the initial concentration of protein in a hydrolytic reaction is usually *much* less than 0.1 M, making α even closer to unity, the hydrolytic reaction can be said to go essentially to completion under these conditions. The question arises, "How much less than 2 must $(K_{pep})_{obs}$ be in order that α be distinguishable from unity, say 0.9?" In other words, we shall assume that experimental methods are available which can detect a value of $\alpha = 0.9$ with a precision of, say, $\pm$ 0.01, so that one could conclude from an experimental value of $\alpha = 0.9$ that the hydrolytic reaction does not go to completion, or that it is a reversible one. For this purpose let M be the molecular weight of the protein and S its concentration in grams per 100 ml. The molarity, $(P)_0$, is then 10 S/M. Therefore, eqn. (54) can be rewritten as

$$(K_{pep})_{obs} = \frac{\alpha^2}{1 - \alpha} \frac{10 S}{M} \tag{55}$$

If $\alpha = 0.9$, then we are seeking conditions such that

$$(K_{pep})_{obs} \leqq \frac{81 S}{M} \tag{56}$$

in order for $(K_{pep})_{obs}$ to be measurable. The values of $(K_{pep})_{obs}$ must be less than the limits where (a) S has its minimum value and M its maximum value, and (b) S has its maximum value and M its minimum value. Taking the range of S as 1 to 10, and of M as 10^4 to 10^6, then α can be 0.9, and therefore experimentally distinguishable from unity, if $(K_{pep})_{obs}$ is smaller than 10^{-4} to 10^{-1}.

Having answered the question as to the values which $(K_{pep})_{obs}$ must have in order that reversibility be demonstrable, the real question now is, "How can we achieve such low values of $(K_{pep})_{obs}$?" Within the framework of the hydrogen-bonding model the answer lies in a consideration of eqn. (49). Taking K_{pep} in the range of 1 to 10, then $(K_{pep})_{obs}$ can be less than 10^{-4} to 10^{-1} if $\Pi(1 + K_{ij})$ is greater than 10 to 10^5. If there are n heterologous single bonds, each with $K_{ij} = 1$, contributing to this product, then we require 4 to 17 such bonds to achieve this stabilization. If K_{ij} were 4, as computed for bovine serum albumin in the previous section, then 2 to 7 such bonds would suffice. This result means that, if one is to observe a hydrolytic reaction which does not go to completion, there must be this number of side-chain hydrogen bonds connecting the core C and the fragment A. Liberation of the fragment during hydrolysis would require the rupture of these hydrogen bonds as well as the breakage of the peptide bond. Since this is a fairly large number of hydrogen bonds we may conclude that there exists a critical size for the fragment A in order that reversibility be observed, *i.e.*, the fragment must be large enough to have the required number of hydrogen-bonded side-chains. If, as an alternative, the side-chain hydrogen bonds are carboxyl–carboxyl, acetic acid dimer type bonds, with $K_{lm} \sim 100$, then only 1 to 3 such bonds would suffice to produce the effect calculated above. The influence of such side-chain hydrogen bonding on the thrombin–fibrinogen reaction has been observed[30]. It may be that reversibility has not been observed in other examples of limited proteolysis because the peptide is too short to have enough stabilizing side-chain hydrogen bonds. However, the subtilisin digestion of ribonuclease[38] may possibly be another example where hydrogen-bonding stabilization is involved.

In cases where there are too few side-chain hydrogen bonds to detect by their effect on $(K_{pep})_{obs}$ it is still possible to infer the existence of such side-chain bonds from $(\Delta H^0_{pep})_{obs}$. Using eqn. (52), we may take ΔH^0_{pep}, as an example, as -1.55 kcal/mole, observed by Dobry, Fruton and Sturtevant[37] for benzoyl-L-tyrosylglycine amide. Even if only one heterologous single bond were involved (with $K_{ij} = 1$ and $\Delta H^0_{ij} = -6$ kcal/mole), $(\Delta H^0_{pep})_{obs}$ would be about $+1.5$ kcal/mole which is distinguishable in a direct calorimetric measurement of the heat of hydrolysis from the value -1.55 kcal/mole for the simple peptide. The effect will be correspondingly larger, the more stabilizing side-chain hydrogen bonds there are. Therefore, calorimetric measurements of $(\Delta H^0_{pep})_{obs}$ should be very useful in the investigation of side-chain hydrogen bonding, even in cases where their effect on $(K_{pep})_{obs}$ cannot be detected.

It has been assumed here that A and C cannot be associated by hydrogen bonds after the peptide bond has been hydrolyzed. However, when there is a large number of such bonds, sufficient to make $(K_{pep})_{obs}$ significantly less than K_{pep}, the possibility increases that such association may actually take place. In such a case, the foregoing treatment breaks down. The possibility of detecting such association resides in a study of the concentration dependence[23,30] of α.

(c) Role of denaturation

According to the foregoing theory the peptide bond should appear normal in the absence of the stabilizing hydrogen bonds. Thus, the hydrolysis of a peptide bond in a denatured protein should be relatively complete, as in the case of a simple peptide, whereas it might not be complete if the required number of hydrogen bonds are present in the native protein. Unfortunately, there are no *equilibrium* data with which to compare the extent of hydrolysis of native and denatured protein in order to verify this point of view. However, data do exist for the *kinetics* of hydrolysis of peptide bonds in native and denatured protein. While the theory presented here applies to the equilibrium situation, and not to the rates of hydrolysis, it can be seen *qualitatively* that stabilizing hydrogen bonds should slow down the rate of hydrolysis. Thus, the *first* peptide bond should be hydrolyzed slower in a native protein than in a denatured one. Numerous examples of this phenomenon are known, *e.g.*, the action of trypsin or chymotrypsin on native ribonuclease is very 'slow but becomes quite rapid if the native structure (presumably including the internal hydrogen bonds) is disrupted by oxidation of the disulfide bridges[39]. Incidentally, the helical, as well as the side-chain, hydrogen bonds no doubt contribute to the stability of the peptide bonds of the native molecule. Further, as hydrolysis of a native molecule proceeds slowly, there will be a disruption of the internal hydrogen bonds. Thus, the succeeding bonds should be hydrolyzed at a faster rate. Under certain circumstances, the rates should increase in such a manner that the reaction might be characterized[40] as a "proteolytic explosion", analogous to the "ionization explosion" discussed in the previous section.

(d) Cyclic stabilization

. There is an alternative possible explanation for the existence of *apparently* strong peptide bonds and "proteolytic explosion" in terms of cyclic struc-

References p. 182

tures. Even in the absence of stabilizing hydrogen bonds, the peptide bond in a cyclic structure would *appear* stronger because its hydrolysis would not lead to the formation of new fragments with an accompanying increase in entropy. However, the subsequent bonds would be easier to hydrolyze since the cyclic structure would have been disrupted after the hydrolysis of the first peptide bond.

There are at least three criteria by which one can distinguish between hydrogen-bonding stabilization on the one hand, and cyclic stabilization, on the other. (1) End group analysis would indicate the presence of cyclic chains. (2) The degree of hydrolysis, α, if measurably less than unity, would be independent of protein concentration if no new fragments were produced (*i.e.*, in the case of cyclic stabilization), but would depend on concentration if a peptide fragment were liberated (*i.e.*, in the case of hydrogen-bonding stabilization). (3) In the case of cyclic stabilization $(\varDelta H^0_{pep})_{obs}$ would be equal to $\varDelta H^0_{pep}$, whereas in the case of hydrogen-bonding stabilization $(\varDelta H^0_{pep})_{obs}$ would be given by eqn. (52), the two situations being distinguishable by a calorimetric determination of the heat of hydrolysis. Of course, it is possible to have both kinds of stabilization, *i.e.*, both cyclic and hydrogen-bonding. In such a case, the pH-dependence of the equilibrium constant might shed light on the problem.

5. Protein association [22]

Protein associations or polymerizations may also involve side-chain hydrogen bonds. As an example of such a reaction we shall discuss the association of fibrin monomers to form intermediate polymers[22]. Referring to eqn. (1), there is no term $\varDelta F^0_{norm}$ for this process, *i.e.*, $\varDelta F^0_{obs}$ is entirely an interaction term, $\varDelta F^0_{interaction}$, arising from the formation of hydrogen bonds between the side-chain groups of the associating molecules. Thermodynamic studies of pH[26,41] and enthalpy[22] changes accompanying association have led to an identification[22,26] of the donor and acceptor groups in this particular case. The association is assumed to involve intermolecular hydrogen bond formation between s equivalent donors on one molecule and s equivalent acceptors on another molecule. Since both the donors and acceptors can ionize, the extent of hydrogen-bond formation is pH-dependent. Each of the donors and acceptors is assumed to be involved in equilibria of the type[22,42]

$$\text{DH} \leftrightharpoons \text{H}^+ + \text{D}^- \tag{57}$$

$$\text{AH}^+ \leftrightharpoons \text{H}^+ + \text{A} \tag{58}$$

$$\text{DH} + \text{A} \leftrightharpoons \text{DH} \ldots \text{A} \tag{59}$$

Formation of a hydrogen bond between a given i^{th} donor and j^{th} acceptor, according to eqn. (59), disturbs the acid–base equilibria of eqns. (57) and (58). Hence, at the low-pH end of the range of polymerization, protons will be produced because of the polymerization-induced dissociation of AH^+, whereas protons will be taken up at the high-pH end of the polymerization range when the polymerization causes D^- groups to combine with hydrogen ions. The theory to be presented below leads to the conclusion that the DH groups are tyrosyl and the AH^+ groups histidyl side-chains.

These effects can be treated quantitatively[22]. The net number of protons released per ij^{th} pair, *after* the solution of monomer is brought to the desired initial pH but *during* the polymerization process, is

$$q \equiv \{ P_{(DH, HA)initial} - P_{(DH, HA)final} \} - \{ P_{(D, A)initial} - P_{(D, A)final} \} \quad (60)$$

where the symbols represent concentration fractions, and the subscripts "initial" and "final" refer to the state of the system at the given initial pH before and after polymerization and the subsequently induced dissociation (or association) of protons have taken place. In the "initial" state no intermolecular hydrogen bonds exist, whereas in the "final" state we have to take into account the presence of the species $P_{(DH...A)}$. Therefore,

$$q = \left\{ \frac{[H^+]/K_2}{1 + K_1/[H^+] + [H^+]/K_2} - \frac{[H^+]/K_2}{1 + K_{ij} + K_1/[H^+] + [H^+]/K_2} \right\}$$

$$- \left\{ \frac{K_1/[H^+]}{1 + K_1/[H^+] + [H^+]/K_2} - \frac{K_1/[H^+]}{1 + K_{ij} + K_1/[H^+] + [H^+]/K_2} \right\}$$

$$= x_{ij} \frac{[H^+]/K_2 - K_1/[H^+]}{1 + K_1/[H^+] + [H^+]/K_2} \quad (61)$$

where x_{ij} is given by eqn. (42). The quantity q will be positive or negative depending on the pH. At low pH it will be positive since dissociation of AH^+ releases protons to the solvent; at high pH it will be negative since D^- will be taking up protons from the solvent; q will be zero when, according to eqn. (61),

$$[H^+] = \sqrt{K_1 K_2} \quad (62)$$

A plot of q against pH (*i.e.*, eqn. (61)) will have a maximum and a minimum which can be obtained as follows. At low pH (*i.e.*, $[H^+] \sim K_2$) we can neglect $K_1/[H^+]$. Since $K_{ij} \sim 1$, these approximations enable eqn. (61) to be reduced to

$$q = \frac{[H^+]/K_2}{1 + [H^+]/K_2} \left(\frac{K_{ij}}{1 + K_{ij} + [H^+]/K_2} \right) \tag{63}$$

at low pH. The maximum in this function occurs at

$$[H^+]/K_2 = \sqrt{1 + K_{ij}} \tag{64}$$

Similarly, at high pH (*i.e.*, $[H^+] \sim K_1$), we can neglect $[H^+]/K_2$ and reduce eqn. (61) to

$$q = \frac{- K_1/[H^+]}{1 + K_1/[H^+]} \left(\frac{K_{ij}}{1 + K_{ij} + K_1/[H^+]} \right) \tag{65}$$

The minimum in this function occurs at

$$K_1/[H^+] = \sqrt{1 + K_{ij}} \tag{66}$$

The complete function, q *vs.* pH, can be plotted according to eqn. (61) with K_1 and K_2 obtained from data of Mihalyi[41] on the pH-dependence of proton production in the association. Mihalyi's data show a maximum at pH 6.0 and the suggestion of a minimum at a pH which may be estimated as 9.8. Applying eqns. (64) and (66) to the maximum and the minimum, respectively, and using a value of unity for K_{ij}, values of $pK_1 = 9.65$ and $pK_2 = 6.15$ are obtained. From these data it may be concluded that the acceptor is the imidazole group of histidine, and that the donor can be either a tyrosyl or an ε-amino group. Mihalyi's experiments have been repeated at two temperatures, 0° and 25°, permitting a calculation of the heat of ionization, ΔH_1^0 of the donor group[26]. The results indicate that the donors are tyrosyl residues. Applying eqn. (62) to the values of K_1 and K_2, q should be zero at pH 7.9. Mihalyi's data show that this condition is met at pH 7.6, in good agreement with the theory. With the above values of K_1, K_2 and K_{ij} it is then possible to compute curves for the pH dependence of x_{ij} and q from eqns. (42) and (61), respectively. Such a theoretical curve for q agrees well with Mihalyi's data.

It is also possible to evaluate the number of donors and acceptors s on each monomer. According to Mihalyi's data the number of hydrogen ions, Δh, released at the maximum (*i.e.*, at pH 6) is 1 per 100,000 g of fibrinogen. Taking the molecular weight as 330,000, this would correspond to 3.3 hydrogen ions per monomer. If eqn. (64) is substituted into eqn. (63) (or, correspondingly, eqn. (66) into eqn. (65)), the following equation is obtained.

$$q_{max} = - q_{min} = \frac{K_{ij}}{(1 + \sqrt{1 + K_{ij}})^2} \tag{67}$$

From eqn. (67), with $K_{ij} = 1$, the value of q_{max} is 0.17. Since the quantity Δh is equal to sq at any pH, the value of sq_{max} is equal to 3.3. Combining this value with the value $q_{max} = 0.17$, a value of $s = 19$ is obtained for the number of donors or acceptors on the polymerization site of the fibrin monomer.

Calorimetric measurements[22] provide additional evidence that hydrogen bonding is involved in the polymerization. The magnitude and pH dependence of the heat evolved upon polymerization of fibrin monomer can be accounted for by means of the same theory. The heat evolved per monomer is taken as equal to the heat evolved per link (*i.e.*, per sx_{ij} hydrogen bonds) formed. At any pH it arises from the formation of hydrogen bonds and from the polymerization-induced ionization of donors and acceptors. It is given by

$$\Delta H = sx_{ij} \left\{ \Delta H^0_{ij} + \frac{([\text{H}^+]/K_2)\,\Delta H^0_2 - (K_1/[\text{H}^+])\,\Delta H^0_1}{1 + K_1/[\text{H}^+] + [\text{H}^+]/K_2} \right\} \tag{68}$$

In eqn. (68), $s = 19$, x_{ij} is a known function of pH, $\Delta H^0_{ij} = -6$ kcal/mole, $\Delta H^0_2 = +7$ kcal/mole, $\Delta H_1 = +6$ kcal/mole, $pK_1 = 9.65$, and $pK_2 = 6.15$. The theoretical curve computed from eqn. (68) agrees well with the experimental data[22] obtained at pH 6.08 and 6.88.

The above thermodynamic theory provides strong evidence that the polymerization of fibrin monomer takes place through a hydrogen-bonding mechanism involving about 19 tyrosyl donors and about 19 histidyl acceptors. It should be emphasized that there are *not* 19 hydrogen-bonds formed in every link but only an average of 19 x_{ij} hydrogen bonds, where the value of x_{ij} depends on pH. Hence, the average *maximum* number of hydrogen bonds per link is about 9, occurring near pH 8, where x_{ij} has its maximum value.

6. Denaturation

We shall use the term "denaturation" for any process in which the configuration of the protein is changed without the rupture of primary valence bonds. The process may, under certain conditions, appear to be reversible. Under others, it may appear to be irreversible. Denaturation can be brought about by a variety of physical and chemical agents. Also, it manifests itself by a change in one or more of many different properties of the protein. These aspects of denaturation have been extensively discussed by Putnam[43] and by Kauzmann[15]. We should like to emphasize one point here. If denaturation is followed, *e.g.*, by observing the loss in solubility of the denatured form, the solubility should be determined under the conditions of the denaturation. For example, if a protein is heated at pH 7 and 80° but its solubility measured at, say, pH 3 and 25°, then there is the possibility

References p. 182

that material denatured at pH 7 and 80° may re-nature in the pH 3 buffer at 25°. Thus, there would be an error in the determination of the amount of insoluble (denatured at pH 7 and 80°) material. Ideally, one should determine the amount of denatured material under the same conditions that the denaturation experiment was performed. This restricts the experimental technique to those such as optical rotation, ultraviolet difference spectrophotometry, etc. where the system can be analyzed without disturbing it.

Having illustrated the role which side-chain hydrogen bonds can play in a variety of protein reactions, we can now formulate a model to account for the pH-dependence of reversible denaturation and also of the pH-dependence of the kinetics of protein denaturation. One should not be surprised to find that the formal equations for denaturation are very similar to those for protein association (except for the sign) since denaturation involves the rupture of hydrogen bonds, whereas association involves their formation. Also, as in the case of association, ΔF^0_{obs} of eqn. (1) arises entirely from $\Delta F^0_{interaction}$.

(a) Reversible denaturation[6, 31]

We may regard a protein molecule as being composed of helical and non-helical regions. The helices may be connected together by cross-links which, in a native protein, are usually disulfide bonds. Further, the side-chains of a given helix or of neighboring helices may be close enough to form hydrogen bonds. We shall regard denaturation as the conversion of the helical parts of the molecule to randomly coiled parts. If the process is reversible, then the overall change in the standard free energy, ΔF^0_{obs}, may be written as

$$\Delta F^0_{obs} = \Delta F^0_{unf} + \Delta F^0_{H} + \Delta F^0_{elec} + \Delta F^0_{comb} - T\Delta S^0_x + \ldots \qquad (69)$$

where ΔF^0_{unf} is the contribution from the unfolding of the backbone helix[6]. It is given by eqn. (2) and is independent of pH since the peptide CO and NH groups do not associate or dissociate protons in the pH range of interest, 1 to 13. The term ΔF^0_{H} is the standard free energy required to rupture the side-chain hydrogen bonds. It is pH-dependent, and already appeared (e.g., in eqn. (51)).

$$\Delta F^0_{H} = - RT \Sigma \ln (1 - x_{ij}) \qquad (70)$$

where x_{ij} is given by eqn. (42). ΔF^0_{elec} is a term arising from the difference in electrostatic free energy between native and denatured forms. It can make a significant contribution to ΔF^0_{obs} (see, e.g., ref. 44), but we shall neglect it here on the assumption that it is small in the presence of excess salt. ΔF^0_{comb} arises from the combination of the randomly coiled form with small molecules and ions, e.g., urea[6]. The cross-links make an entropy contribution[45], ΔS^0_x given by

$$\Delta S_x^0 = - (3 \, Rv/4) \, [\ln n' + 3] \qquad (71)$$

where v is the number of cross-linked helices and n' is the number of statistical elements (assumed here equal to n) between cross-links. Other terms could be added to eqn. (69) to take account of other structural features such as hydrophobic bonds, etc.

When a protein is reversibly denatured, the fraction of the molecules denatured, α, may be written as[6]

$$\alpha = [1 + e^{\Delta F_{obs}^0/RT}]^{-1} \qquad (72)$$

The value of α is zero at low temperature and approaches unity at high temperature. At some intermediate temperature, T_{tr}, referred to as the "transition temperature", the value of ΔF_{obs}^0 becomes equal to zero, and α equal to 0.5. Thus, a plot of denaturation data as α vs. T at a given pH, urea concentration, etc. permits one to determine the transition temperature under the given set of conditions.

We shall first discuss urea denaturation at a pH where no hydrogen bonds occur so that eqn. (69) becomes

$$\Delta F_{obs}^0 = \Delta F_{unf}^0 + \Delta F_{comb}^0 - T \Delta S_x^0 \qquad (73)$$

Schellman[6] has shown that, for urea denaturation,

$$\Delta F_{comb}^0 = - 2 \, p \, RT \ln (1 + Kc) \qquad (74)$$

for $p > 20$, where p is the number of amino acid residues which may react with urea when the helix is unfolded, K is the equilibrium constant for the binding of a urea molecule to a C=O or N—H group of a peptide unit, and c is the concentration of urea in moles/l. For small c, $Kc \ll 1$ and eqn. (74) may be rewritten as

$$\Delta F_{comb}^0 = - 2 \, p \, RT \, Kc \qquad (75)$$

The temperature dependence of K may be written as

$$K = K_{25} \exp \left[- \frac{\Delta H_u}{R} \, (1/T - 1/T_{25}) \right] \qquad (76)$$

where K_{25} is the value of K at 25° and ΔH_u is the heat of formation of the complex between urea and the peptide CO or NH group.

If the transition temperature is determined at various urea concentrations, then we can obtain eqn. (77) by setting ΔF^0_{obs} of eqn. (73) equal to zero, and substituting from eqn. (2) for ΔF^0_{unf}, from eqns. (75) and (76) for ΔF^0_{comb}, and from eqn. (71) for ΔS^0_x.

$$\frac{1}{T_{tr}} = \frac{(n-1)\Delta S^0_{res} + \Delta S^0_x}{(n-4)\Delta H^0_{res}} + \frac{2pRcK_{25}}{(n-4)\Delta H^0_{res}} e^{\Delta H_u/RT_{25}} e^{-\Delta H_u/RT_{tr}} \quad (77)$$

ΔS^0_x can be determined from the known structure of the protein (amino acid sequence and disulfide bridge location). An assumed model for the helical portion of the protein will give n. Thus a plot of $1/T_{tr}$ against $c\,e^{-\Delta H_u/RT_{tr}}$ will give a straight line from which ΔH^0_{res} and ΔS^0_{res} may be obtained. Once these parameters are known, they can be used for subsequent experiments at other pH's, in the *absence* of urea, for which cases eqn. (69) becomes

$$\Delta F^0_{obs} = \Delta F^0_{unf} + \Delta F^0_H - T\Delta S^0_x \quad (78)$$

We shall next consider the pH-dependence[31] of ΔF^0_{obs} of eqn. (78). According to the assumption implicit in our model, the pH-dependence of ΔF^0_{obs} arises entirely from the pH-dependence of ΔF^0_H. The function ΔF^0_H is such that, *e.g.*, for a tyrosyl-carboxylate ion hydrogen bond, it is zero at high and low pH, where the donor has lost its proton and where the acceptor has gained a proton, respectively. Only in the intermediate pH region, where the donor is in the form DH and the acceptor in the form A, does the side-chain hydrogen bond make a positive contribution to ΔF^0_H, which stabilizes the helical form of the protein against unfolding. Thus, the maximum stability of the native protein, *i.e.*, the maximum value of ΔF^0_H, will be at a pH intermediate between the pK's of the donor and acceptor groups. These pK's can therefore be determined from data on the pH-dependence of ΔF^0_{obs}, and the stabilizing side-chain groups can be identified.

These same considerations apply to the phenomenon of shrinkage in protein fibers. In fact, the shrinkage phenomenon is in a sense an experimental device to study denaturation. The reader is referred elsewhere to an analysis of experimental data on ribonuclease films and insulin fibers from the point of view presented here[14].

(b) Kinetics of protein denaturation[32]

Since the reversibility of relatively few denaturation reactions has been demonstrated, it is not surprising that most denaturation studies have been concerned with the kinetics of denaturation.

The transition-state theory is used and it will be assumed that the only barrier to the transition from the native to the activated state is the presence in the native state of several intramolecular hydrogen bonds between polar side-chain groups which must be simultaneously ruptured in the activated state. The first task then is to compute the equilibrium constant, $K^{\ddagger}$, for the formation of the activated complex from the native protein. A molecule qualifies as an activated complex if, after instantaneous equilibrium of the native protein with its environment (*i.e.*, pH, temperature, urea concentration, etc.), a specified number of side-chain hydrogen bonds are *simultaneously* broken while the helices remain intact. The concentration of such species will be very small, leading to a measurable rate of denaturation under appropriate conditions. In its simplest form, we may write the transition-state theory expression for the first order specific reaction rate constant, k_1, as

$$k_1 = \frac{kT}{h} K^{\ddagger} \tag{79}$$

where h is Planck's constant and k is Boltzmann's constant.

If activation required the rupture of only one side-chain hydrogen bond, then the value of $K^{\ddagger}$ would be

$$K^{\ddagger} = \frac{1 - x_{ij}}{x_{ij}} \tag{80}$$

for a heterologous single bond, with a corresponding expression in terms of x_{lm} for a homologous double bond. Eqn. (80) can be rewritten as

$$\frac{K^{\ddagger}}{1 + K^{\ddagger}} = 1 - x_{ij} \tag{81}$$

Since $K^{\ddagger}$ is very small for denaturation reactions which proceed at measurable rates we may replace $K^{\ddagger}/(1 + K^{\ddagger})$ by $K^{\ddagger}$ and write

$$K^{\ddagger} = 1 - x_{ij} \tag{82}$$

If activation requires the simultaneous rupture of n side-chain hydrogen bonds, then $K^{\ddagger}$ is given by

$$K^{\ddagger} = \Pi(1 - x_{ij}) \tag{83}$$

where the product is taken over the n bonds.

(i) pH-independent denaturation

If denaturation involves the rupture of side-chain hydrogen bonds in a pH region where the donors DH cannot dissociate protons and the acceptors A cannot associate protons, then the rate will be independent of pH. The expression for x_{ij} will be given by eqn. (43).

$$x_{ij} = \frac{K_{ij}}{1 + K_{ij}} \tag{84}$$

In this treatment there is essentially no difference in the pH-independent region between the expressions involving the constants K_{ij}, K_{lm}, K_{rs}, the only difference arising from their magnitude and the corresponding heat of formation. Combination of eqns. (79), (83) and (84) gives

$$k_1 = \frac{kT}{h} \Pi \left(\frac{1}{1 + K_{ij}} \right) \tag{85}$$

By analogy with eqns. (51), (52) and (53) we obtain

$$\Delta F^{\ddagger} = RT \, \Sigma \ln (1 + K_{ij}) \tag{86}$$

$$\Delta \Pi^{\ddagger} = - \Sigma \frac{K_{ij}}{1 + K_{ij}} \Delta H_{ij}^0 \tag{87}$$

$$\Delta S^{\ddagger} = - R \, \Sigma \ln (1 + K_{ij}) - \frac{1}{T} \Sigma \frac{K_{ij}}{1 + K_{ij}} \Delta H_{ij}^0 \tag{88}$$

These changes arise because of the rupture of the side-chain hydrogen bonds and the increased freedom of torsional oscillation of the side-chain groups in the activation process.

From eqn. (85) it can be seen that the rate will be slower, for a given K_{ij}, the larger the number of hydrogen bonds which must be ruptured in the activation process. This number can be computed by comparing experimental and theoretical values of $\Delta F^{\ddagger}$, $\Delta H^{\ddagger}$ and $\Delta S^{\ddagger}$.

(ii) pH-dependent denaturation

If the rupture of the side-chain hydrogen bonds occurs in a pH region in which the donors or acceptors can ionize, then the rate of denaturation will be pH-dependent.

For heterologous single bonds the expression for x_{ij} is given by eqn. (42). Hence, the rate constant is

$$k_1 = \frac{kT}{h} \Pi \left[\frac{1 + K_1/[\text{H}^+] + [\text{H}^+]/K_2}{1 + K_{ij} + K_1/[\text{H}^+] + [\text{H}^+]/K_2} \right] \tag{89}$$

assuming that the electrostatic factor w is the same for both the native protein and for the activated complex.

Since kinetic data are usually plotted as $\log k_1$ vs. pH, it is of interest to compute the slope.

$$\frac{d \log_{10} k_1}{d \text{ pH}} = - [\text{H}^+] \frac{d \ln k_1}{d[\text{H}^+]} = \Sigma \, x_{ij} \frac{K_1/[\text{H}^+] - [\text{H}^+]/K_2}{1 + K_1/[\text{H}^+] + [\text{H}^+]/K_2} = \Sigma \, q_{ij}^{\ddagger} \quad (90)$$

The quantity $\Sigma q_{ij}^{\ddagger}$ is the apparent order of the reaction with respect to hydrogen ion. If all the groups are equivalent $\Sigma q_{ij}^{\ddagger} = 0$ at

$$[\text{H}^+] = \sqrt{K_1 K_2} \quad (91)$$

i.e., the $\log k_1$ vs. pH curve will have a minimum at a pH given by eqn. (91). This equation is of some use in determining K_1 and K_2. At pH's other than that at which the minimum occurs, one or the other of the terms $K_1/[\text{H}^+]$ or $[\text{H}^+]/K_2$ will be the predominant one. Hence, eqn. (90) can be simplified to

$$\Sigma \, q_{ij}^{\ddagger} = - \Sigma \frac{K_{ij}}{1 + K_{ij} + [\text{H}^+]/K_2} \left(\frac{[\text{H}^+]/K_2}{1 + [\text{H}^+]/K_2} \right) \quad (92)$$

on the acid side of the minimum ($[\text{H}^+] \sim K_2$), and to

$$\Sigma \, q_{ij}^{\ddagger} = \Sigma \frac{K_{ij}}{1 + K_{ij} + K_1/[\text{H}^+]} \left(\frac{K_1/[\text{H}^+]}{1 + K_1/[\text{H}^+]} \right) \quad (93)$$

on the basic side ($[\text{H}^+] \sim K_1$). The slope, $\Sigma q_{ij}^{\ddagger}$ will be negative on the acid side and positive on the basic side. If the experimental slopes are fitted by these equations, and a value is assumed for K_{ij}, it is possible to identify K_1 and K_2 if all the groups are assumed to be equivalent.

The maxima in these slopes (i.e., the pH where the rate is most pH-dependent) are given by the following equations for n equivalent groups

$$[\text{H}^+]/K_2 = \sqrt{1 + K_{ij}} \quad (94)$$

$$K_1/[\text{H}^+] = \sqrt{1 + K_{ij}} \quad (95)$$

The value of the maximum slope is

$$(\Sigma \, q_{ij}^{\ddagger})_{\text{max}} = \pm \frac{n \, K_{ij}}{(1 + \sqrt{1 + K_{ij}})^2} \quad (96)$$

Eqns. (94), (95) and (96) provide additional equations for the determination of K_1, K_2 and K_{ij} for the side-chain hydrogen bonds involved in denaturation. While no accurate data are available to test these equations for the rupture of side-chain hydrogen bonds, they have been applied to the reverse process (the *formation* of hydrogen bonds in a protein association reaction), *i.e.*, eqns. (61)–(67).

The heat of activation is obtained by differentiation of $\ln k_1$ (from eqn. (89)) with respect to T at constant pH.

$$\Delta H^\ddagger = \Sigma \, x_{ij} \left[-\Delta H_{ij}^0 + \frac{(K_1/[\mathrm{H}^+]) \, (\Delta H_1^0) - ([\mathrm{H}^+]/K_2) \, (\Delta H_2^0)}{1 + K_1/[\mathrm{H}^+] + [\mathrm{H}^+]/K_2} \right] \quad (97)$$

The temperature coefficient of k_1 thus provides additional information about the nature of the side-chain groups involved in the activation process.

A similar treatment can be provided if the bonds involved are homologous double bonds. For this case the rate constant is given by

$$k_1 = \frac{kT}{h} \, \Pi \, (1 - x_{lm}) \quad (98)$$

where x_{lm} is given by

$$x_{lm} = \frac{K_{lm}}{1 + K_{lm} + 2 \, K_2/[\mathrm{H}^+] + (K_2/[\mathrm{H}^+])^2} \quad (99)$$

The calculation of $\Sigma q_{lm}^\ddagger$, $\Delta H^\ddagger$ etc. is straightforward.

Complex combinations of these and other types of hydrogen-bonding situations can occur. In such cases the plot of $\log k_1$ vs. pH may show more than one maximum and minimum. The application of the foregoing analysis to the kinetics of protein denaturation will require accurate data on slopes of the $\log k_1$ vs. pH plot.

From the theory presented in this section, it can be seen that studies of the pH-dependence of denaturation can provide valuable information for assessing the role of side-chain hydrogen bonding and the nature of the groups involved in the stabilization of the native protein.

7. Concluding remarks

A variety of protein reactions have been considered in this chapter. These have been discussed from the point of view of a specific model. If experiments are carried out, in which a protein undergoes these various reactions, then data will be available to test the model and also to provide information about specific interactions within the molecule. It is hoped that a knowledge of the location of such interactions will some day lead to the detailed configuration of a native protein in solution and to an understanding of its reactivity.

As already pointed out, side-chain hydrogen bonding is not the only kind of interaction in the tertiary structure. However, it is hoped that a detailed treatment of other types of interaction, *e.g.*, hydrophobic bonding, will be developed soon, so that these interactions can be incorporated into a more complete theory.

ADDENDUM

The writing of this section was completed in September 1960. Since then there have been several developments which are directly related to the material presented here. First of all, Lifson and Roig[46] have developed an elegant statistical mechanical theory of the helix-to-random coil transition in polypeptides. Secondly, the theory of side-chain interactions, presented in this section, has been extended further by inclusion of the effects of hydrophobic bonding[47-51]. Inclusion of these effects rationalizes the values[51] cited in eqns. (6), among other things.

REFERENCES

[1] K. U. LINDERSTRØM-LANG, *Lane Medical Lectures*, Stanford University Press, Stanford, Calif., 1952, p. 58.

[2] L. PAULING, R. B. COREY AND H. R. BRANSON, *Proc. Natl. Acad. Sci., U.S.*, 37 (1951) 205.

[3] R. B. COREY AND L. PAULING, *Proc. Roy. Soc. (London)*, B 141 (1953) 10.

[4] L. PAULING AND R. B. COREY, *Proc. Roy. Soc. (London)*, B 141 (1953) 21.

[5] P. J. FLORY, *Principles of Polymer Chemistry*, Cornell University Press, Ithaca, N.Y., 1953, pp. 399, 495.

[6] J. A. SCHELLMAN, *Compt. rend. trav. lab. Carlsberg, Sér. chim.*, 29 (1955) 223, 230.

[7] T. L. HILL, *J. Polymer Sci.*, 23 (1957) 549.

[8] J. A. SCHELLMAN, *J. Phys. Chem.*, 62 (1958) 1485.

[9] B. H. ZIMM AND J. K. BRAGG, *J. Chem. Phys.*, 28 (1958) 1246; 31 (1959) 5261.

[10] J. H. GIBBS AND E. A. DiMARZIO, *J. Chem. Phys.*, 28 (1958) 1247; 30 (1959) 271.

[11] L. PELLER, *J. Phys. Chem.*, 63 (1959) 1194, 1199.

[12] S. A. RICE AND A. WADA, *Abstracts of the 134th meeting of the Am. Chem. Soc.*, Chicago, Ill., Sept., 1958, 41 S.

[13] G. I. LOEB AND H. A. SCHERAGA, *J. Am. Chem. Soc.*, 84 (1962) 134.

[14] A. NAKAJIMA AND H. A. SCHERAGA, *J. Am. Chem. Soc.*, 83 (1961) 1575, 1585.

[15] W. KAUZMANN, *Advances in Protein Chem.*, 14 (1959) 1.

[16] I. M. KLOTZ, *Science*, 128 (1958) 815.

[17] I. M. KLOTZ, *Brookhaven Symposia in Biology*, 13 (1960).

[18] H. A. SCHERAGA AND G. NEMETHY, Discussion at end of ref. 17.

[19] G. NEMETHY AND H. A. SCHERAGA, *Abstracts of the 138th meeting of the Am. Chem. Soc.*, New York, N.Y., Sept., 1960, 4C.

[20] C. TANFORD AND J. G. KIRKWOOD, *J. Am. Chem. Soc.*, 79 (1957) 5333.

[21] M. LASKOWSKI JR. AND H. A. SCHERAGA, *J. Am. Chem. Soc.*, 76 (1954) 6305.

[22] J. M. STURTEVANT, M. LASKOWSKI JR., T. H. DONNELLY AND H. A. SCHERAGA, *J. Am. Chem. Soc.*, 77 (1955) 6168.

[23] M. LASKOWSKI JR. AND H. A. SCHERAGA, *J. Am. Chem. Soc.*, 78 (1956) 5793.

[24] G. I. LOEB AND H. A. SCHERAGA, *J. Phys. Chem.*, 60 (1956) 1633.

[25] H. A. SCHERAGA AND M. LASKOWSKI JR., *Advances in Protein Chem.*, 12 (1957) 1.

[26] S. EHRENPREIS, E. SULLIVAN AND H. A. SCHERAGA, *Abstracts of the 133rd meeting of the Am. Chem. Soc.*, San Francisco, Calif., April, 1958, 26C.

[27] M. LASKOWSKI JR., *Abstracts of the 134th meeting of the Am. Chem. Soc.*, Chicago, Ill., Sept., 1958, 51C.

[28] H. A. SCHERAGA, *Ann. Rev. Phys. Chem.*, 10 (1959) 191.

[29] M. LASKOWSKI JR., S. J. LEACH AND H. A. SCHERAGA, *J. Am. Chem. Soc.*, 82 (1960) 571.

[30] M. LASKOWSKI JR., S. EHRENPREIS, T. H. DONNELLY AND H. A. SCHERAGA, *J. Am. Chem. Soc.*, 82 (1960) 1340.

[31] H. A. SCHERAGA, *J. Phys. Chem.*, 64 (1961) 1917.

[32] M. LASKOWSKI JR. AND H. A. SCHERAGA, *J. Am. Chem. Soc.*, 83 (1961) 266.

[33] I. M. KLOTZ in H. NEURATH AND K. BAILEY (Eds.), *The Proteins*, Vol. Ib, Academic Press, New York, 1953, p. 727.

[34] K. LINDERSTRØM-LANG, *Compt. rend. trav. lab. Carlsberg*, 15 (1924) No. 7.

[35] C. TANFORD, S. A. SWANSON AND W. S. SHORE, *J. Am. Chem. Soc.*, 77 (1955) 6414.

[36] N. M. GREEN AND H. NEURATH in H. NEURATH AND K. BAILEY (Eds.), *The Proteins*, Vol. IIb, Academic Press, New York, 1954, p. 1057.

[37] A. DOBRY, J. S. FRUTON AND J. M. STURTEVANT, *J. Biol. Chem.*, 195 (1952) 149.

[28] F. M. RICHARDS, *Federation Proc.*, 17 (1958) 296.

[39] C. H. W. HIRS, S. MOORE AND W. H. STEIN, *J. Biol. Chem.*, 235 (1960) 633.

[40] A. TISELIUS AND I. B. ERIKSSON-QUENSEL, *Biochem. J.*, 33 (1939) 1752.

[41] E. MIHALYI, *J. Biol. Chem.*, 209 (1954) 723, 733.

[42] H. A. SCHERAGA, *Ann. N.Y. Acad. Sci.*, 75 (1958) 189.

[43] F. W. PUTNAM in H. NEURATH AND K. BAILEY (Eds.), *The Proteins*, Vol. Ib, Academic Press, New York, 1953, p. 807.

[44] J. HERMANS JR. AND H. A. SCHERAGA, *J. Am. Chem. Soc.*, 83 (1961) 3283, 3293.
[45] P. J. FLORY, *J. Am. Chem. Soc.*, 7 (1956) 5222.
[46] S. LIFSON AND A. ROIG, *J. Chem. Phys.*, 34 (1961) 1963.
[47] H. A. SCHERAGA, *J. Phys. Chem.*, 65 (1961) 1071.
[48] C. TANFORD, *Physical Chemistry of Macromolecules*, John Wiley, New York, 1961, p. 129.
[49] G. NEMETHY AND H. A. SCHERAGA, *J. Chem. Phys.*, 36 (1962) 3382, 3401; *J. Phys. Chem.*, in the press.
[50] H. A. SCHERAGA, G. NEMETHY AND I. Z. STEINBERG, *J. Biol. Chem.*, 237 (1962) 2506.
[51] G. NEMETHY, I. Z. STEINBERG AND H. A. SCHERAGA, *Abstracts of the 142nd meeting of the Am. Chem. Soc., Atlantic City, N.J., Sept. 1962*, 58C. *J. Polymer Sci.*, in the press.

Chapter V

Thermodynamic Properties of Proteins Found
From Osmotic Experiments

ROBERT L. BALDWIN

*Department of Biochemistry, Stanford University Medical Center,
Palo Alto, Calif. (U.S.A.)*

In studying the chemistry of simple molecules, thermodynamic properties are used in several ways: to correlate different experiments, to test models for molecular behavior, and to aid in characterizing unknown substances. The protein chemist usually is interested in the last of these. For example, he wants to know the molecular weight of a protein, which is a thermo-dynamic property. As the number of thermodynamic experiments which he uses becomes larger, the protein chemist becomes more interested in properties such as activity coefficients and partial specific volumes which are useful chiefly in correlating these experiments.

In this chapter we will discuss the thermodynamic properties which are found from osmotic experiments. In such experiments, a protein solution is placed on one side of a semi-permeable membrane and solvent on the other; equilibrium is reached by osmosis, which is the movement of small molecules through the membrane*. Essentially the complete theory of osmotic measurements can be found in the classic article of Scatchard[2]. The theory, together with other aspects of osmotic pressure measurements, is the subject of a very clear and informative discussion by Edsall[3].

A diagrammatic sketch of an osmotic pressure experiment is shown in Fig. 1. It is based on the the apparatus used by Güntelberg and Linderstrøm-Lang[4] but has been simplified for the purposes of discussion. A layer of protein solution is placed inside a thistle tube, closed at the bottom with a semi-permeable membrane, and the tube is filled with toluene. The dialysis membrane (which sometimes is made of collodion but often is a commercial

---

Analogous experiments can be made without the use of membranes when the solvent passes from one liquid phase to another by evaporation and condensation: see the "isopiestic method" and the "porous-disc osmometer" in Robinson and Stokes[1].

cellulose tubing) is supported by a stainless steel plate, with many holes cut into it, and this plate also fastens the membrane to the thistle tube. The osmotic pressure is *defined* to be the difference in hydrostatic pressure, at equilibrium, on the two sides of the membrane. It is measured either from the height to which liquid rises in the thistle tube (corrected for capillary

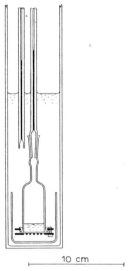

10 cm

Fig. 1. Diagram of an apparatus used to measure osmotic pressures of protein solutions (see text): from Güntelberg and Linderstrøm-Lang[4]. The purpose of the isolated glass tubing (above, left) is to emphasize that a correction must be made for the capillary rise.

rise[5]) or by using a manometer to find that pressure which prevents flow of liquid across the membrane. For the latter, "dynamic" measurement, the protein solution must first be dialyzed to equilibrium against the buffer solution.

Many different types of osmometers have been described; one might mention those of Güntelberg and Linderstrøm-Lang[4], Smithies[6], and Rowe and Abrams[7], who worked with proteins and who studied the precision of their results. The classic early work of Adair[8] deserves study. The protein concentration usually is found with a differential refractometer[9-11] or by determining nitrogen or the light absorbed near 280 mμ.

1. Fundamental equations

Osmotic equilibrium is one type of equilibrium between phases: the protein solution inside the osmometer is one phase and the "solvent" outside is the other. The theory of equilibria between phases was worked out by Gibbs[12]; it follows directly from his formulation of the first two laws of thermodynamics. A fundamental result of the theory is that, neglecting external fields, the *chemical potential* of any component which can pass from one phase to another has the same value in both phases.

$$\mu_k^\alpha = \mu_k^\beta \tag{1}$$

Here μ is Gibbs' symbol for the chemical potential*, the superscripts α and β refer to the phases (β will be used for the protein solution, α for the phase without protein), and the subscript k refers to the component.

The word "component" requires special definition when it is used in thermodynamics. A component is a substance, or combination of substances, which can be added *by itself* to a phase: thus NaCl may be a component but chloride ion may not, because one can handle only electrically neutral substances. After listing all the substances in a solution, one has considerable freedom in choosing the components. However, when appropriate amounts of these components are added up, one must obtain exactly the contents of the solution. In order to find the molecular weight of a component by a thermodynamic method, one must be able to measure the amount (*e.g.* dry weight) of this component.

Proteins exist in solution as ions and an ion cannot be chosen as a component unless its net charge is zero. Consequently in choosing components some combination of counter-ions must be added to make an electrically neutral component. Often the equations can be made simpler in form by a special choice of components[2,14] but it may be difficult to measure the amounts and properties of these components without additional information such as the charge carried by the protein. We will use here the simple choice of components in which a single type of counter-ion is added in amount sufficient to neutralize the charge of the protein ion.

The chemical potential per mole of an ion, or of a non-ionizing molecule, is related to its concentration by[1,15]

$$\mu_i = \mu_i^0 + RT \ln \gamma_i m_i \tag{2}$$

where R is the gas constant ($8.314 \cdot 10^7$ ergs deg^{-1} mole^{-1}), T is the absolute temperature, m_i is the number of moles of i per 1000 g solvent, μ_i^0 is a reference potential which depends only on temperature and pressure, and γ_i is the activity coefficient of i on the molal concentration scale. The activity

---

* The chemical potential is called the partial molal free energy by Lewis and Randall[13] who use for it the symbol $\bar{F}_k$.

coefficient, which depends on temperature, pressure, and the concentration of each solute, can always be made to approach 1 as the concentration of every solute approaches zero*.

$$\lim_{\substack{m_i \to 0 \\ m_k \to 0}} \gamma_i = 1 \tag{3}$$

The chemical potential of a neutral component is simply the sum of the chemical potentials of its ions[1,15].

$$\mu_{PX_z} = \mu_P + z\mu_X \tag{4}$$

$$\mu_{PX_z} = \mu_{PX_z}^0 + RT \ln (\gamma_P m_P) (\gamma_X m_X)^z \tag{4a}$$

If the molecular weight of i is unknown, then m_i also is unknown; consequently we will need an additional concentration scale, w, which gives the weight of solute per 1000 g solvent. Two standard thermodynamic results[13,16] will be needed. One is the Gibbs-Duhem relation

$$\sum_{i=0}^{s} n_i \, d\mu_i = V' \, dP - S' \, dT \tag{5}$$

in which n_i is the number of moles of i in the volume V', with entropy S', and the number of components is $s + 1$, the solvent being labeled zero. The other equation gives the variation of chemical potential with pressure.

$$\left(\frac{\partial \mu_i}{\partial P} \right)_{T,m} = M_i \bar{v}_i = \left(\frac{\partial V'}{\partial n_i} \right)_{T,P} \tag{6}$$

In this equation M_i is the molecular weight of i, $\bar{v}_i$ is its partial specific volume (ml per g) and the subscripts T,m mean that these quantities are held constant in taking the partial derivatives. Subscripts will often be omitted once a particular derivative has been introduced.

The theory for osmotic equilibrium is simplified considerably[4,17] by the following experimental arrangement. The osmotic pressure is measured in a series of experiments in which the protein concentration is varied but the temperature, pressure and composition of the phase without protein are held constant. Experimentally this may be accomplished by making the volume of the protein phase small compared to that of the other phase. Thus, for any dialyzable component, the chemical potential does not vary from one experiment to the next in either phase (see eqn. 1).

---

* This requirement fixes the value of the reference potential.

We will write equations for the β (or protein) phase, because this is the phase in which the pressure varies.

$$d\mu_k = 0 = \left(\frac{\partial \mu_k}{\partial P}\right)_{T,m} dP + \sum_{i=1}^{s} \left(\frac{\partial \mu_k}{\partial m_i}\right)_{T,P,m} dm_i \quad (k = \text{dialyzable}) \quad (7)$$

To find the osmotic pressure we will apply this relation to the solvent (component o) and use the Gibbs-Duhem relation to express $\partial\mu_o/\partial m_i$ in terms of the s independent derivatives of chemical potential.

$$\left(\frac{\partial \mu_0}{\partial m_i}\right)_{T,P,m} = -\left(\frac{M_0}{1000}\right) \sum_{j=1}^{s} m_j \left(\frac{\partial \mu_j}{\partial m_i}\right)_{T,P,m} \quad (8)$$

Substitution of this relation into eqn. (7), for $k = $ component o, gives

$$d\pi = \left(\frac{1}{1000 \, \bar{v}_o}\right) \sum_{i=1}^{s} \sum_{j=1}^{s} m_j \frac{\partial \mu_j}{\partial m_i} dm_i \quad (9)$$

where π is the osmotic pressure, $P^\beta - P^\alpha$. The dialyzable components can be eliminated from the summation by means of eqn. (7): we will number the non-dialyzable components $1, \ldots, q$ and the dialyzable ones $(q + 1)$, $\ldots, s$. The result is a basic differential equation for the osmotic pressure.

$$V \, d\pi = \sum_{i=1}^{s} \sum_{j=1}^{q} m_j \frac{\partial \mu_j}{\partial m_i} dm_i \quad (10)$$

V is the volume of solution containing 1000 g solvent plus corresponding amounts of the other dialyzable components.

$$V = 1000 \, \bar{v}_o + \sum_{k=q+1}^{s} m_k M_k \bar{v}_k \quad (k = \text{dialyzable}) \quad (11)$$

In the following sections eqn. (10) will be evaluated for various cases, to show the effects of a net charge carried by the protein, the consequences of using a mixed solvent, and so forth.

2. Measurement of molecular weights

As a starting point, consider the case in which the protein component PX_z is dissolved in water. This is a two-component system ($s = 1$) since the protein is supposed homogeneous. Eqn. (10) reduces, for this case, to

$$\frac{d\pi}{dm_1} = \left(\frac{1}{1000 \, \bar{v}_o} \right) m_1 \frac{\partial \mu_1}{\partial m_1} \tag{12}$$

The chemical potential of the protein component may be written (see eqn. 4a) as

$$\mu_1 = \mu_1^0 + (z + 1) \, RT \ln m_1 \gamma_1 \tag{13}$$

$$\gamma_1^{z+1} = \gamma_P \gamma_X^z \tag{13a}$$

$$m_1 = m_P = (m_x)/z \tag{13b}$$

Thus eqn. (12) becomes

$$\frac{d\pi}{dm_1} = \frac{(z + 1) \, RT}{1000 \, \bar{v}_o} \left(1 + m_1 \frac{\partial \ln \gamma_1}{\partial m_1} \right) \tag{14}$$

or, on the w scale of concentration,

$$\frac{d\pi}{dw_1} = \left(\frac{z + 1}{M_1} \right) \left(\frac{RT}{1000 \, \bar{v}_o} \right) \left(1 + w_1 \frac{\partial \ln \gamma_1}{\partial w_1} \right) \tag{14a}$$

Eqn. (14) reveals one of the critical problems in measuring molecular weights of proteins: using a system of two components, protein and water, one obtains not the molecular weight of the protein component but the ratio $M_1/(z + 1)$. The number of counter-ions, z, which is determined by the net charge on the protein, is difficult to measure with the accuracy needed to find M_1 by eqn. (14a). This problem can be side-stepped by adding a salt, often referred to as "swamping electrolyte". Thus we are led to a discussion of the measurement of molecular weights in a three-component system ($s = 2$).

Let the three components be: $0 = $ solvent, $1 = PX_z$, $2 = BX$, where BX is the additional salt. Both 1 and 2 are assumed to be completely dissociated. Eqn. (10) gives

$$V \frac{d\pi}{dm_1} = m_1 \frac{\partial \mu_1}{\partial m_1} + m_1 \frac{\partial \mu_1}{\partial m_2} \frac{dm_2}{dm_1} \tag{15}$$

Although the chemical potential of component 2 is constant, its concentration in the protein phase can vary with the protein concentration (see the section on study of interaction). The derivative dm_2/dm_1 may be expressed by eqn. (7), with $k = 2$.

$$\frac{dm_2}{dm_1} = - \left(\frac{\partial \mu_2}{\partial m_1} + M_2 \bar{v}_2 \frac{dP}{dm_1} \right) \Big/ \left(\frac{\partial \mu_2}{\partial m_2} \right) \tag{16}$$

Substitution of this into eqn. (15) gives

$$\frac{d\pi}{dm_1} = \frac{m_1 \dfrac{\partial \mu_1}{\partial m_1} + m_1 \Gamma \dfrac{\partial \mu_1}{\partial m_2}}{V \left[1 - m_1 \left(\Gamma M_2 \bar{v}_2 / V \right) \right]} \tag{17}$$

$$\Gamma = - \left(\frac{\partial \mu_2}{\partial m_1} \right)_{T,P,m_2} \Big/ \left(\frac{\partial \mu_2}{\partial m_2} \right)_{T,P,m_1} \tag{17a}$$

In order to evaluate the derivatives of chemical potential which appear here, we make use of eqn. (4a) and note that

$$m_P = m_1 \tag{18a}$$

$$m_B = m_2 \tag{18b}$$

$$m_X = zm_1 + m_2 \tag{18c}$$

Consequently the chemical potentials of the neutral components are

$$\mu_1 = \mu_1^0 + RT \ln (m_1) (zm_1 + m_2)^z + (z + 1)RT \ln \gamma_1 \tag{19}$$

$$\mu_2 = \mu_2^0 + RT \ln (m_2) (zm_1 + m_2) + 2 RT \ln \gamma_2 \tag{20}$$

where γ_1 is still defined by eqn. (13a) and γ_2 by

$$\gamma_2^2 = \gamma_B \gamma_X \tag{20a}$$

When the derivatives in eqn. (17) are evaluated in this way, the resulting equation for the osmotic pressure is

$$\frac{d\pi}{dm_1} = \frac{RT}{V} [1 + 2 BM_1 m_1 + o (m_1^2)] \tag{21}$$

or, on the w scale,

$$\frac{d\pi}{dw_1} = \frac{RT}{M_1 V} [1 + 2 Bw_1 + o (w_1^2)] \tag{21a}$$

where B is the second virial coefficient, which will be discussed in the next section. The notation $o(w_1^2)$ means that terms of order w_1^2 and higher have been omitted. Integration of eqn. (21a) is straightforward.

$$\frac{\pi}{w_1} = \frac{RT}{M_1 V}\left[1 + Bw_1 + o\,(w_1^2)\right] \tag{22}$$

Eqn. (22) shows that, by adding a salt, one now obtains M_1 rather than $M_1/(z + 1)$ from the value of (π/w_1) at $w_1 = 0$. One would guess that it must make a difference how much salt is added: it seems unlikely that adding only a trace of salt could accomplish this valuable result. The expression for B, in the next section, shows that it is the slope of (π/w) vs. w which changes as the concentration of salt is varied.

The answer to another important question also is contained in eqn. (22): is the value of π/w at $w = 0$ (which gives the molecular weight) influenced by a preferential interaction of the protein with one of the two small molecules present? The answer clearly is no, and one might suppose that this is never a problem. However, one usually has to measure Γ (eqn. 17a) in order to find M: compare the theory for light scattering[18,19] or equilibrium sedimentation[20].

Γ is likely to be significant whenever a mixed solvent is used in which the amounts of the two components are comparable: for example, when concentrated solutions of urea or guanidine are used to dissociate a protein into subunits (see the early work of Burk and Greenberg[21]). However, by using osmotic pressure, rather than light scattering or sedimentation, one need not measure Γ. Fig. 2 shows the results of a study by Kupke and Linderstrøm-Lang[22] on the minimum molecular weight of insulin dissolved

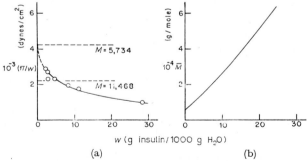

Fig. 2. The study of an associating system by osmotic pressure: data of Kupke and Linderstrøm-Lang[22] for the minimum molecular weight of insulin in 6 molal guanidine hydrochloride. On the left the ratio of osmotic pressure to concentration is plotted against concentration. On the right the apparent weight-average molecular weight is shown as a function of concentration (see eqn. 37).

in 6 molal guanidine hydrochloride. At the time of their study it was not certain whether the monomer of beef insulin has a molecular weight of 5,734 or 11,468. Their results confirm the conclusion of Harfenist and Craig[23] that the correct value is near 6,000. Calculation of the average molecular weight at each concentration (Fig. 2b) is discussed in the section on study of interaction.

Protein preparations often are heterogeneous, either because of difficulties in fractionation or because the protein aggregates on storage. One should ask, then, what type of average molecular weight is obtained from measurements of osmotic pressure. To answer this question we will suppose, for simplicity, that we have a system of q non-ionizing macromolecules plus a solvent (component o). Let the total concentration be $\bar{w}$

$$\bar{w} = \sum_{i=1}^{q} w_i \tag{23a}$$

and the weight fraction of solute i be f_i.

$$f_i = w_i/\bar{w} \tag{23b}$$

Then eqn. (10) becomes

$$\frac{d\pi}{dw} = \left(\frac{1}{M_n}\right)\left(\frac{RT}{1000\ \bar{v}_o}\right)[1 + 2\ \bar{B}\bar{w} + o\ (\bar{w}^2)] \tag{24}$$

where $\bar{B}$ is discussed in the next section and M_n is given by

$$\left(\frac{1}{M_n}\right) = \sum_{i=1}^{q} \frac{f_i}{M_i} = \sum_{i=1}^{q} n_i \Big/ \sum_{i=1}^{q} n_i M_i \tag{25}$$

M_n is called the *number-average* molecular weight because, in taking the average, the molecular weight of each species is weighted by the number of molecules of that kind, divided by the total number. Light scattering and equilibrium sedimentation yield *weight-average* molecular weights (M_w) in which the molecular weight of each species is weighted by its weight fraction f_i; other averages can also be found. The difference between a number and weight average can be very large: for a mixture of two proteins with molecular weights of 10,000 and 100,000, present in equal amounts by weight, $M_n = 18,000$ while $M_w = 55,000$.

3. Properties of the second virial coefficient

The coefficient B, which is measured from the initial slope of (π/w) against w, is referred to as the second virial coefficient. The name is taken by analogy from the virial equation of state for a gas, in which the pressure is written as a power series in the density of the gas. From the point of view of finding molecular weights, the magnitude of B is important because it determines how close to $w = 0$ the measurements of π must be made for a safe extrapolation of (π/w) to $w = 0$. From another point of view B is of interest because it contains information about the activity coefficient of the solute, and can be used in correlating different experiments.

The second virial coefficient contains not the activity coefficients themselves but certain derivatives which we will abbreviate, in Scatchard's notation[2] as β_{ik}.

$$\beta_{ik} = v_i \left(\frac{\partial \ln \gamma_i}{\partial m_k} \right)_{T,P,m} \tag{26}$$

Here v_i is the number of ions contained in a molecule of i. For protein components* the β_{ik} usually can be treated as constants and then $\ln \gamma_i$ is given by

$$v_i \ln \gamma_i = \sum_{k=1}^{s} m_k \beta_{ik} + o\,(m^2) \tag{27}$$

since $\ln \gamma_i = 0$ at zero concentration of all solutes (see eqn. 3).

When there are only two components, β_{11} alone determines the dependence of π/w on w (see eqn. 14). For the three-component system (eqn. 22) B contains several terms**.

$$B = [2\,M_1(2 + m_2\beta_{22})]^{-1}\,[z^2\,(\beta_{22} + 1/m_2)$$
$$+ \beta_{11}(2 + m_2\beta_{22}) - \beta_{12}(2\,z + m_2\beta_{12})$$
$$- (M_2\bar{v}_2/V)\,(z + m_2\beta_{12})] \tag{28}$$

One can see from this equation that: (1) even when the activity coefficient of the protein is constant (i.e. $\beta_{11}, \beta_{12} = 0$), B is not zero — in fact, the term in z^2 can be quite large; (2) when z is zero, B depends not only on β_{11} but also on β_{12}.

Fig. 3 shows the data of Scatchard et al.[24] for the variation of B with z,

---

* In the case of the three-component system discussed above, β_{22} is not independent of the salt concentration m_2, and β_{22} (as well as m_2) in the expression for B should be evaluated at m_2^a, which does not vary with m_1.
** This equation may be derived from Scatchard's[2] eqn. (35), for which the components are $1' = PX_z - (z/2)BX$, $2' = BX$, by noting that he has omitted the term in $(M_2\,\bar{v}_2/V)$, which is small, and that $\beta'_{11} = \beta_{11} - z\beta_{12} + (z^2/4)\beta_{22}$, $\beta'_{12} = \beta_{12} - (z/2)\beta_{22}$, and $\beta'_{22} = \beta_{22}$. Here z is the number of counter-ions X needed to neutralize the charge carried by P, and the primes refer to Scatchard's choice of components. Note that $m'_1 = m_1$ but $m'_2 = m_2 + (z/2)m_1$, and that the numbering of his components differs from this.

for bovine plasma albumin dissolved in 0.15 molal sodium chloride. The
dashed line shows the curve predicted by eqn. (28) if β_{11} and β_{12} are zero;
in order to make z vary, the pH, and hence the number of protons bound,

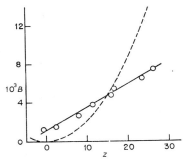

Fig. 3. The result of Scatchard *et al.*[24] for the second virial coefficient of bovine plasma
albumin in 0.15 molal NaCl, at various pH's. The dashed line shows the values of B
predicted from z (eqn. 28) when the activity coefficient of the protein is constant; z,
which is numerically equal to the charge carried by the protein, was calculated from the
electrophoretic data of Alberty[25]. See eqn. (22) for the computation of B from osmotic
pressure results.

was varied*. Note that, even at this high salt concentration, the value of B
is determined chiefly by the charge on the protein and that the minimum
occurs at $z = 0$.

The value of B at $z = 0$ is small compared to the values which are found
for synthetic polymers, and this is true generally of the "globular" proteins.
This result is predicted by theory[17,28]. For a solute which does not ionize
and which is dissolved in a solvent of only one component, Zimm[28] predicts
the following values for π when the solute is a compact sphere

$$\frac{\pi}{c_1} = \frac{RT}{M_1}(1 + 4\,\bar{v}_1 c_1) \tag{29}$$

and for long, cylindrical rods (or even for flexible polymers whose diameter
is large compared to the solvent)

---

* These values of z were computed from the electrophoretic data of Alberty[25] by
using the conversion factor $\Delta u/\Delta z$ of Longsworth and Jacobsen[26] who measured it from
the graph of electrophoretic mobility u against the number of protons bound. Their
electrophoretic studies were made in an acetate buffer where the binding of ions other
than protons is believed to be small. They found $\Delta u/\Delta z$ to be $0.20 \cdot 10^{-5}$ at 0.10 ionic
strength; at the ionic strength (0.15) used by Alberty $\Delta u/\Delta z$ should then be $0.17 \cdot 10^{-5}$,
according to Henry's theory[27] for the variation of u with ionic strength. The advantage
of using u to find z is that one can take account of the strong binding of chloride ions
by bovine albumin. The calculation would be more accurate if the electrophoretic and
osmotic experiments had not been made at different temperatures (*ca.* 5° and 25°,
respectively).

$$\frac{\pi}{c_1} = \frac{RT}{M_1} [1 + (l/d)\bar{v}_1 c_1] \tag{30}$$

Here l is the length and d the diameter of the rod, and the concentration scale used in eqns. (29) and (30) is: $c_1 = $ g of 1 per ml of solution. One can see from Fig. 3 that the value of B at $z = 0$ is less than that predicted for compact spheres; however, the theory is not strictly applicable because the "solvent" contains two components (NaCl, H_2O). Myosin, which is believed to be a rod-shaped molecule[29], shows a large dependence of (π/c) on concentration[30], and the slope is predicted rather well[29] by the dimensions of the molecule and eqn. (30).

For a heterogeneous system (see eqn. 24) the average virial coefficient $\bar{B}$ is given by

$$\bar{B} = \left(\frac{1}{2}\right) \sum_{i=1}^{q} \sum_{k=1}^{q} f_i f_k \left(\frac{M_n}{M_k}\right) \left(\frac{\partial \ln \gamma_k}{\partial w_i}\right)_0 \tag{31}$$

where the derivatives $(\partial \ln \gamma_k / \partial w_i)_0$ are evaluated at zero concentration of all solutes, and the f_i are weight fractions defined by eqn. (23b). This is a different average for B than the one given by light scattering[18] or equilibrium sedimentation[31].

4. The study of interaction

In Fig. 2a the downward curving plot of (π/w) against w suggests that the insulin polymerizes to an extent dependent on concentration, even in 6 molal guanidine hydrochloride. If this were merely an effect of charge or varying activity coefficients one would expect (π/w) to increase, and in a linear manner (see eqn. 22). The question arises, how can osmotic pressure results be used to determine the average degree of polymerization at a given concentration?

We will consider the case of monomer in equilibrium with dimer, trimer,... $(q - 1)$mer (cf. refs. 4,32). The molecular weight of i-mer is iM_1 where 1 stands for monomer. The equations take a simple form when the association equilibria are written

$$w_i = K_i w_1^i \tag{32}$$

Thus the total concentration is

$$\bar{w} = \sum_{i=1}^{q} K_i w_1^i \tag{32a}$$

K_i is the product of the thermodynamic equilibrium constant K_i', which does not vary with concentration, and a ratio of activity coefficients which may vary.

$$K_i = K_i' \gamma_1^i / \gamma_i \tag{33}$$

In general one must make some non-thermodynamic assumption in order to measure association. If

$$\left(\frac{\partial \ln \gamma_i}{\partial \bar{w}}\right)_{T,P} = i \left(\frac{\partial \ln \gamma_1}{\partial \bar{w}}\right)_{T,P} \tag{34}$$

then K_i is independent of concentration even though the individual activity coefficients vary. With the use of this assumption, the basic equation for osmotic pressure becomes

$$\frac{d\pi}{dw_1} = \left(\frac{RT}{1000 \, \bar{v}_0}\right)\left(\frac{1}{M_1}\right) \sum_{i=1}^{q} \frac{w_i}{w_1}\left[1 + i \frac{\partial \ln \gamma_1}{\partial \bar{w}} \bar{w} \frac{\partial \bar{w}}{\partial w_i}\right] \tag{35}$$

It follows from eqn. (32) that

$$\frac{\partial \bar{w}}{\partial w_i} = \frac{1}{iw_i} \sum_{k=1}^{q} kw_k \tag{36}$$

so that eqn. (35) reduces to

$$\frac{d\pi}{d\bar{w}} = \left(\frac{RT}{1000 \, \bar{v}_0}\right)\left(\frac{1}{\bar{M}}\right)\left[1 + \bar{w}\left(\frac{\bar{M}}{M_1}\right)\frac{\partial \ln \gamma_1}{\partial \bar{w}}\right] \tag{37}$$

where $\bar{M}$ is the weight-average molecular weight at the concentration $\bar{w}$.

$$\bar{M}(\bar{w}) = \sum_{i=1}^{q} M_i(w_i/\bar{w}) \tag{38}$$

It can be shown from eqns. (32) and (38) that $\bar{M}$ approaches M_1 in the limit as $\bar{w}$ approaches zero.

Thus the slope $d\pi/d\bar{w}$ bears a simple relation to the average molecular weight but the expression for $(\pi/\bar{w})$ is quite complex. Comparison of Fig. 2a with 2b shows that $(\pi/\bar{w})$ gives an apparent molecular weight which is very different from $\bar{M}$. Note that one must still make an assumption about $\partial \ln \gamma_1/\partial \bar{w}$ to find $\bar{M}^*$. Computation of the various equilibrium constants from the curve of $\bar{M}$ vs. $\bar{w}$ is discussed by Steiner[32].

Osmotic measurements are widely used to study the preferential interaction of a protein with a small molecule. In fact the literature in this field is vast, and there is not space to review the subject here. Excellent discussions

---

* Fig. 2b was obtained by drawing a smooth curve through the experimental points[22] for π vs. $\bar{w}$, differentiating by graphical means to find $d\pi/d\bar{w}$, and then calculating $\bar{M}$ from eqn. (37) with $\delta \ln \gamma_1/\delta \bar{w} = 0$.

of the measurement and interpretation of binding can be found in chapters by Edsall and Wyman[33] and Klotz[34].

Whether or not specific binding occurs, the parameter Γ can be used to measure preferential interaction of the protein with a small molecule. As pointed out above, Γ is needed in finding molecular weights by light scattering or equilibrium sedimentation. The term preferential is used because Γ is zero when the ratio of solvent to component 2 remains the same on both sides of the membrane. Neglecting the small term in dP/dm_1, Γ can be measured from eqn. (16).

$$\Gamma \cong \frac{dm_2}{dm_1} \tag{39}$$

This derivative is found from the slope of the plot of $m_2{}^\beta$ vs. $m_1{}^\beta$, when $m_2{}^\alpha$ remains constant. Although it is said to measure preferential interaction, Γ need not be zero even when the activity coefficient of the protein is unaffected by the small molecule. Eqns. (17a) and (20) show that, for the three-component system discussed here,

$$\Gamma = -\left(\frac{z + m_2\beta_{21}}{2 + m_2\beta_{22}}\right) + o\,(m_1) \tag{40}$$

and so the charge carried by the protein contributes to Γ.

When the interaction is believed to be stoichiometric, the term "binding" is used to describe it and eqns. (1)–(4) to measure it. Thus if component 2 is a non-ionizing small molecule, the ratio of its concentrations in the two phases is given by

$$\frac{m_2^\beta}{m_2^\alpha} = \frac{\gamma_2^\alpha}{\gamma_2^\beta} \tag{41}$$

where the small dependence of reference potential on pressure has been omitted. Again some assumption about activity coefficients must be made. Usually the activity coefficient of the unbound small molecule is set equal in the two phases, and the activity coefficient of the bound molecule is said to be zero; then it follows from eqn. (41) that m_2 (bound) equals $m_2{}^\beta - m_2{}^\alpha$.

When it comes to the binding of ions, the situation is more complex. According to eqns. (1), (4a) and (18), for the three-component system discussed here,

$$\frac{m_B^\beta}{m_B^\alpha} = 1 - \frac{zm_P}{2m_B^\alpha} + o\,(m_P^2) \tag{42}$$

even when there is no binding and $\gamma_2^{\alpha} = \gamma_2^{\beta}$: this is the Gibbs–Donnan equilibrium. In addition Overbeek[35] has shown that the activity coefficient of an ion will be different in the two phases with and without protein for purely electrostatic reasons. Consequently, in order to diminish charge effects, it is wise to measure the binding of ions in the presence of another salt but this also raises certain problems: cf. Edsall and Wyman[33].

REFERENCES

1 R. A. Robinson and R. H. Stokes, *Electrolyte Solutions*, Butterworths, London, 1955.
2 G. Scatchard, *J. Am. Chem. Soc.*, 68 (1946) 2315.
3 J. T. Edsall in H. Neurath and K. Bailey (Eds.), *The Proteins*, Vol. IB, Academic Press, New York, 1953.
4 A. V. Güntelberg and K. Linderstrøm-Lang, *Compt. rend. trav. lab. Carlsberg, Sér. chim.*, 27 (1949) 1.
5 S. Glasstone, *Textbook of Physical Chemistry*, Van Nostrand, New York, 1946.
6 O. Smithies, *Biochem. J.*, 55 (1953) 57.
7 D. S. Rowe and M. E. Abrams, *Biochem. J.*, 67 (1957) 431.
8 G. S. Adair, *Proc. Roy. Soc. (London), A*, 108 (1925) 627; 109 (1925) 292.
9 L. G. Longsworth, *Ind. Eng. Chem., Anal. Ed.*, 18 (1946) 219.
10 R. Cecil and A. G. Ogston, *J. Sci. Instr.*, 28 (1951) 253.
11 H. Svensson, *J. Opt. Soc. Am.*, 44 (1954) 140.
12 J. W. Gibbs, *The Collected Works of J. Willard Gibbs*, Yale University Press, New Haven, Conn., 1948.
13 G. N. Lewis and M. Randall, *Thermodynamics*, McGraw-Hill, New York, 1923.
14 E. F. Casassa and H. Eisenberg, *J. Phys. Chem.*, 64 (1960) 753.
15 H. S. Harned and B. B. Owen, *The Physical Chemistry of Electrolytic Solutions*, Reinhold, New York, 1958.
16 K. G. Denbigh, *The Principles of Chemical Equilibrium*, Cambridge University Press, 1955.
17 L. Onsager, *Ann. N.Y. Acad. Sci.*, 51 (1949) 627 (see p. 628).
18 J. G. Kirkwood and R. J. Goldberg, *J. Chem. Phys.*, 18 (1950) 54.
19 W. H. Stockmayer, *J. Chem. Phys.*, 18 (1950) 58.
20 J. W. Williams, K. E. Van Holde, R. L. Baldwin and H. Fujita, *Chem. Rev.*, 58 (1958) 715.
21 N. F. Burk and D. M. Greenberg, *J. Biol. Chem.*, 87 (1930) 197.
22 D. W. Kupke and K. Linderstrøm-Lang, *Biochim. Biophys. Acta*, 13 (1954) 153.
23 E. J. Harfenist and L. C. Craig, *J. Am. Chem. Soc.*, 74 (1952) 3087.
24 G. Scatchard, A. C. Batchelder and A. Brown, *J. Am. Chem. Soc.*, 68 (1946) 2320.
25 R. A. Alberty, *J. Phys. Chem.*, 53 (1949) 114.
26 L. G. Longsworth and C. F. Jacobsen, *J. Phys. Chem.*, 53 (1949) 126.
27 D. C. Henry, *Proc. Roy. Soc. (London), A*, 133 (1931) 106.
28 B. H. Zimm, *J. Chem. Phys.*, 14 (1946) 164.
29 W. W. Kielley and W. F. Harrington, *Biochim. Biophys. Acta*, 41 (1960) 402.
30 H. Portzehl, *Z. Naturforsch. Pt. b*, 5 (1950) 75.
31 H. Fujita, *J. Phys. Chem.*, 63 (1959) 1326.
32 R. F. Steiner, *Arch. Biochem. Biophys.*, 49 (1954) 400.
33 J. T. Edsall and J. Wyman, *Biophysical Chemistry*, Vol. I, Academic Press, New York, 1958.
34 I. M. Klotz in H. Neurath and K. Bailey (Eds.), *The Proteins*, Vol. IB, Academic Press, New York, 1953.
35 J. Th. G. Overbeek, *Progr. Biophys. Biophys. Chem.*, 6 (1956) 58.

Chapter VI

Sedimentation, Diffusion and Partial Specific Volume

KAI O. PEDERSEN

Institute of Physical Chemistry, University of Uppsala (Sweden)

1. Introduction

Sedimentation and diffusion measurements have been used in protein chemistry to determine the molecular weight of these substances and as an aid in following the fractionation procedure. These methods started a new epoch when they, and later on electrophoresis, were introduced in the study of protein solutions. For the first time one could get a visual picture of what was going on in the fractionation procedure and how the purification was proceeding. In this section no account shall be given of experimental details nor of the theory of sedimentation and diffusion. For this the reader is referred to Vols. 2 and 3 of this series and to the monographs[1, 2] and papers discussing the theoretical problems connected with these methods[3, 4]. After a historical introduction some of the special problems connected with the use of these methods in protein chemistry will be discussed.

2. Sedimentation

Most of our knowledge about the molecular weights of the proteins has been gained from sedimentation measurements carried out since 1930. Up to that time very little was known about the size and shape of the soluble protein molecules. It was assumed that their particle weights were in the region of some thousands, perhaps up to some ten thousands. Some attempts had been made to get an idea of the size of the particles in protein solutions, but results obtained were not convincing. The most reliable experiments were those based on osmotic pressure measurements. Thus Sörensen concluded from such measurements[5] that egg albumin had a molecular weight of about 34,000. This was back in 1917. Thirty years later Linderstrøm-Lang made a critical study of Sörensen's experimental data[6]. He found hereby that a molecular weight of about 45,000 would fit Sörensen's old data much better than 34,000 chosen by Sörensen. Maybe Sörensen at that time thought that 34,000 was already a very high molecular weight for a protein, so he had difficulty in trusting the still higher values a great number of his experiments indicated.

From chemical analysis of the iron content of haemoglobin it was known that its minimum molecular weight was 16,700. However, it was not known whether this was also the weight of the kinetic unit in haemoglobin solutions. For the interpretation of the oxygen binding curve for haemoglobin it was important to know the size of this kinetic unit. Adair had therefore started an investigation of the osmotic pressure of haemoglobin solutions and in 1924 the first results were published[7], but this paper was hardly noticed when Svedberg and Fåhraeus started their study of haemoglobin in the ultracentrifuge[8]. At that time Svedberg had built his first low speed ultra-centrifuge and it was his intention to start using it for the study of particle size distribution in colloidal systems, including if possible the proteins.

He had shown that two different sedimentation methods could be used for calculating the particle size or molecular weight in colloidal solutions. If the centrifugal field was sufficiently intense, so that a sedimenting bounda-ry would leave the meniscus at an early time during the experiments, the sedimentation coefficient, s, could be calculated from the movement of the sedimenting boundary. Svedberg defined s as the sedimentation velocity (in cm per sec) in unit field of force (1 dyne per gram of mass) or $s = (\partial r/\partial t)/r\omega^2$, where r is the distance of the sedimenting boundary from the axis of rotation and ω is the angular velocity of the centrifuge rotor. If we know the molecular frictional coefficient, f, the molecular weight, M, may be calculated from the following expression $M = sf_s/(1 - \bar{v}\rho)$, where $\bar{v}$ is the partial specific volume of the solute and ρ is the density of the solution. Einstein has shown that in an ideal dilute solution f is related to the diffusion coefficient, D, in the following way: $f_D = RT/D$, where R is the gas constant and T the absolute temperature. Assuming f_s equal to f_D we obtain

$$M = \frac{RTs}{D(1 - \bar{v}\rho)} \tag{1}$$

which is usually called Svedberg's equation. It has been extensively used in the calculation of protein molecular weights from sedimentation and diffusion measurements.

If the centrifugal field is less intensive, a gradual change in the concentra-tion of the solute takes place and eventually an equilibrium is established between sedimentation towards the periphery of the cell and diffusion in the opposite direction. Under the same conditions as above the following equation is valid

$$M = \frac{2RT \ln(c_2/c_1)}{(1 - \bar{v}\rho)\omega^2(r_2^2 - r_1^2)} = \frac{RT(\partial c/\partial r)}{(1 - \bar{v}\rho)\omega^2 rc} \tag{2}$$

where c_1 and c_2 are the concentrations of the solute at the distances r_1 and r_2, respectively, from the axis of rotation. For further details of the methods see refs. 1 and 2.

If the protein solution does not behave ideally, an additional term must be added to the Svedberg equation and to the sedimentation equilibrium expression. They then change to

$$M = \frac{RTs}{(1 - \bar{v}\rho)D}\left(1 + c\frac{d \ln y}{dc}\right) \tag{1a}$$

or

$$M = \frac{2 RT \ln (c_2/c_1)}{(1 - \bar{v}\rho)\omega^2(r_2^2 - r_1^2)}\left(1 + c\frac{d \ln y}{dc}\right) \tag{2a}$$

where y is the activity coefficient for the macromolecule. From the form of the non-ideality term it is seen that for $c \to 0$ one gets $[1 + c(d \ln y/dc)] \to 1$. The values to be used for s and D in the Svedberg equation should therefore be those reduced to zero protein concentration, whereas the values from eqn. (2a) should be extrapolated to $c = 0$ in order to get the proper M.

While in most of the colloidal systems studied by Svedberg there was a considerable difference in density between the particles and the solvent, this was not the case with haemoglobin. With the centrifugal fields available it was necessary therefore to use the sedimentation equilibrium method. Svedberg and Fåhraeus made four series of measurements with horse haemoglobin and found that the factor with which the minimum molecular weight (16,700) had to be multiplied was 4.06 and 4.25 for CO-haemoglobin and 4.18 and 3.73 for methaemoglobin. They therefore concluded that the factor should be 4 and $M = 66,800$. In their paper they say: "These measurements should be regarded more as an illustration of the method than as a precision determination of the molecular weight of haemoglobin. A more refined technique of measurement will, we hope, enable us to communicate such determinations later on"[8].

The molecular weight for egg albumin and haemoglobin made it clear that at least some proteins had molecular weights in the region 30,000 to 70,000. However, the osmotic measurements could only give a number average molecular weight (M_n) for the protein, but could not tell anything about the uniformity of the size of the molecules. Sedimentation equilibrium gives the weight average molecular weight (M_w) and will give some indication of the uniformity of the particles. It is difficult, however, to get more detailed information about the homogeneity of a dissolved protein from these methods.

If an analysis of the homogeneity or of the polydispersity should be made, it was necessary to use the sedimentation velocity method, where in a dilute solution of a monodisperse substance the shape of the boundary should be determined solely by its diffusion coefficient. A larger spreading of the boundary than corresponding to the diffusion of the substance, or the appearance of separate boundaries would indicate inhomogeneity of the material. From the molecular weight of egg albumin and haemoglobin it was estimated that a centrifugal field of at least 100,000 times gravity would be necessary. That meant a 20-fold increase in the centrifugal field available. For this purpose Svedberg designed a completely new and different type of ultracentrifuge in 1925–26.

At that time the proteins were generally assumed to be typical examples of lyophilic colloids with no definite molecular weight but rather with a certain particle size distribution, or they were assumed to form some kind of reversible, dissociable systems. It was therefore quite unexpected that almost all the proteins first studied in the high speed ultracentrifuge were found to be monodisperse, meaning that the dissolved particles were all of the same size within the experimental error of the method. In a few cases the solutions were found to be paucidisperse, meaning that two or more distinctly different size classes were present. By suitable fractionation such solutions could often yield monodisperse protein solutions. In one case only a real polydisperse protein was found, *viz.* gelatin, which at that time was often used as a *model-protein*. Nowadays one would hardly consider gelatin a typical soluble protein.

After some years' study of the proteins it appeared to Svedberg that the molecular weights for most of the proteins were multiples of that for egg albumin ($\sim 35,000$) and in 1929 he put forward a hypothesis of the multiple law for the molecular weight of the soluble proteins[9]. In the following years a large number of different proteins were studied in the ultracentrifuge in order to prove or disprove the hypothesis of the multiple law and to find proteins with molecular weights below 35,000. Some proteins with M around 17,000 were also found, and studies of dissociation and association reactions on respiratory proteins showed that these molecules could often be reversibly split or associated to molecules having the same M as those belonging to other groups of respiratory proteins. On the basis of these studies[1,10] it was assumed that the molecular weights of the proteins could be arranged in groups that were simple multiples (1, 2, 4, 6, 8, 16, 24, 48, 96, 192 and 384) of a basic molecular weight of 17,600.

Svedberg's multiple law hypothesis meant a great stimulus to protein chemistry. It gave rise to much speculation about the formation and struc-ture of protein molecules. Simultaneously a lot of more experimental data was collected. However, from the beginning of the 1940's several proteins having molecular weights below 17,600 were found and from then on an increasing number of proteins were disclosed whose molecular weights did not fit into the Svedberg system of multiples. Svedberg's hypothesis has therefore been severely critisized by several authors who claim that there are no molecular weight classes and that the multiple hypothesis is disproved by the statistical analysis of the published molecular weights for the proteins. All our present knowledge indicates also that Svedberg's hypothesis is not of such a general validity as it was first thought to be. On the other hand there seems to be much evidence against the statement that all the M values are completely randomly distributed. Thus there are large numbers of proteins which serve the same purpose in different organisms, but are chemically different and still have about the same value for M or at least for their sedimentation constants, s_{20}. As examples may be mentioned several of the plasma proteins, a number of seed proteins and various groups of respiratory proteins (for reviews and references see refs. 11 and 12). For the last group of proteins it seems appropriate to assume that their M's fit into a few multiple systems with different basic units.

Sedimentation studies have been widely used in following the fractionation of protein solutions and ascertaining the homogeneity and purity of protein preparations. In their native state these substances are often present in mixtures with several other proteins. Frequently these various proteins have different sedimentation constants and consequently they will appear as individual components when investigated in the ultracentrifuge. The progress of a fractionation can thus easily be followed by studying the sedimentation diagrams obtained from the various fractions. The presence of a single symmetrical peak in a (dc/dr), r-diagram is a necessary, but not sufficient test of purity for a protein. If the protein also shows a single, symmetrical peak at different pH values in electrophoretic experiments, it is often taken as a criterion that the preparation has resulted in a pure protein. However, these two criteria are necessary, but they may not be sufficient. It may quite well be that one has only succeeded in getting a population of closely related members of a protein family, where the spread in the values of the sedi-mentation coefficients is too small to be discovered by a mere visual inspec-tion of the sedimentation diagram. By a detailed analysis of the spreading of the sedimenting boundary with time and by comparing it with the spreading due to diffusion it is possible, however, to get an idea of the homogeneity of the protein[13].

For several proteins, *e.g.* the γ-globulins, we must assume that they represent populations of closely related members of a family of proteins with about the same size and structure, but with somewhat different amino acid composition. For a number of other proteins with very specific biological action as for instance some of the enzymes and protein hormones, there is reason to believe that they in their native state form a collection of identical molecules with only minor differences from species to species, as for instance in the case of insulin, where the only differences for five species (cattle, pig, sheep, horse and whale) were limited to the three amino acid residues occupying positions 8–10 in the A chain[14].

By our methods of preparation, however, we may sometimes produce slight changes in some of the individual molecules, so that we in these cases also end up with protein preparations consisting of populations of closely related members of a family instead of collections of identical molecules. Some authors are inclined to assume that there is always some kind of microheterogeneity even in highly purified protein preparations[15].

(a) Sedimentation coefficients

In order to get comparable values for the sedimentation coefficients it is customary to reduce the values found to some standard temperature and solvent. Usually water at 20° is chosen for this purpose, but a few American authors have started to refer their values to water at 25°. If we express the sedimentation coefficient reduced to its calculated value in water at 20° as $s_{20,w}$, it will be related in the following way to the value, s_t, found in another solution at t:

$$s_{20,w} = s_t \frac{\eta_t}{\eta_{20}^\circ} \frac{1 - \bar{v}_{20}\rho_{20}^\circ}{1 - \bar{v}_t\rho_t}$$

Here η_t and η_{20}° are the viscosities, ρ_t and ρ_{20}° the densities of the solutions at $t°$ and water at 20°, respectively. Theoretically a correction term allowing for the variation of η, ρ and $\bar{v}$ with pressure should have been included in the above expression. Practically it may be neglected for aqueous solutions in the temperature interval 15–30°.

The formula relating s_t to $s_{20,w}$ is based on the expression for s in a two-component system and on the assumption that the frictional coefficient, f, is proportional to the viscosity of the solvent. This also means that the shape of the particle shall be independent of the temperature, $viz.$ $(f/\eta) = $ constant. However, diffusion measurements carried out on bovine serum albumin in the temperature interval 1° to 25° have shown a small decrease in (f/η) with temperature[16]. Since also the variation of $\bar{v}$ with temperature is usually not too well known, the importance of making the experiments as close as

References p. 214

practicable to the reference temperature, wherever possible, should be emphasized. Furthermore, one should be very cautious in drawing far reaching conclusions from experiments carried out at different temperatures.

For obtaining the sedimentation constant the values for $s_{20,w}$ must be plotted against protein concentration and extrapolated to $c = 0$. In sedimentation experiments c should refer to the initial concentration or rather to the average protein concentration in the *plateau region* in the solution during the run. Generally s decreases linearly with increase in c. In a few cases a plot of $1/s$ *versus* c may fit the experimental values better. For the proteins this decrease in s should amount to at least about 1% for an increase in protein concentration of 1 g/100 ml of solution. Usually it is greater. If $s_{20,w}$ is independent of concentration or increases with c, it shows that association takes place with increase in protein concentration. In such cases sedimentation equilibrium experiments or the so-called Archibald method may give valuable information (see later).

Sedimentation studies on proteins must almost always be carried out in salt solutions in order to get unambiguous values for s. When the proteins are not at their isoelectric point they will carry an electric net charge that will always tend to reduce the rate of sedimentation. In a salt-free protein solution even minor changes in its pH may result in marked changes in s. The maximal result of a pure *electrical* charge effect on sedimentation[17] is a 50% reduction in s. In a salt-free solution any decrease in s greater than 50% must be caused by a change in the protein molecule (change of shape, dissociation, etc.). Addition of neutral salts to as little as 0.01 M will greatly reduce the electric charge effect. It will be negligible for most proteins in a 1% solution being 0.1 to 0.2 M with respect to NaCl.

The slope $(ds_{20,w}/dc)$ of the $s_{20,w},c$ line will vary from protein to protein. It is highly dependent upon the net charge on the protein and on the ionic strength of the solution.

Besides their *swamping* of charge effects on sedimentation, the ions of neutral salts as well as of buffer salts may have specific and unspecific effects on the sedimentation of proteins. Thus a number of anions bind to certain proteins (change their isoelectric points, etc.) resulting in different values of s, even near the isoelectric point of the protein as shown for serum albumin in Table I (s is given in Svedberg units and c in g protein/ml solution).

Such indifferent ions as the alkali ions may also be bound to the proteins on the alkaline side of their isoelectric points or carried along with the sedimenting protein ion in such a way that marked differences may be observed between solutions containing various alkali ions[17]. Thus bovine serum albumin solutions at pH 9 containing 0.2 M LiI or 0.2 M CsI gave $s_{20,w} = 4.39$ S and 4.82 S, respectively, when extrapolated to zero protein concentration.

TABLE I

VARIATION OF THE SEDIMENTATION CONSTANT FOR BOVINE SERUM
ALBUMIN $(c=0)$ IN DIFFERENT SALT SOLUTIONS

Salt	0.2 M NaCl	0.2 M CsCl	0.5 M KCl	0.5 M KCl	0.2 M LiBr	0.2 M KSCN
pH	4.92	4.70	5.20	4.08	5.13	—
$s_{20,w}$	4.44	4.54	4.44	4.25	4.59	4.60
$-(ds_{20.w}/dc)$	24.9	24.3	27.8	22.9	28.4	32.2

Since for a protein the sedimentation constant $(c = 0)$ as well as the slope of the $s_{20,w},c$ curve may depend upon the nature of the salt, the pH and the ionic strength of the solution, it is evident that one can only expect to find identical values for proteins that have been studied in identical media. Similar values obtained at a single concentration may not be conclusive.

(b) Sedimentation equilibrium and the Archibald method

During the first 10 years after the introduction of the ultracentrifuge a certain fraction of the total number of runs was carried out as sedimentation equilibrium measurements. However, the time to reach equilibrium generally took many days, and this, in addition to some technical difficulties, resulted in discrediting this method for many years. However, there is reason to believe that the equilibrium method will be used more in the future. It has thus been shown that the height of solution in the cell may be reduced so much that equilibrium for proteins is practically reached in less than a day[18]. The availability of a low speed attachment to the Spinco ultracentrifuge makes it also easier to carry out successful equilibrium experiments with this instrument.

It has been pointed out by Archibald that since there should not be any net flow of solute through the surfaces at the meniscus or bottom of the cell, the condition which exists at equilibrium at any level in the cell, *viz.*

$$c_i s\omega^2 r_i = D(\partial c/\partial r)_i$$

should for a monodisperse substance be valid at all times during an experiment at the meniscus (r_m) and at the bottom of the cell (r_b). Thus by knowing the concentration at the meniscus and at the bottom of the cell and by extrapolating $(\partial c/\partial r)$ to these places, values for $(s\omega^2/D)$ corresponding to r_m and r_b, respectively, may be calculated. A monodisperse ideal solute results in identical values at r_m and r_b. (For details see ref. 2, p. 181, and ref. 19.)

References p. 214

If the two values are different and change with time it is an indication that the solute is either polydisperse or that there is some kind of equilibrium between the monomer and polymers. If the equilibrium is constantly maintained, Archibald runs combined with sedimentation velocity runs may give very valuable information about the nature of such equilibria in protein systems[20]. Even in the study of polydisperse systems Archibald runs may be of great help[21].

(c) Some other uses of sedimentation methods

Whenever a reaction with proteins produces a marked change in the particle size, sedimentation studies may yield valuable information about the process. As an example shall be mentioned an extended series of studies of soluble antigen–antibody complexes (for references see ref. 22).

The largest numbers of ultracentrifugations have probably been carried out on lipoprotein solutions isolated by centrifugal flotation from normal and pathological sera. By means of their flotation rates in certain standard salt solutions it was possible to divide the lipoproteins into certain classes and characterize them, which had not been possible earlier[23]. Because of the implications of serum lipoproteins with atherogenesis a large number of publications have appeared dealing with this subject[24].

For many years a certain pathological globulin, the Waldenström macro-globulin, could only be unambiguously disclosed from the appearance of a large $s_{20} \sim 19$ S component in the sedimentation diagram. The ultra-centrifuge has been used in the study of this protein and different types of high molecular weight antibodies[25]. Another plasma protein, fetuin, was first discovered by its unexpected presence in the sedimentation diagrams from some globulin fractions from calf serum[26].

As the density of the solvent (including salt and buffer substances) approaches that of the macromolecular solute, the rate of sedimentation becomes more sensitive to small differences in $\bar{v}$ and may manifest themselves either as an increased spreading of the sedimenting boundary or the appear-ance of new peaks in the sedimentation diagrams. Such experiments may be valuable in the study of lipoproteins for example, where $\bar{v}$ depends so much on the ratio between the lipid and protein moiety of the molecule.

By making the runs in concentrated salt solutions (e.g. CsCl) a strong density gradient may be produced by the dense salt in the cell, and the protein will sediment and float towards the level in the cell where the density is equal to that of the macromolecule including bound salt ions. If the protein is homogeneous as regards density, a single, narrow protein band is observed in the cell, and from its shape at equilibrium its molecular weight may be calculated[27]. If it is heterogeneous as regards density, several bands may appear or the protein distribution in the band may be un-symmetrical. The method has mainly been used in the study of nucleic acids and viruses, but it seems to possess potentialities even for the study of proteins. One merit of the method is that very little material is needed of the macromolecular substance.

3. Diffusion

The first diffusion measurements on proteins were made by Graham in the middle of last century. About fifty years later, when the mathematical theory of diffusion had been developed, Graham's data were used to cal-culate a molecular weight for egg albumin, assuming spherical molecules[28]. The value found was 33,000. However, it was not until the end of the twenties that interest in the diffusion of proteins really started in connection with the introduction of the ultracentrifuge.

From measurements of the diffusion and sedimentation coefficients and by using the Svedberg equation (p. 201), values for the molecular weights of the proteins could be calculated. In the beginning the values for D were either computed from separate diffusion experiments or from the spreading of the sedimenting boundary in centrifuge runs. The methods for measuring diffusion coefficients were at that time rather coarse, but the need for values of D in connection with protein studies also stimulated the development of new and more accurate methods and apparatus for measuring diffusion coefficients.

The introduction of the Gouy and the Rayleigh interference methods in combination with special boundary sharpening techniques increased the accuracy so much that diffusion coefficients in two-component systems may now be correct to about 0.1% (for description of methods and references see ref. 4). By these improved methods it was also found that the interacting flows in systems with more than two components play a much more important role than anticipated earlier. Since in such systems with two solute com-ponents we have to deal with four diffusion constants, viz., D_{11} and D_{22}, for the two individual diffusion coefficients, plus D_{12} and D_{21} for the cross-term diffusion coefficients, and since in most cases $D_{12} \neq D_{21} \neq 0$ they will all make some contribution to the experimentally measured value for the diffusion coefficient, $\mathscr{D}_A$, even when the concentration of the second solute is almost the same on the two sides of the diffusing boundary. Simple model experiments with raffinose and KCl in water or raffinose and urea in water have shown that $\mathscr{D}_A \neq D_{11}$ even when for the second solute $\Delta c \sim 0$ across the diffusing boundary[29]. Since proteins are ampholytes and it is very difficult in salt-free solution to have them exactly at their isoelectric point, they must in practice be studied in some kind of salt solutions, which means that in diffusion experiments we must at least have to deal with two solutes, and D_{11} will in general be different from $\mathscr{D}_A$.

Before the middle of the 1950's it has been customary to treat the buffer system—*i.e.* the solvent (water) and low molecular salts—as a single component, thus putting $\mathscr{D}_A = D_1$. The majority of the values for D given in the literature must therefore be regarded as approximate.

In diffusion experiments it has been common practice to dialyze the protein, dissolved in a salt or buffer solution, against the same buffer before starting the experiment. This practice cannot be recommended. It seems more appropriate to keep the salt and buffer concentration as closely alike as possible in the two solutions before the start of the experiment.

The whole question of the mathematical treatment of the experimental data from diffusion measurements with interacting flow appears still to be in a state of development. If under these conditions precision determination of the diffusion coefficient for a protein should be carried out, it would seem advisable to run the experiments in the following way. With constant salt and buffer concentration a series of experiments are made with decreasing mean protein concentration, allowing extrapolation of $\mathscr{D}_A$ to zero protein concentration. Similar series of runs are made with some different buffer concentrations (same buffer composition) each time extrapolating $\mathscr{D}_A$ to zero protein concentration. Finally all these $\mathscr{D}_A$ values are extrapolated to zero buffer concentration. It is thus a very time-consuming procedure.

If, however, the main purpose of the diffusion measurements is to get values for D to be used in the Svedberg equation, it would at the present time seem better to refrain from the diffusion experiment and instead make either sedimentation equilibrium or Archibald runs on the protein.

Just as in the case of the sedimentation coefficients it has been customary to reduce the values for D_t obtained in some buffer solution at $t°$ to those in water at $20°$ by means of the following equation

$$D^*_{20,w} = D_t(\eta_t/\eta^\circ_{20})[293.18/(273.18 + t)]$$

The expression for $D^*_{20,w}$ is unsatisfactory, however, since it does not take into account the thermodynamic term. It is therefore more correct to use

$$D_{20,w} = \frac{D^*_{20,w}}{1 + \bar{c}(d \ln y/dc)}$$

where $\bar{c}$ is the mean of the protein concentration on the two sides of the boundary, and then extrapolate to $\bar{c} = 0$. Furthermore the necessity should be emphasized of carrying out the experiment at a temperature as close as possible to the reference temperature[16].

4. Partial specific volume factor

For the calculation of molecular weights from sedimentation measurements it is necessary to know the partial specific volume of the macromolecular substance at the same temperature and in the same solution in which it has been run in the centrifuge.

Since for the proteins $(1 - \bar{v}\rho)$ is of the order 0.25 to 0.30 it means that an error in the determination of $\bar{v}$ is multiplied by a factor of 3 to 4. It is therefore important that the proper values for $\bar{v}$ be used in the calculation of M.

According to definition

$$\bar{v} = \left(\frac{\partial V}{\partial c}\right)_{T,P}$$

and the partial specific volume is accordingly calculated from density determinations on differently concentrated solutions. The densities were generally obtained from pycnometer measurement[1, 30, 31], but the accuracy of the $\bar{v}$ determined from this kind of experiment is seldom better than about 1 %. The introduction of the magnetic float method[32] instead of the pycnometer greatly increased the accuracy of the density determinations and thus diminished the error in $\bar{v}$. It also made studies on the dependence of $\bar{v}$ on pH, salts, etc. possible[33]. Until then very little attention had been given to the variation of $\bar{v}$ with temperature. Based on a few old determinations of $\bar{v}$ at different temperatures, values of $\bar{v}_t$ for *an average protein* were given for the temperature interval 15–35° in Appendix II of ref. 1. The justification of this correction term was rather uncertain, so it has probably been used very little outside Uppsala. After the introduction of the magnetic float method, the variation of $\bar{v}$ with temperature has been studied for a few proteins[34] and the values found for $d\bar{v}/dt$ were about the same as those given in ref. 1, or an increase of a little less than 1 % in $\bar{v}$ for an increase of 1°. It is thus an appreciable variation of $\bar{v}$ and it cannot be neglected when correcting sedimentation coefficients from one temperature to another.

The hydrostatic pressure in the centrifuge cell increases from zero at the meniscus to several hundred atmospheres at the periphery of the solution. A change in $\bar{v}$ with pressure would therefore have to be taken into account. Unfortunately such measurements have not yet been published. However, there is reason for believing that for proteins such changes in $\bar{v}$ with pressure are so small that they may generally be neglected. For the evaluation of $\bar{v}$ from density determinations it is of interest to know whether $\bar{v}$ varies

TABLE II

Protein	Origin	$s_{20,w}$	$D_{20,w}$	$\bar{v}_{20}$	M	Literature
α_1-Glycoprotein (orosomucoid)	Human serum	3.11	5.27	0.675	44,000	38
Fetuin	Calf serum	2.86	5.2	0.712	45,000	39
Albumin	Human serum	4.32*	5.9	0.736	67,000	40
Albumin	Bovine serum	4.41	5.9	0.734	67,000	32, 41, 42
Transferrin	Porcine serum	5.37	5.8	(0.725)	79,000	43
Haptoglobin Type I-I	Human serum	4.2	4.8	0.72	85,000	44, 45
Plasminogen	Human serum	4.28	2.9	(0.75)	143,000	46
γ-Globulin	Human serum	6.6*	4.0	0.718	142,000	40
γ-Globulin	Bovine serum	7.1*	3.8	0.732	170,000	40
Fibrinogen	Human plasma	7.63	1.97	0.723	340,000	47
Fibrinogen	Bovine plasma	7.8	2.02	0.718	330,000	48–50

In Table II and III $s_{20,w}$ is given in Svedberg units and $D_{20,w}$ in Fick units.

TABLE III

Protein	Origin	$s_{20,w}$	$D_{20,w}$	$\bar{v}_{20}$	M	Literature
Hordein	Barley	1.9*	6.5	(0.729)	26,000	1
α-Globulin	Barley	2.3*	7.4	0.72	27,000	51, 52
Gliadin	Wheat gluten	2.1	6.7	0.724	27,500	1, 53
Zein	Maize	1.9	4.0	0.776	51,000	12, 53, 54
Vicilin	Seed from pea	7.5*	4.26	0.752	170,000	52
γ-Globulin	Wheat embryo	8.0*	3.6	(0.72)	190,000	52
Excelsin	Brazil nuts	13.3	4.26	0.743	295,000	1
Legumin	Seed from pea	11.7*	3.49	0.735	310,000	52
Amandin	Almonds	12.5	3.62	0.746	330,000	1, 55
Edestin	Hemp seeds	12.8	3.18	0.744	380,000	1, 55

with the protein concentration or is independent of it. Investigations on haemoglobin up to about 40% concentration have shown $\bar{v}$ to be constant for this protein[35].

One of the difficulties with the determination of $\bar{v}$ is that the protein should preferably be available in gram quantities. For many biologically active proteins this may be a serious drawback. Various methods have therefore been tried to circumvent this difficulty, but they all show some kind of ambiguity. They are generally based on measurement of the rate of sedimentation in various dense solutions, and $1/v$ is put equal to the interpolated density of the solution, where the protein neither sediments nor floats. However, the value found for v is not the partial specific volume of the protein, but some kind of specific volume for the hydrated protein.

It is often dependent upon the substances that have been used for increasing the density of the solutions.

Where the amino acid compositions of the proteins are known, fairly good approximate values for $\bar{v}$ have been computed from the volume of their constituent amino acid residues[31]. The method neglects electrostriction that is due to charged groups in the protein molecule. Consequently it might be expected that the calculated values for the specific volumes would be higher than those observed. In the beginning some marked discrepancies were found for certain proteins between the calculated and the observed values. Better values for the amino acid compositions and more exact determinations of $\bar{v}$ for these proteins have reduced these discrepancies considerably[31,33]. The success of these calculations suggests that the effect of electrostriction is to a large extent compensated by other effects in the protein molecule.

5. Molecular constants for some proteins

In Tables II and III values for $s_{20,w}$, $D_{20,w}$, $\bar{v}_{20}$ have been given together with the molecular weights calculated from these values by means of the Svedberg equation. As most of the diffusion measurements were made before the middle of the 1950's the diffusion coefficients can only be regarded as approximate (see p. 210). Some of the earlier determinations of $\bar{v}_{20}$ may also be less correct. The $s_{20,w}$ values marked with an asterisk have been corrected for a systematic error in the determination of the ultracentrifuge cell temperature in Uppsala[17]. Taken together, the various sources of error may cause an uncertainty in the molecular weights of the order of 5 %, in a few cases perhaps up to about 10%. There is no doubt, however, that it is now possible to determine the molecular constants for a pure protein with considerably greater accuracy.

In Table II molecular constants are given for some of the plasma proteins. Values for other proteins belonging to this group may be found in refs. 36 and 12. Table III includes some of the seed proteins; further information regarding these proteins may be found in refs. 11 and 12. The largest number of determinations of molecular constants for a single group of proteins have been carried out on the enzymes[12,37]. A number of measurements have also been made on the protein hormones[12,37]. Comparative studies have been made of the constants for a number of respiratory proteins belonging to different classes of the animal kingdom[1,11].

REFERENCES

[1] T. SVEDBERG AND K. O. PEDERSEN, *The Ultracentrifuge*, Clarendon Press, Oxford, 1940 (Reprinted by Johnson Reprint Corporation, New York, 1959.)

[2] H. K. SCHACHMAN, *Ultracentrifugation in Biochemistry*, Academic Press, New York, 1959.

[3] J. W. WILLIAMS, K. E. VAN HOLDE, R. L. BALDWIN AND H. FUJITA, *Chem. Revs.*, 58 (1958) 715.

[4] L. J. GOSTING, *Advances in Protein Chem.*, 11 (1956) 429.

[5] S. P. L. SÖRENSEN, *Compt. rend. trav. lab. Carlsberg*, 12 (1917) 255.

[6] A. V. GÜNTELBERG AND K. LINDERSTRØM-LANG, *Compt. rend. trav. lab. Carlsberg*, *Sér. chim.*, 27 (1949) 1.

[7] G. S. ADAIR, *Proc. Cambridge Phil. Soc., Biol. Ser.*, 1 (1924) 75.

[8] T. SVEDBERG AND R. FÅHRAEUS, *J. Am. Chem. Soc.*, 48 (1926) 430.

[9] T. SVEDBERG, *Nature*, 123 (1929) 871.

[10] T. SVEDBERG, *Proc. Roy. Soc. (London)*, A,170 (1939) 40; B,127 (1939) 1.

[11] K. O. PEDERSEN, *Cold Spring Harbor Symposia Quant. Biol.*, 14 (1949) 140.

[12] K. O. PEDERSEN, *Inst. intern. chim. Solvay, Conseil chim., 9th Conseil*, Brussels, (1953) 19.

[13] R. L. BALDWIN, *Biochem. J.*, 65 (1957) 49C, 503.

[14] J. I. HARRIS, F. SANGER AND M. A. NAUGHTON, *Arch. Biochem. Biophys.*, 65 (1956) 427.

[15] J. R. COLVIN, D. B. SMITH AND W. H. COOK, *Chem. Revs.*, 54 (1954) 687.

[16] L. G. LONGSWORTH, *J. Phys. Chem.*, 58 (1954) 770.

[17] K. O. PEDERSEN, *J. Phys. Chem.*, 62 (1958) 1282.

[18] K. E. VAN HOLDE AND R. L. BALDWIN, *J. Phys. Chem.*, 62 (1958) 734.

[19] R. TRAUTMAN AND C. F. CRAMPTON, *J. Am. Chem. Soc.*, 81 (1959) 4036.

[20] G. KEGELES AND M. S. N. RAO, *J. Am. Chem. Soc.*, 80 (1958) 5721, 5724.

[21] S. R. ERLANDER AND J. F. FOSTER, *J. Polymer Sci.*, 37 (1959) 103.

[22] F. A. PEPE AND S. J. SINGER, *J. Am. Chem. Soc.*, 81 (1959) 3878.

[23] F. T. LINDGREN, H. A. ELLIOTT AND J. W. GOFMAN, *J. Phys. & Colloid Chem.*, 55 (1951) 80.

[24] F. T. LINDGREN AND A. V. NICHOLS in F. W. PUTNAM (Ed.), *Plasma Proteins*, Vol. 2, Academic Press, New York, 1960, p. 1.

[25] H. G. KUNKEL in F. W. PUTNAM (Ed.), *Plasma Proteins*, Vol. 1, Academic Press, New York, 1960, p. 279.

[26] K. O. PEDERSEN, *Nature*, 154 (1944) 575.

[27] M. MESELSON, F. W. STAHL AND J. VINOGRAD, *Proc. Natl. Acad. Sci. U.S.*, 43 (1957) 581.

[28] W. SUTHERLAND, *Phil. Mag.*, 9 (1905) 781.

[29] P. J. DUNLOP, *J. Phys. Chem.*, 61 (1957) 994, 1619.

[30] C. DRUCKER, *Arkiv Kemi, Mineral. Geol.*, 14A (1941) No. 15.

[31] J. T. EDSALL, in H. NEURATH AND K. BAILEY (Eds.), *The Proteins*, Vol. I B, Academic Press, New York, 1953, p. 562.

[32] M. O. DAYHOFF, G. E. PERLMANN AND D. A. MacINNES, *J. Am. Chem. Soc.*, 74 (1952) 2515.

[33] P. A. CHARLWOOD, *J. Am. Chem. Soc.*, 79 (1957) 776.

[34] C. M. KAY, *Biochim. Biophys. Acta*, 38 (1960) 420.

[35] G. S. AND M. E. ADAIR, *Proc. Roy. Soc. (London)*, B,120 (1949) 422.

[36] R. A. PHELPS AND F. W. PUTNAM in F. W. PUTNAM (Ed.), *Plasma Proteins*, Vol. 1, Academic Press, New York, 1960, p. 153.

[37] W. B. DANDLIKER, in H. NEURATH AND K. BAILEY (Eds.), *Proteins*, Vol. I B, Academic Press, New York, 1953, p. 634.

[38] E. L. SMITH, D. M. BROWN, H. E. WEIMER AND R. J. WINSLER, *J. Biol. Chem.*, 185 (1950) 569.

[39] H. F. DEUTSCH, *J. Biol. Chem.*, 208 (1954) 669.

[40] K. O. PEDERSEN, *Ultracentrifugal Studies on Serum and Serum Fractions*, Thesis, Uppsala, 1945, p. 148.

[41] G. I. LOEB AND H. A. SCHERAGA, *J. Phys. Chem.*, 60 (1956) 1633.

[42] M. L. WAGNER AND H. A. SCHERAGA, *J. Phys. Chem.*, 60 (1956) 1066.
[43] C.-B. LAURELL AND B. INGELMAN, *Acta Chem. Scand.*, 1 (1947) 770.
[44] M. F. JAYLE AND G. BOUSSIER, *Exposés ann. biochim. méd.*, 17 (1955) 157.
[45] M. NYMAN, *Scand. J. Clin. & Lab. Invest.*, 11 (1959) Suppl. 39.
[46] S. SHULMAN, N. ALKJAERSIG AND S. SHERRY, *J. Biol. Chem.*, 233 (1958) 91.
[47] E. A. CASPARY AND R. A. KEKWICK, *Biochem. J.*, 56 (1954) XXXV.
[48] S. SHULMAN, *J. Am. Chem. Soc.*, 75 (1953) 5846.
[49] R. A. KEKWICK, *Biochem. J.*, 32 (1938) 552.
[50] H. A. SCHERAGA, W. R. CARROL, L. F. NIMS, E. SUTTON, J. K. BACKUS AND J. M. SAUNDERS, *J. Polymer Sci.*, 14 (1954) 427.
[51] O. QUENSEL, *Untersuchungen über die Gerstenglobuline*, Thesis, Uppsala, 1942.
[52] C. E. DANIELSSON, *Biochem. J.*, 44 (1949) 387.
[53] J. F. FOSTER AND D. FRENCH, *J. Am. Chem. Soc.*, 67 (1945) 687.
[54] C. C. WATSON, S. ARRHENIUS AND J. W. WILLIAMS, *Nature*, 137 (1936) 322.
[55] E. M. BEVILACQUA, E. B. BEVILACQUA, M. M. BENDER AND J. W. WILLIAMS, *Ann. N.Y. Acad. Sci.*, 46 (1945) 309.

Chapter VII

Spacial Configuration in Proteins

D. W. GREEN[*]

*Davy Faraday Research Laboratory of the Royal Institution,
London (Great Britain)*

1. Introduction

Perhaps the simplest way to explain the fascination and purpose of studies of spacial configuration in biological materials is by means of a mechanical analogy. Enzymes, for example, have often been called the machine tools of the living cell because of their key role in controlling the intricate reaction pathways of metabolism; while the nucleic acids may justly be likened to filing systems within which plans and specifications of these machine tools are stored away. To know the pattern in which the component parts of such mechanisms are fitted together is to know something of the way they were made, and something of the way they work. Similarly, we believe that knowledge of protein structure, for example, will be an essential part of our understanding of the synthesis of enzymes and of the reactions which take place with their substrates.

It is clear that this knowledge must extend down to the level at which the spacial positions of the component atoms are known. Very early it was found that the specificity of enzymes, the aspect in which their controlling function is most evident, operates at the level of single atoms: any α-glycoside is safe in the presence of a β-glucosidase! Correspondingly, on the enzyme surface there must be a structure sufficiently precise to effect this distinction between configurations around a single atom. Later, the crystallisation of enzymes, which can be very rapid once they have been separated from other components of the cell, showed that the globular protein molecule must be a well defined and rigid body within which the specification of coordinates for the atoms would be possible and meaningful. More recently, the complete elucidation of the amino acid sequences in insulin and ribonuclease, and the identification of single amino acid replacements as the basis of variation

---

[*] Member of the External Staff of the Medical Research Council.

among the mutant forms of haemoglobin, has shown that the genetic control of protein synthesis also operates close to the atomic level. The successful incorporation of unnatural amino acids such as *p*-fluorophenylalanine shows that the specificity is not absolute, but, clearly, the synthetic mechanism distinguishes between closely similar pairs such as leucine and iso-leucine, or serine and threonine.

Exposure to temperatures outside the natural range, or to extremes of pH, leads to denaturation, in which the covalent linking is conserved, but, generally, the enzymatic activity is lost. Apparently, the amino acid sequence alone does not determine the biological activity: the catalytically active part of the surface may include side chains from amino acids well separated in the sequence, but brought together by the folding back of the main chain of covalent bonds. However, it is conceivable that in the special circumstances of protein synthesis, when the molecule may be assembled in an ordered way, the sequence does contain within itself the design for arranging all the atoms correctly in space. At present this can only be a speculation: we know only the simplest rules governing the construction of protein molecules, and these do not enable us to predict the configuration from the sequence with any certainty.

It is the aim of this chapter to discuss the few rules which are known, and to describe techniques by which more may be learned in the future. It is written from the point of view of the X-ray crystallographer, with some apology, for this is not the only means by which the structure of proteins has been studied. However, it does appear to be much the most powerful technique available at the present time, and the results gained in this way during the last few years have led to a remarkably coherent picture of protein structure. Fortunately, the reader can be referred to the excellent survey of general X-ray diffraction methods by Bullen (see Volume 3, Chapter II, p. 33); only the extensions which have been specially developed for protein structure work will be described in any detail here.

2. Stereochemical principles

(a) Amino acids

It is generally accepted that twenty amino acids occur commonly in proteins. The list given in Table I is something of a convention since it includes cystine and hydroxyproline, but leaves out glutamine and asparagine. The last two are certainly distinguished from glutamic and aspartic acids in the amino acid sequences of proteins, whereas cystine is probably derived from two cysteine residues, and hydroxyproline is rarely found outside the special class of collagen-type proteins. The occurrence of several unusual amino acids has been reviewed by Desnuelle[1].

TABLE I

AMINO ACIDS COMMONLY OCCURRING IN PROTEINS
Crystal structure analysis

Name	Symbol	Side chain	Compound	Configuration	Data*
Glycine	Gly	—H	Gly	—	3D
Alanine	Ala	—CH$_3$	Ala	DL	3D
Valine	Val	—CH(CH$_3$)$_2$			
Leucine	Leu	—CH$_2$CH(CH$_3$)$_2$			
Isoleucine	Ileu	—CH(CH$_3$)CH$_2$CH$_3$	Ileu·HCl Ileu·HBr	D	2 × 2D
Serine	Ser	—CH$_2$OH	Ser	DL	3D
Threonine	Thr	—CH(OH)CH$_3$	Thr	L$_s$	3D
Cysteine	Cys	—CH$_2$SH			
Cystine	Cys | Cys		Cys | Cys	L	3D
Methionine	Met	—CH$_2$CH$_2$SCH$_3$	Met	DL	2D
Phenylalanine	Phe	—CH$_2$C$_6$H$_5$			
Tyrosine	Tyr	—CH$_2$C$_6$H$_4$OH	Tyr·HBr Zn	L	2 × 2D
Aspartic acid	Asp	—CH$_2$COOH	Co·Asp·H$_2$O Ni	L	3D
Glutamic acid	Glu	—CH$_2$CH$_2$COOH	Glu	L	3 × 2D
Lysine	Lys	—CH$_2$CH$_2$CH$_2$CH$_2$NH$_2$	Lys·HCl·H$_2$O	L	2 × 2D
Arginine	Arg	—CH$_2$CH$_2$CH$_2$NHC(NH)NH$_2$			
Histidine	His	—CH$_2$—C——CH | || HN N _C⁄ H$_2$	His·HCl·H$_2$O	D or L	3D
Tryptophan	Try	—CH$_2$—C———— || HC | | _N⁄ H			
Proline	Pro	CH$_2$—CH$_2$ (complete | | formula) H$_2$C CHCOOH _N⁄ H			
Hydroxyproline	Hypro	HOCH——CH$_2$ (complete | | formula) H$_2$C CHCOOH _N⁄ H	Hypro	L	3D

---

* 3D for a complete three-dimensional set; 2 × 2D for two planes of the reciprocal lattice, etc.

Among the twenty, all except glycine are optically active, and have the same L-configuration about the α-carbon atom, as shown in Fig. 1. In all the crystal structures studied so far the amino acids have been found as zwitterions $NH_3^+CH(R)COO^-$ rather than as uncharged molecules. In this form resonance within the carboxyl group makes the two C–O bonds equal

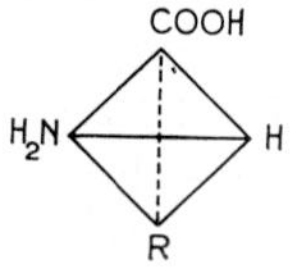

Fig. 1. L-Configuration at the α-carbon atom of the natural amino acids.

at about 1.26 Å, though this symmetry may be slightly disturbed by the formation of hydrogen bonds with neighbouring molecules. As expected, C_α has always been found very close to the plane of the carboxyl group, and the C_α–C bond to the carboxyl group has been found to have little double-bond character, averaging 1.53 Å in length. However, there is a definite tendency for the nitrogen atom to lie near the carboxyl plane, the greatest departure from this plane being about 0.6 Å. The C_α–N bond is definitely longer than the usual C–N bond (1.50 Å rather than 1.475 Å), but the significance of this is not clear. All the interbond angles have been found to be close to the expected values, e.g. the tetrahedral angle of 109° for bonds from C_α, and 125° for the $O=C-O^-$ angle. A very full collection and evaluation of the experimental data has been given by Hahn[2].

Configurations within the side chain are not particularly significant, except for isoleucine, threonine and hydroxyproline, which contain a second asymmetric carbon atom. In working out the structure of D-isoleucine from crystals of the hydrochloride and hydrobromide, Trommel and Bijvoet[3] were able to collect data for the anomalous scattering of uranium $L_{\alpha 1}$ X-rays by the bromine atom. This extension of the usual X-ray technique enables the absolute configuration of asymmetric atoms to be determined. It was established that D(−)isoleucine is D-α-amino-D-β-methylvaleric acid, so the natural L(+)isoleucine has the mirror-image configuration shown in Fig. 2(a).

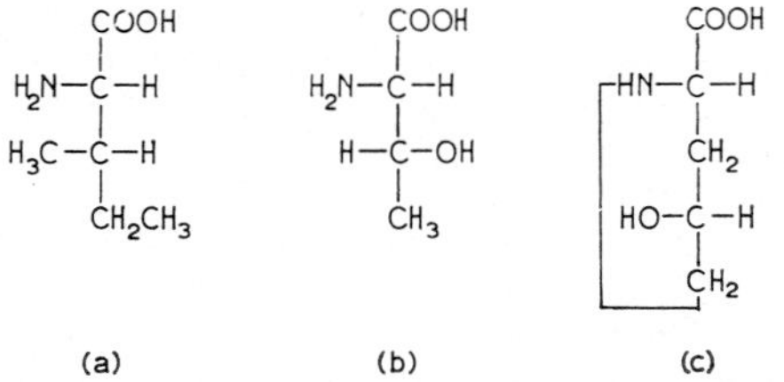

(a)   (b)   (c)

Fig. 2. Configurations of the natural amino acids with secondary asymmetric centres, according to the Fischer convention. (a) isoleucine; (b) threonine; (c) hydroxyproline.

References p. 267

For threonine the configuration shown in Fig. 2(b) was first demonstrated chemically, and has since been confirmed by crystal structure analysis[4]. In hydroxyproline the hydroxyl and carboxyl groups are *trans* to the ring, as in Fig. 2(c); again chemical and crystallographic data are in agreement[5].

Cystine is a particularly interesting case. In three crystal structure analyses of different cystine compounds the molecule has been found to be symmetrical, with a twofold axis through the centre of the S–S bond[6–8]. For hexagonal L-cystine[6] the S–S bond is 2.03 Å long (essentially a single bond), the angle at the sulphur atom is 114°, and the dihedral angle of the C–S–S–C bridge is 106°. Similar values were found in the other compounds, and are likely to be repeated in the arrangement of the disulphide bridge between chains in proteins.

(b) Peptides

A further vital piece of information has come from the crystal structure studies of amides (including glutamine) and small peptides. In all cases the C–N bond of the amide group or peptide link is about 1.32 Å long, which corresponds to 50% of double-bond character. Also, the six atoms of the peptide group C_α–CO–NH–C_α lie in a plane, with the two α-carbon atoms *trans* to the C–N bond (Fig. 3). As we shall see later, this axiom of the planarity of the peptide link was brilliantly used by Pauling and Corey[14] in choosing the most satisfactory configurations for regular polypeptide chains.

The stereochemical principles described so far are beautifully illustrated in the crystal structure of glutathione, recently determined by Wright[10]. References to several earlier determinations of amide and peptide structures may be found in a review by Kendrew and Perutz[11]. Glutathione is a tripeptide: γ-L-glutamyl–L-cysteinyl–glycine. The configuration found in the crystal structure is shown in Fig. 4. Both the peptide groups $C_4-N_2-C_6-O_4-C_7$ and $C_2-N_1-C_3-O_3-C_4$ have the CO and NH groups in *trans* configuration, and are planar, the greatest deviation from the mean planes being 0.12 Å for N_2. Their C–N bonds are short: $C_6-N_2 = 1.31$ Å, $C_3-N_1 = 1.32$ Å, whereas C_4-N_2 is 1.46 Å long, and is essentially a single bond. C_4, supporting the reactive SH-group, is a central pivot shared by the two planar groups, which have some freedom of rotation about the single bonds C_4-N_2 and C_4-C_3. In the crystal the angle between the planes is 94.4°.

(c) Polypeptides

Peptide chains in proteins are long. A typical chain length among the globular proteins is between 100 and 150 residues, while in the natural and artificial polypeptide fibres the lengths are yet greater. Knowing the stereochemistry of the backbone atoms in a single residue, and the geometry expected for the link between residues, it is possible to predict dimensions for polypeptide chains in which the residues are regularly arranged[12]. Random arrangements are by no means improbable, since there is great freedom of rotation about the C_α-linked bonds of the backbone chain. Indeed, a thoroughly denatured pure protein preparation would demonstrate the myriad possibilities of randomness very effectively by the difficulty of detecting any group of "molecules" having the same configuration. However, we know that proteins produced by the living organism are regular in structure: the fibrous ones are not like rubber, but show considerable strength, while the globular ones are crystallisable. Both give X-ray diffraction patterns in which the detail is a direct reflection of the regularity in structure.

The simplest regular form is the fully extended chain shown in Fig. 3. In this, each residue is related to the next by a rotation of 180° and a translation, always in the same direction. These movements may be regarded as the basic operations by which the symmetry of the structure is generated. The two other classical symmetry operations of reflection in a mirror and inversion through a centre of symmetry must be rejected in building up polypeptide chains other than polyglycine, because either of them would change the hand of the asymmetric carbon atoms from L to D. With more general rotations and translations, regularly repeated, one builds up a helix. If one turn is exactly filled by a simple number of residues, the helix is called integral, but non-integral helices are perfectly regular objects. Attractive examples of this more subtle symmetry can be found in the patterns of spines on some ornamental cacti. Helical symmetry is also familiar in crystals, but there the geometrical conditions are more restrictive: only integral helices with 2, 3, 4, or 6 pattern-units per rotation will allow a regular side-by-side packing which fills the whole three-dimensional space. However, for an isolated regular polypeptide chain, a non-integral helix is *a priori* the most likely form.

The precise dimensions of any helical model have to be decided on stereochemical grounds. Apart from the covalent bond geometry which has already been discussed, one must take into account the possibilities of forming hydrogen bonds between the more electronegative atoms oxygen and nitrogen, and the van der Waals repulsion between atoms which are brought too close. Generally, all the possible hydrogen bonds *are* formed, and it is sound practice to check model structures to see if this is so. Usually, a good hydrogen bond can only be formed if the hydrogen atom lies naturally close to the line joining the two electronegative centres, and the distance between them is reasonable, *i.e.* near to 2.6 Å for $O-H\ldots O$ and 2.8 Å for $N-H\ldots O$. For a thoroughgoing discussion with many examples the reader is referred to a review by Donohue[13]. Some useful Van der Waals

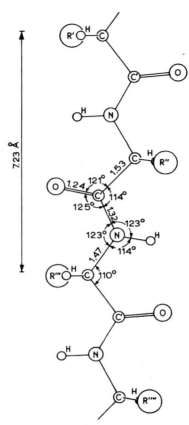

Fig. 3. Dimensions of the fully extended polypeptide chain. (From Pauling and Corey[14]).

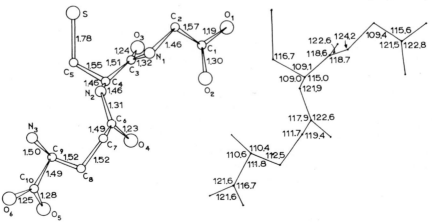

Fig. 4. Configuration of glutathione found in the crystal structure. (From Wright[10].)

radii are: H 1.2 Å; N 1.5 Å; O 1.4 Å; CH₃ 2.0 Å; but these should be taken only as a rough guide: closer contacts than would be expected from the sum of these radii may be found in special situations.

The number of structures which can be made to satisfy all the stereo-chemical requirements is always quite small, indeed, for the polypeptide chain it is probable that only one configuration, the α-helix of Pauling *et al.*[9] (Fig. 5), is completely acceptable. However, rather than merely describe this one particular form, it seems worthwhile to discuss the general way in

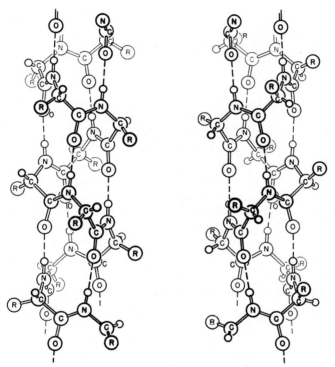

Fig. 5. Left- and right-handed α-helices. (Drawings from Pauling *et al.*[9].)

which the problem can be approached. It is hoped in this way to emphasize the value of stereochemical knowledge gained from crystal structure studies, and to bring out the reasons why the α-helix is preferred above all others.

If the configuration is a helix, the general direction of the covalent bonds –CH(R)–CO–NH–CH(R)– will be along the thread, and to hold successive turns in register one above the other there must be subsidiary hydrogen bonding in the general direction of the helix axis. Since the NH

References p. 267

and CO groups will be the ones involved in regular hydrogen bonding, the plane of the peptide link, which contains these bonds, must be roughly parallel to the helix axis too. With this situation two orientations of the peptide link are possible, as shown in Fig. 6. Roughly speaking they are related by rotation through 180° about the thread direction, but a better description can be given in terms of the sense, or polarity, of the peptide

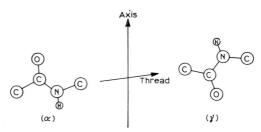

Fig. 6. Alternative orientations of the peptide link in helical structures.

link in relation to the sense of the rotation and translation producing the basic helix. Suppose rotation and translation together produce a movement from one α-carbon to the next along the thread in the direction $C_{\alpha_1} \to C \to N \to C_{\alpha_2}$ then, for the first orientation (α) the simultaneous axial translation is in the sense $H \to N \to C \to O$; for the second orientation (γ) the same sense for the thread corresponds to the opposite direction for the axis, *i.e.* $O \to C \to N \to H$. With the α orientation, the hydrogen bonds between turns close off rings of atoms with the general formula

$$CO - [NH - C_\alpha - CO]_n - NH$$

whereas with the γ orientation the general formula for the hydrogen bonded ring is

$$NH - [C_\alpha - CO - NH]_n - C_\alpha - CO$$

Depending on the way the links are made, n can, in principle, take on any integral value, but not all the resulting structures are stereochemically satisfactory.

In the α-helix (the original example of the α-class) the NH of each peptide link is hydrogen bonded to the CO of the third peptide link further round the thread, *i.e.* the ring closed by the hydrogen bond has the formula

$$CO - [NH - C_\alpha - CO]_3 - NH$$

There are 3.6 residues per turn, and the axial translation is 1.5 Å. A notation for helical structures introduced by Bragg *et al.*[15] would have this configuration designated 3.6_{13}, or generally S_R where S is the number of residues per turn, and R is the number of atoms in the hydrogen bonded ring. This structure is completely satisfactory stereochemically: the peptide groups are strictly planar, and the bond angle at the α-carbon atom is tetrahedral. The van der Waals contacts are close, but not too close (N...N 2.9 Å; N...O 3.0 Å; C...O 2.7 Å; C...C 2.9 Å), so there is a small gain of stability from the van der Waals attraction, and no loss due to repulsion. The hydrogen atoms lie in the line of the hydrogen bond, which is 2.86 Å long. Other members of the series with $n = 1$, 2 or 4 can be built ($n = 4$ gives the π-helix of Low and Baybutt), but these are all somewhat less stable, as Donohue has shown[16].

In the γ series, the prototype γ-helix with $n = 4$, also proposed by Pauling, Corey and Branson, appears to be considerably less stable than the α-helix, firstly because the N–H bond is some 30° off the line of the N−H...O hydrogen bond, and secondly because it is a very open structure lacking stabilisation from close Van der Waals contacts. The members of this series with $n = 1$ and 2 cannot be built without intolerable distortions of bond angles, but the helix with $n = 3$ appears possible though rather less stable than the $n = 4$ γ-helix. Again the reader must be referred to Donohue's paper[16] for detailed assessments.

Until now we have left aside the question of the hand of the helix, and at first sight there would appear to be no important difference between left-handed and right-handed versions since one can be turned into the other by reflection in a mirror. Although this is true for the backbone atoms alone, it no longer holds when the configuration around the α-carbon atom is taken into account. If the first atom of the side chain, C_β, (excepting glycine) is always placed so that C_α has the L-configuration, as in the natural amino acids, left- and right-handed helices become metrically distinguishable, and may be expected to differ slightly in energy. In a left-handed α-helix of L-amino acids C_β comes rather close to the carboxyl oxygen (Fig. 5), while in the right-handed version the bond to C points more directly outward from the axis, giving greater freedom to the side chain. This suggests that the right-handed α-helix may be the more stable form for proteins.

This concludes the discussion of stereochemical principles, and we must now pass on to consider the experimental evidence for the presence of helical polypeptide chains in natural and synthetic materials.

3. X-ray diffraction by fibres

The natural protein fibres hair, wool and silk contain polypeptide chains running roughly parallel to the length. Similarly, artificial polypeptides, such as poly-γ-methyl-L-glutamate and poly-L-alanine, can be spun into fibres with the molecular chains rather well oriented along the length. These fibres are not crystalline, since there is no special orientation around the fibre axis, and indeed no well defined *molecule* in register with other molecules along this axis. The best one can hope to do, therefore, in describing their structures is to give the rules by which one residue is related to the others over the most prominent regular regions. Now, any complex pattern which is regular over a reasonably large number of repeats can be analysed into the sum of simpler repeating patterns. For example, the α-helix, regarded as an array of point atoms, could be subdivided into simple helices each containing only one type of atom: all would have the same translation and rotation parameters, but the radii would be different. For a continuous periodic distribution such as that of the electrons in the α-helix (and it is the electrons which scatter the X-rays) a particularly convenient way of simplifying the pattern is to split it into its Fourier components, that is to

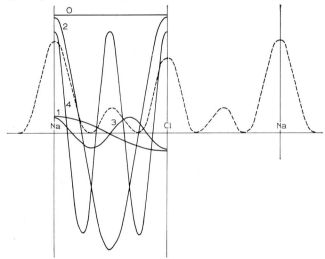

Fig. 7. Addition of Fourier components to make up the pattern of electron density along the [111] direction in crystalline sodium chloride. The order number of each wave is shown. The spurious peak between Na and Cl atoms arises from the use of too few Fourier waves in building up the curve.

represent it as the sum of a number of sinusoidal plane waves. The wavelengths of these Fourier components must, of course, be integrally related to the fundamental period of the structure, *i.e.* the first order component has one wave fitting into the fundamental repeat, the second order component has two waves to the repeat, and so on. This is very easily illustrated in one dimension. Fig. 7 shows the way one could build up a picture of the electron density along the body-diagonal of the cubic unit cell of crystalline sodium chloride, starting with the first few Fourier components. The beauty of this

Fourier representation is that it corresponds to the way in which a structure is "seen" by X-rays. For each Fourier wave there is a corresponding spot in the X-ray diffraction pattern: if the Fourier wave has a large amplitude the X-ray spot is strong; in fact its intensity is proportional to the square of the amplitude of the Fourier wave. It is convenient to think of the diffraction pattern as existing in so-called *reciprocal space*. Each spot can be plotted out in this three-dimensional space by measuring out from the origin, in the direction perpendicular to the corresponding Fourier wave, a length inversely proportional to the Fourier wavelength, and marking at that point the square of the amplitude. Thus, if we had a fibre made up of equally thick discs of high and low electron density stacked alternately, *i.e.* with a strong periodicity in the vertical direction, the representation in reciprocal space would show a number of equally spaced spots along the vertical axis, the first being the strongest since the first order Fourier component is the most important. Similarly, if the fibre contains chains stacked regularly side by side, the horizontal plane in reciprocal space will contain spots corresponding to the lateral Fourier waves making up the pattern of electron density as seen down the fibre axis.

An X-ray photograph is essentially a sample of the intensity distribution in reciprocal space. Unfortunately, when taken in the usual way, with the fibre at right angles to the X-ray beam and the photographic film behind, it is a rather odd sample. For the X-ray spot to be recorded experimentally each set of Fourier waves has to be at the correct angle to the X-ray beam. This angle θ is given by the Bragg equation $\lambda = 2d \sin \theta$, where λ is the wavelength of the X-rays being used and d is the wavelength of the Fourier waves. The situation is best visualised through a construction due to Ewald. First the distribution in reciprocal space is taken to be drawn on such a scale that a Fourier wave of wavelength d gives a spot $1/d$ cm from the origin. Then the direction of the incident X-rays is shown by a line through this origin, and a sphere of radius $1/\lambda$ cm is drawn around this line as diameter and with the surface passing through the origin point (Fig. 8). Only those spots in reciprocal space which lie on the surface of the sphere are correctly oriented to give traces on the photographic film. It is easily verified from Fig. 8 that for all these points the Bragg equation is satisfied. Other regions of the pattern in reciprocal space can, of course, be recorded by tipping the fibre, since the reciprocal space pattern will rotate with the fibre.

The usual fibre diffraction arrangement, then, records the reciprocal space pattern on a spherical surface. It would be preferable to record the intensity distribution in the plane at right angles to the X-ray beam, and this can be done with appropriate apparatus, but for most purposes the simple arrangement is satisfactory since it does approximate to the ideal one for small θ-values. Conventionally the fibre is mounted vertically; the vertical

References p. 267

axis of the photograph is then called the meridian, and the horizontal axis the equator. Here these terms will be used to refer to axes in the true reciprocal plane at right angles to the X-ray beam.

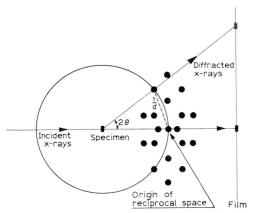

Fig. 8. Diffraction by a fibre. Sampling by the Ewald sphere of the intensity distribution in reciprocal space.

Very early, the natural polypeptide fibres were assigned to two classes, α and β, according to the characteristics of their diffraction photographs. The unstretched keratin fibres of hair, horn and wool gave the distinctive

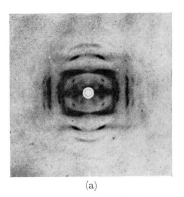
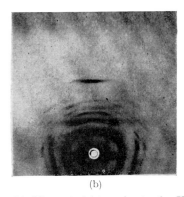

(a)   (b)

Fig. 9. Fibre photographs of α-poly-L-alanine. (a) Fibre at right angles to the X-ray beam; (b) fibre tipped through $31°$ to record the 1.5 Å reflection. (From Brown and Trotter[17].)

α-pattern, while stretched keratin (elongated by more than 30%), and silk were representative of the β-class. Synthetic polypeptides have also been found to give typical α and β patterns, the type of structure often depending on the nature of the solvent from which they are precipitated. Sometimes the synthetic materials have given much better diffraction pictures than the natural fibres, particularly where only one type of side chain has been present.

Fig. 9 shows two particularly fine photographs of poly-L-alanine in the unstretched α-form. In the first (a) the fibre was at right angles to the incident X-ray beam, so the spots near the centre give a good idea of the intensity distribution around the origin on the reciprocal plane normal to the X-rays. In the second (b) the fibre was tipped through 31° to bring the high order part of the meridian (around 1.5 Å spacing) into the reflecting position. As was first pointed out by Perutz[18], the very strong spot on the meridian at 1.5 Å spacing is characteristic of the α-helix, being the Fourier component in step with the fundamental axial translation of 1.5 Å from one residue to the next. None of the other helical structures has this axial spacing. The strong layer line, which also shows up well in the second photograph, crosses the meridian at a spacing of 5.4 Å, which is just the pitch of the α-helix, and the strong off-meridian spots on this layer line correspond to Fourier components in step with the inclined turns of the helix. The equatorial spots, seen best in the first picture, are all orders of a hexagonal array, such as would be expected from a close-packed bundle of cylinders, the diameter of each cylinder being 8.55 Å. The pattern from the α-form of poly-γ-methyl glutamate is similar, except that the lateral spots correspond to a hexagonal array of cylinders 12 Å in diameter, the greater separation being accounted for by the bulkier side chain. The most detailed comparison of observed diffraction intensities with those calculated from various α-helical models has been made by Elliott and Malcolm for poly-L-alanine[19]. They found very good agreement with right-handed α-helices packed together with the sense of the peptide sequence in neighbouring chains completely random. Left-handed helices definitely did not give such close agreement.

In the natural α-keratin structure found in hair, myosin, tropomyosin, fibrinogen, epidermis, and porcupine quill, there appears to be a further degree of organisation superimposed on the α-helices. The diffraction pattern shows the characteristic meridional reflection at 1.5 Å, but the other meridional reflection corresponding to the pitch of the helix is not at 5.4 Å but 5.1 Å. Crick and, separately, Pauling and Corey pointed out that this could be explained by twisting α-helices together to form a slowly coiling flex or cable (Fig. 10). This supercoiling might be produced by interactions between side chains in a specially repeating sequence[20], or by the requirements of packing neighbouring non-integral helices together as closely as possible[21].

The β-type photographs, of which Fig. 11 is a good example, show the strongest spots near "layer-lines" which arise from a vertical repeat of

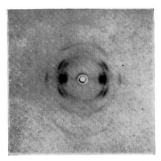

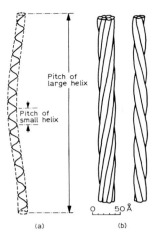

Fig. 10. Coiled-coil type of structure proposed for α-keratin. (From Pauling and Corey[20]).

Fig. 11. Fibre photograph of β-poly-L-alanine; fibre at right angles to the X-ray beam. (From Brown and Trotter[17].)

6.9 Å in the fibre. Clearly, the polypeptide chain must be in an almost completely extended form, for, as shown in Fig. 3, the repeat distance between similarly oriented residues in the fully extended chain is only 7.2 Å. Neighbouring extended chains can be coupled laterally through $N-H-O$ hydrogen bonds to form sheet structures in two ways: either with all the chains running in the same direction (parallel pleated sheet of Pauling and Corey[22]), or with the chains running alternately up and down (antiparallel pleated sheet) as shown in Fig. 12. With the most favourable configurations for the bonds the parallel pleated sheet has an axial repeat of 6.5 Å, while the repeat for the antiparallel sheet is 7.0 Å. The first has been proposed as the structure for β-keratin, and the second for silk and β-polyalanine, but there still seems to be some doubt whether the chains may not be sometimes coupled one way and sometimes the other way in the same fibre. An interesting situation occurs if, in any way, odd-numbered amino acids are distinguished from even-numbered ones in the sequence. The sheet structures then become polar, with the side chains of different types on opposite sides. For example, it has been suggested by Marsh *et al.*[23] that the silk of *Bombyx mori* consists largely of chains of alternate glycine and alanine residues. Pairs of sheets can then be packed back-to-back with

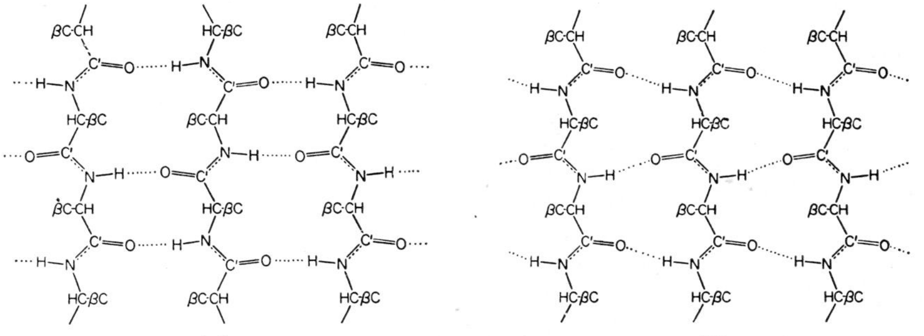

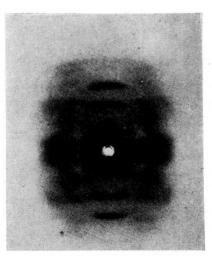

Fig. 12. Parallel (a) and antiparallel (b) sheet structures. (From Pauling and Corey[22]).

a separation of 5.6–5.7 Å where the alanine methyl groups are in contact, but only 3.5–3.7 Å where the hydrogens of glycine touch. In Tussah silk, though, the proportion of alanine is higher, and, indeed, the diffraction

Fig. 13. Fibre photograph of dry collagen stretched 8%. Fibre at right angles to the beam. (From Cowan *et al.*[25].)

pattern is very similar to that of β poly-L-alanine. For these two materials the sheets appear to be packed together in a random way[24].

Collagen gives a diffraction pattern which is quite unlike those of the α- or β-polypeptides (Fig. 13); also it is unique in its high content of glycine (about 33 %), and proline plus hydroxyproline (about 22 %). Two constituents, hydroxyproline and hydroxylysine, are only found in collagen and closely related materials. The two imino acids, proline and hydroxyproline, have no NH-group with which to form a hydrogen bond, so a single chain structure with regular axial hydrogen bonds cannot be built. Following a suggestion

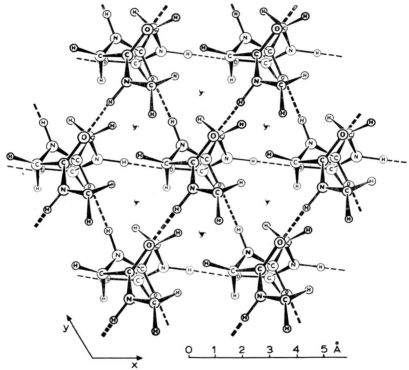

Fig. 14. Structure of polyglycine II. Projection down the threefold axis showing seven chains of the infinite network. (From Crick and Rich[27].)

by Ramachandran and Kartha[26], it has become clear that the deficiency is made up by taking three chains together, and forming hydrogen bonds between them. The whole configuration, which is quite complex, is most readily understood by looking first at the structure proposed for polyglycine II by Crick and Rich[27] (Fig. 14). Here each polyglycine chain is a simple helix with exactly three residues per turn, and adjacent helices are joined by lateral hydrogen bonding to form an infinite three-dimensional network. The structure of collagen proposed by Rich and Crick[28] can be derived from this by taking three interlinked chains out of the three dimensional network and replacing the non-hydrogen bonded outside residues by proline

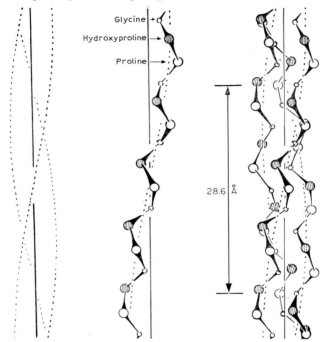

Fig. 15. Principles of the collagen structure. Only C_α carbon atoms are shown. Small circles show the sites which must be glycine; large and shaded circles can be proline or hydroxyproline. (From Rich and Crick[28].)

or hydroxyproline. The three stranded rope is then twisted into a super helix in such a way that the rotation per residue is reduced from 120° to 108° (Fig. 15). There are, in fact, two distinct sets of triple strands in the structure of polyglycine II, and, correspondingly, two proposed structures for collagen following this general plan. One of these is much preferred, since it gives better agreement with the diffraction pattern, and is rather more satisfactory stereochemically. The model does, of course, predict that every third residue in the sequence should be glycine, and this is in agreement with the chemical studies, but it offers no special explanation for the frequent occurrence of the peptide -Gly-Pro-Hypro-Gly-.

Apart from this, which might be termed the secondary structure, collagen gives beautiful evidence of tertiary structure in the regular banding at a spacing of 640 Å which is so characteristic in electron microscope pictures. Several orders of this spacing are observed in the low angle X-ray diffraction pattern, but the basis of the tertiary structure is not known.

4. X-ray diffraction of globular proteins

The X-ray crystallographic study of globular proteins, with which the remainder of this chapter is mainly concerned, makes use of the concepts of the crystallography of small molecules such as unit cell, space group, asymmetric unit, axis of symmetry, etc. These terms will be used without further explanation, since they have all been defined by Bullen (see Volume 3, Chapter I, p. 1). A description of the special techniques of isomorphous replacement as applied to proteins will be given later, but some of the more straightforward results of examining protein crystals with X-rays will be mentioned first.

The atlas of crystalline enzymes prepared by Dixon and Webb[29] contains more than sixty different enzymes, not counting differences in the species of origin, and does not include other non-enzyme proteins such as haemoglobin, β-lactoglobulin, and serum albumin which have been available in crystalline form for many years. It is remarkable that such large molecules (the majority of molecular weights are around 60,000) should crystallise so readily, for crystallisation implies that the choice of configurations for the molecule is small. In fact the great majority which have been studied have at least one crystal form in which only a single configuration is used. The conditions of crystallisation are usually close to the physiological; indeed, some mammalian haemoglobins can be crystallised inside the red blood cells, merely by lowering the temperature to 0°. Also, the molecular environment inside the crystals is not as different from that in solution as might at first appear. In between the molecules as they are stacked in the crystal there are large gaps filled with the crystallisation medium: a typical protein crystal will have 40% of its volume occupied by this mother liquor. The limited choice of configurations, and the rather slight change of molecular environment on crystallisation, make it unlikely that there is any great configurational change between physiological solution and the crystals, but there is really no detailed evidence on this point.

It is difficult to discuss the possible degrees of structural variation without a generally agreed terminology. Here the division into primary, secondary and tertiary structure suggested by Linderstrøm-Lang (and extended to quaternary structure by Bernal) is useful, because it can, to a large extent, be defined operationally. By primary structure is meant the conventional chemical structural formula, expressed as the sequence of amino acids along the polypeptide chain, together with any other covalent bonding, through

—S–S— bridges, for example. Secondary structure refers to spacial relationships between adjacent residues, particularly any patterns of regularity such as the formation of helical structures. If such regular groupings do occur, it may be convenient to envisage a higher scheme of organisation between them, and call this the tertiary structure. Secondary and tertiary structure, however, are both aspects of folding the polypeptide chain, and are not always readily distinguishable. Quaternary structure covers the association of already folded units into relatively stable aggregates, the implication being that the units are capable of independent existence. The protein coats of viruses are examples of such high order aggregates, and other examples can be found among the larger protein molecules.

Until recently all our knowledge of the primary structure of proteins has been won through developments in the analytical techniques of peptide chemistry. The pioneering work of Sanger and his collaborators[30] on insulin has been rapidly followed by success with larger polypeptide chains in ribonuclease[31], tobacco mosaic virus[32], haemoglobin[54], and cytochrome c[83]. Only in the case of myoglobin[17] has a crystallographic analysis been taken far enough for individual side chains to be recognisable in the electron density maps.

As has been remarked already, a large proportion of the volume of protein crystals is occupied by the mother liquor. Apart from a layer of more ordered solvent and ions over the surface of the protein molecules, most of this liquid is in no way special, and quite large molecules, up to the size of dyes, can be diffused into it from outside the crystal. If a crystal is removed from the mother liquor and allowed to dry, the unbound water is lost. At first the structure may shrink a little, still preserving a very high degree of order, but eventually it collapses, leaving the molecules close packed but disoriented. During the X-ray exposure, therefore, the crystal must be kept wet, which is done by sealing it in a thin walled glass capillary. A few drops of mother liquor are left in the capillary, but the crystal itself is blotted dry so that unwanted absorption and scattering of the X-rays are reduced to a minimum. In these conditions the diffraction pattern extends out to spacing of 1.5 to 2 Å. The example shown in Fig. 16 includes reflections out to 2.7 Å spacing, where the average intensity is still quite high.

The cell dimensions and space group are immediately available from the first few photographs. Combined with a knowledge of the water content, or an approximate value of the molecular weight, these data enable one to decide the size of the asymmetric unit of pattern. Very often this will contain just one protein molecule, sometimes there will be two or more, occasionally only a half or some other simple fraction of the molecular weight found by hydrodynamic methods. In one form of horse haemoglobin[34], for example, the asymmetric unit contains only half the usual molecular weight of

68,000. This molecule, therefore, was known to be composed of two very similar, if not identical, parts long before the chemical identification of four polypeptide chains—two of one type, and two of another—had been made. However, if a protein molecule is composed of sub-units, this fact is not necessarily revealed in the crystallography: it is only when these

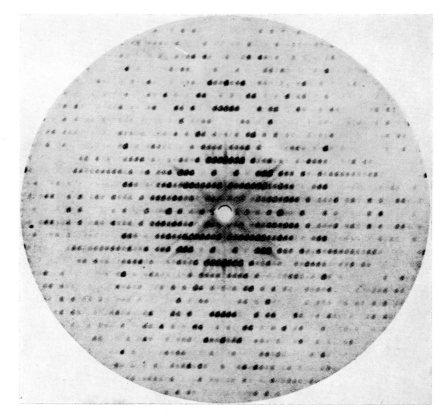

Fig. 16. Diffraction pattern from a single crystal of a globular protein. Finback whale myoglobin type F, c-projection. (From Kendrew and Kraut[33].)

sub-units are arranged symmetrically, and the molecular symmetry is aligned with the extended symmetry of the crystal, that it becomes immediately obvious. Insulin provides an example of hidden sub-units: the monomer is known to have a molecular weight of 6,000, but the asymmetric unit weight in both common crystal forms is 12,000.

A quick examination of X-ray photographs can sometimes tell one if varieties of a protein from different sources, distinguishable perhaps by immunological tests or electrophoretic mobility, have the same configuration, though differing in primary structure. Quick results are again a matter of luck, as one can see from the example of β-lactoglobulin. Two genetically controlled forms of this protein are found in pooled milk: they differ in electrophoretic mobility[35]. Cows which are homozygous for the lactoglobulin gene are easily detected, so the pure A and B forms of this protein can be prepared and crystallised. When this was first done, the crystal forms of A and B were found to be different, though the molecular weights could be shown to be the same. Later a second crystal form of the B protein was found which was virtually indistinguishable from A, the intensities on the diffraction photographs matching spot by spot out to 3.5 Å spacing[36]. A and B β-lactoglobulins do not differ in configuration, therefore, even though some differences in composition have been found by chemical methods. The same is true of normal human haemoglobin and the sickle cell variant[37]. These have been shown to differ by the exchange of a valine residue for one of glutamic acid[38], but the diffraction photographs are practically identical. Among the myoglobins, too, preparations from sperm whale, finback whale, blue whale, sei whale, lesser rorqual, and common porpoise all give crystals of the same type[39].

This insensitivity of the diffraction data seems to set a limit to the capabilities of the X-ray method, and it is of some interest to know where this limit lies. Since X-rays are scattered by electrons, the way to regard the exchange of amino acids is as the replacement of one electron density pattern by another, within the volume occupied by the side chain. The electron density patterns involved are principally made up of peaks at the C, N, and O atoms, at the most about 4 Å apart, and considerably spread out by thermal vibration. The changes will be small, since none of the atoms has a high atomic number, and they will, in general, vary from positive to negative over a distance of 2 Å or less. If this pattern of changes is split into Fourier components, as described in the introduction to fibre diffraction, one may expect the most prominent waves to have wavelengths of less than 4 Å. This means that the largest changes in the diffraction pattern should appear at spacings less than 4 Å, *i.e.* only among the higher order reflections, which are not usually the first to be recorded, will they be obvious.

5. Isomorphous replacement

Amino acid exchanges in proteins are not useful to the crystallographer because they involve atoms which scatter X-rays too feebly, and they are too much spread out in space. The situation is completely transformed if derivatives containing heavy atoms can be prepared and crystallised in a form isomorphous with the untreated protein, *i.e.* unaltered in any other way. The basic difficulty in X-ray analysis, the phase problem, can then be overcome, enabling the protein structure to be revealed by methods which are quite direct and free from assumptions. But the first step is a difficult one to take. Derivatives are needed in which the heavy atoms occupy a small number of specific sites on the protein molecule. Very few reactions by which such sites can be picked out have been developed, though the advantages of this approach to protein chemistry were pointed out by Cohn[40] in 1948, and the strength of his arguments has increased greatly since then. Among the few possibilities, the blocking of sulphydryl groups with mercurials has been studied most, and was the first to be used in the X-ray work. For enzymes there is an attractive opportunity to block the active site with an inhibitor or substrate analogue containing a heavy atom, but no success has yet been reported with this method. Schemes for reactions at the N-terminal α-amino group, and with some of the rarer amino acids such as tyrosine and tryptophan also appear possible, but have not been exploited. Fortunately, a less systematic approach has produced suitable derivatives of myoglobin and haemoglobin, but there remains a great need for methods which can be applied, with reasonable hope of success, to a majority of proteins. It is doubtful if anything useful can be said about the further difficulties to be overcome in crystallising derivatives isomorphously!

The way in which such isomorphous derivatives have been used will be described in terms of the situation where only one heavy atom is present in the asymmetric unit, but there is no difference of principle involved in dealing with two or three heavy atoms attached to a typical protein of, say, 30,000 molecular weight. Ideally, the difference between the protein crystal and its isomorphous heavy atom derivative should appear, to the X-ray eye, as a very high peak in the distribution of electron density. To build up such a peak by adding Fourier components, one must use waves of all possible wavelengths, with their crests all adding at the peak, but cancelling with troughs in other waves elsewhere. In order to specify the way in which Fourier waves should be added to produce such a picture it is convenient to introduce the concept of a *phase* for each wave. This is merely an expression for the position of the Fourier wave relative to a conveniently chosen origin. If the wave is placed with a peak precisely in register with the origin, its phase is 0°; if it has the trough at the origin the phase is 180°; at the negative-going zero the phase is 90°, and so on; one wavelength corresponding to one complete cycle of 360°. A few waves of different phase (and amplitude), adding up to a peak some distance from the origin, are shown in Fig. 17. Precisely the same definition of phase is suitable for waves in two and three dimensions. Since a peak must be built up from all the available waves, one may expect every reflection in the diffraction pattern to be affected by this difference in the electron density. Here we are again making use of the correspondence between reflections and Fourier components which

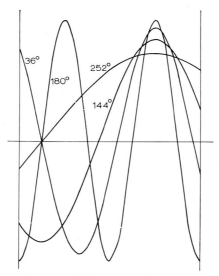

Fig. 17. Fourier component waves of different amplitude and phase adding up in a peak away from the origin.

was introduced in the discussion of fibre diffraction patterns. However, this general argument has taken no account of the symmetry of the crystal: it is true for a triclinic protein crystal with only one heavy atom per unit cell, but, more usually, there will be a few heavy atoms, related in position by the symmetry of the space group. For a few reflections the separate contributions of these related atoms may interfere and cancel completely, producing no change of intensity, but, in general, interference will leave some contribution from the heavy atoms to change the reflection.

The simplest way of representing this interference between scattering contributions from different atoms, or sets of atoms, is by means of a vector diagram (Fig. 18b). The length of the vector is drawn to represent the amplitude, F_1, while the angle between the vector and some axis of reference, usually taken pointing to the right, represents the phase φ. The precise formulae for calculating the amplitudes and phases of scattering are given by Bullen: it is sufficient for the present purpose to point out that the amplitude of scattering from a single atom varies only with the Bragg spacing, *i.e.* the distance from the centre of the diffraction pattern, decreasing as this distance increases; while the phase depends on the position of the atom relative to conveniently chosen axes. Where there are symmetry axes, these are always chosen to define the coordinate system because the representation of phase can then be simplified. This can be illustrated by a two-dimensional case with symmetry, such as the projection of a crystal structure onto a plane at right angles to a twofold symmetry axis. Here the origin would be chosen at the twofold axis, so that the atoms are related in pairs symmetrically through the origin. The phases of the scattering contributions from the two members of each pair are also symmetrically related, as is shown in Fig. 18b for two pairs, one heavy (large amplitude) and one light (small amplitude). It is easy to see that the sum total of such contributions, however many atoms there are in the unit cell, must always lie, positively or negatively, along the direction of zero phase, *i.e.* the phase angle is either 0° or 180°. Such reflections are said to have *real* amplitudes, and are conventionally termed *plus* and *minus* for the 0° and 180° phase angles. This restriction to real amplitudes is only valid for those special reflections in the diffraction pattern which correspond to centrosymmetry in the structure. Proteins are, of course, asymmetric, with all the molecules of the same hand, so it is impossible that the crystal as a whole should be centrosymmetric; only views down the even-fold symmetry axes can be treated this way. All the other reflections, that is the great majority for any protein, are quite unrestricted in phase. Here we have the crux of the problem in X-ray analysis, for there is no technical means of recording the phases of reflections, one can only measure the intensities.

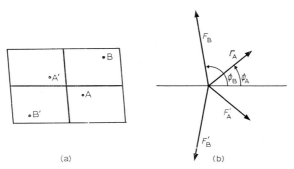

Fig. 18. (a) Centrosymmetric arrangement of two pairs of atoms; (b) Vector representation of the contributions from each atom to one particular reflection.

The effect of the heavy atom is most easily interpreted for the real reflections, and in the cases which have been worked out so far the first step has been to extract all the information which they can give. Since the phases are simply positive or negative, the effect of the heavy atom on any particular

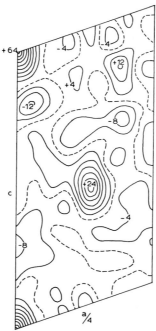

Fig. 19. Difference Patterson for two heavy atoms in the unit cell. Horse haemoglobin, C2 form, *b*-projection, SH-derivative with PCMB. (From Green *et al.*[41].)

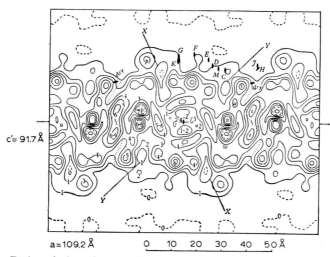

Fig. 20. Projected view of a row of haemoglobin molecules in salt-free water. The dyad axis relating the two halves of the molecule is at the centre. (From Bragg and Perutz[42].)

reflection is very easily understood. Three cases can arise: first, when the contribution from the heavy atom F_H is in phase with the scattering from the protein alone F_P, the resultant F_{PH} is merely the sum $F_P + F_H$; second, when they are out of phase, and the heavy atom contribution is smaller than that of the protein, $|F_{PH}| = |F_P| - |F_H|$; third, when they are out of phase, but the heavy atom contribution is greater than that from the protein, $|F_{PH}| = |F_H| - |F_P|$. In this third case the reflection changes sign, but this will not be obvious when photographs of the native protein and the derivative are compared. Fortunately, the number of reflections on which this happens may be expected to be small, since the general scattering power of the whole protein is very much greater than that of the heavy atoms. For the first two cases, the size of the heavy atom contribution can be worked out from measurements on the photographs, since each reflection intensity is proportional to F^2; thus

$$|F_H| = \left|\sqrt{F_{PH}^2} - \sqrt{F_P^2}\right|$$

The third case cannot be detected at this stage, but this quantity, the difference of amplitudes for the protein and the derivative, is worked out for every reflection, and then squared. F_H^2 is just the intensity of scattering which would have been produced by the heavy atom alone (excepting case 3). The variation in F_H^2 from one reflection to another, being largely due to interference between the heavy atoms, can be used to give some information about their positions in the unit cell. All the values of F_H^2 are combined into a difference Patterson synthesis, which shows the length and direction of every line which can be drawn between the heavy atoms in the unit cell. For the derivation and an explanation of the Patterson synthesis the reader must again be referred to the chapter by Bullen (see Volume 3, Chapter I, p. 19). If there are not too many heavy atoms, their positions in the unit cell can be deduced from the difference Patterson diagram. When there are only two atoms in the cell the interpretation is particularly straightforward since only one line can be drawn: Fig. 19 is an example of such a case. Once the positions of the heavy atoms are known, the expected magnitudes and signs of their contributions can be calculated for every reflection, and used, by checking whether the reflection went up or down between F_P^2 and F_{PH}^2, to give signs to the reflections from the protein alone[41]. At this stage the mistaken cases where the sign of the reflection was changed by the heavy atom, and $|F_H|$ should have been $|F_{PH}| + |F_P|$, can be corrected.

In practice not all the signs of the real reflections can be determined by a single isomorphous replacement because, on some reflections, the effect of the heavy atom is too small to measure. One or two further derivatives, with the heavy atoms in new positions, would enable the whole field of these special reflections to be covered. Having determined all the signs, the way is open to calculate an electron density map for the protein. This will necessarily be a projection, since we have only discussed the use of real reflections. An example is shown in Fig. 20: the projected view of a row of haemoglobin molecules, seen at a resolution of 6 Å. It is unreasonable to expect that any familiar chemical features would be recognised in such a picture, for there are too many atoms on top of one another in the great thickness of the projection (63 Å). It is essential to build up a three-dimensional picture by releasing the information locked away in the remainder of the diffraction pattern.

The task of dealing with the remaining great majority of reflections which are not restricted in phase is more difficult. At least two isomorphous

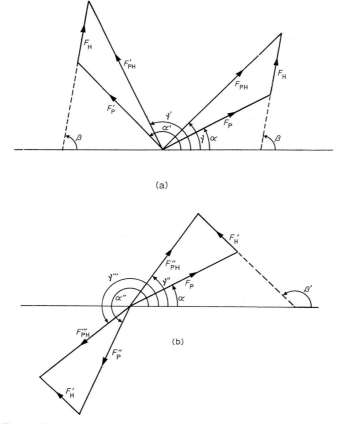

Fig. 21. The ambiguity in phase determination with a single isomorphous replacement (a), resolved with a second isomorphous replacement (b). For description see text.

replacements are required to determine the phase of any reflection, and the lengths and directions of the vectors between the two sets of heavy atom positions must be known. The situation for one reflection is illustrated in Fig. 21a: the protein part F_P has the phase α, the heavy atom part F_H phase β, and their resultant F_{PH} for the derivative has phase γ. The problem is to determine α from the diffraction measurements, which give the lengths F_P and F_{PH}, together with calculations of the heavy atom contribution, which give F_H and β. It can be seen from Fig. 21a that two vector triangles may be drawn, both of which satisfy the requirements, since they are symmetrical about the only known direction, that of the heavy atom vector F_H. The ambiguity in the phase of the protein part (α or α') can only be resolved by carrying out another isomorphous replacement at a new set of positions in the unit cell. For the reflection which we have been using as an example, the new heavy atom contribution F'_H (Fig. 21b) may be supposed to have a different phase β', so the choice of phase for F_P now lies between α and α''. The correct phase α is common to the solutions for both isomorphous replacements. In practice, experimental errors make the determination of phase angles much less certain than the determination of signs among real reflections, and, again, several isomorphous replacements are needed. It is beyond the scope of this chapter to describe the ways of combining data from the various derivatives to the best advantage in the face of considerable errors of measurement. For discussions of this, and the determination of relative heavy atom positions in non-centrosymmetric situations, reference must be made to the original papers[43, 44].

6. Results of isomorphous replacement studies

(a) Myoglobin

Although several proteins have been studied by X-ray crystallographic methods for some years, the analyses of haemoglobin and myoglobin are outstandingly the most advanced. The myoglobin structure, which is the work of Kendrew and his collaborators[44-47], is known in more detail, and will be described first since it provides a guide to interpreting the more complex situation in haemoglobin.

Myoglobin, of molecular weight 17,000, has a single polypeptide chain and carries a prosthetic group, haem, whose chemical structure is known. It functions as a store for oxygen in muscle, one molecule of oxygen being linked to each haem group through the central iron atom. The protein contains no cysteine, so the only obvious site at which heavy atoms might be attached is the haem group itself, and many attempts were made to exploit the affinity of the haem for imidazoles, isocyanides, and nitroso compounds. None of these efforts produced a completely satisfactory derivative, largely because the affinity of myoglobin for oxygen is very high, and the more weakly bound ligands were displaced by traces of atmospheric oxygen. However, one compound which could be linked to the haem, *p*-iodophenylhydroxylamine, did prove useful as a heavy atom label for the haem group at a later stage of the analysis.

The first useful derivative was prepared by crystallising sperm whale myoglobin from ammonium sulphate solution in the presence of one or two equivalents of mercuri-iodide ion (HgI_4^{2-}). This was known to form complexes with dialkyl thio-ethers, and was introduced in the hope of labelling

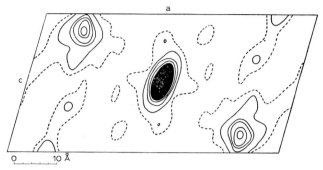

Fig. 22. Difference Patterson for HgI_4^{2-} derivative of sperm whale myoglobin. Type A crystals, *b*-projection. (From Bluhm *et al.*[45].)

the methionine residues, of which there were believed to be two in myoglobin. The crystal form was monoclinic (space group $P2_1$) with two molecules in the unit cell, related by the twofold screw axis. The view down the screw axis is, of course, centrosymmetric, and the corresponding reflections are real. The difference Patterson map which was computed from the intensity changes among these real reflections is shown in Fig. 22. Apart from the origin, there is only one important peak (with its centrosymmetric mate), so we have the simplest possible case: one heavy group per asymmetric unit producing, on the difference Patterson map, one vector to the symmetry-related position.

Many further trials of crystallisation in the presence of various heavy metal ions produced some other suitable derivatives. Those with *p*-chloro-mercuribenzene sulphonate (PCMBS), aurichloride ($AuCl_4^-$), and mercury diammine ($HgAm_2$; prepared by dissolving mercuric oxide in hot concentrated ammonium sulphate solution) were particularly useful because of their close approximation to one site per asymmetric unit. The two coordinates x and z for these heavy atoms were obtained from the real reflections (Fig. 23). The determination of the separations of the various sets of heavy atom positions along the twofold screw axis posed an interesting

References p. 267

crystallographic problem which was satisfactorily solved by more than one method[44,48].

In principle, the way was then open to obtain a map of the electron density in three dimensions, but the intensity measurements had to be made,

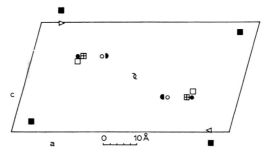

Fig. 23. Projected positions of the heavy-atom groups in various isomorphous replacements in sperm whale myoglobin. (From Bluhm *et al.*[45].) Myoglobin, type A: positions of heavy atoms. □ PCMBS; △ Au, Ag; ○ HgI$_4$$^{2-}$; ● IC$_6H_4$NO; ⊞ PCMS-SC$_6H_4$NC, ▲ I; ■ Hg diammine.

Myoglobin Type A 6A 3 dim' Fourier synthesis

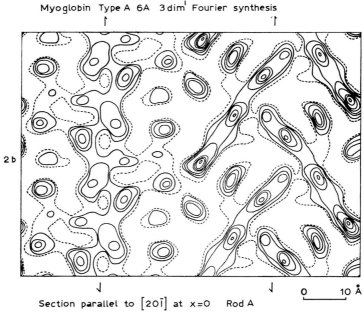

Section parallel to [20ī] at x=0   Rod A

Fig. 24. Section through the 6 Å three-dimensional electron density map of sperm whale myoglobin showing (on the right) straight rods 40 Å long. (From Bodo *et al.*[44].)

and computer programmes had to be devised for phase-determination and the calculation of electron density maps. The whole diffraction pattern for this crystal form of myoglobin contains some 20,000 different reflections. To start with, only the 400 or so reflections with Bragg spacings greater than 6 Å were used. This limit is not a completely arbitrary one, in fact the mean intensity of the reflections, which is a maximum in the region of 10 Å spacing, falls to a minimum at 6 Å, so making a natural cut-off point. Also, it was realised that the physical basis of the variation in the mean intensity of the reflections must be the presence of structures, such as helical polypeptide chains, with characteristic dimensions of 10 Å, which would be plainly revealed by taking the resolution to 6 Å.

The actual Fourier synthesis required to produce this first three-dimensional electron density map for a protein was carried out on a high speed electronic computer, and the results were plotted as contour maps on sixteen planes at equally spaced levels throughout the unit cell. The chief characteristic of the map is illustrated well in the section reproduced in Fig. 24: there are circular rods of high electron density, sometimes running straight for 30 Å, but with sharp corners between them, producing a most irregularly contorted bundle. These rods showed the polypeptide chain folded into some compact form, but the precise configuration could not be determined at 6 Å resolution, and it was difficult to trace a unique path

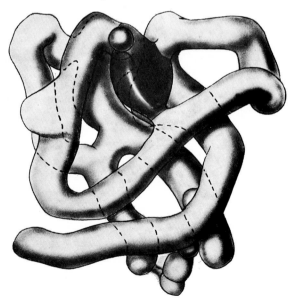

Fig. 25. Model showing the main chain configuration and orientation of the haem group in myoglobin. (From Kendrew *et al.*[47].)

through the molecule for the one chain. The haem group could be identified immediately, for the iron atom produced the highest peak in the electron density, and the difference electron density for the derivative with *p*-iodo-phenylhydroxylamine revealed the iodine atom in an appropriate place.

Fig. 26. (a) Cylindrical projection of a helical segment of polypeptide chain from the 2 Å electron density map of myoglobin, with a skeleton of the α-helix superimposed. (b) Key to the arrangement of atoms in the α-helix. The points marked β and β′ are the two alternative projected positions of Cβ. β′ is the position in a left-handed and β that in a right-handed helix. (From Kendrew *et al.*[47].)

Since this result was first published, the uncertainties in the continuity of the polypeptide chain have been cleared away, and Kendrew has produced a model showing this and the position of the haem group very clearly (Fig. 25).

The extension of the resolution to 2 Å, a task involving the measurement of 10,000 reflections for the native protein and each of four derivatives, together with the associated calculations, now demanding the use of a much more powerful electronic computer, was completed recently[47]. In the result it is possible, for the first time, to get a detailed impression of the atomic structure of a globular protein: atoms connected by covalent bonds are not resolved from one another, but groups which are in van der Waals contact are distinctly separated, so rigid associations of a few atoms, such as the indole group of tryptophan or the phenyl group of phenylalanine, are recognisable.

The rods of high density which appeared in the 6 Å map now look like tubes, the density being low at the centre. Closer examination reveals the wall to be made from strands of high density wound helically, with a pitch of 5.4 Å. This is shown in Fig. 26, which was constructed from a typical length of such a tube by projecting the electron density in the wall onto a cylindrical surface at 1.95 Å radius, then cutting this cylinder parallel to the axis and unrolling it. Superimposed on the contours of electron density is the corresponding cylindrical projection of a skeletal α-helix. Surely, this is a most beautiful justification of the long efforts of the Pasadena school to establish the stereochemical principles leading up to its prediction, and of the Cambridge school in building up the method which led to its revelation. The α-helix is the dominant motif in the structure of myoglobin, some 75% of the polypeptide chain being in this configuration. All the lengths of

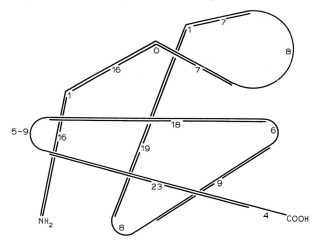

Fig. 27. Distribution of amino acid residues among the α-helical lengths and "corners" in the molecule of sperm whale myoglobin. α-helical sections are indicated by the double line.

α-helix are right handed: the first atom of each side chain C_β can be seen projecting from the main chain in a direction opposite to the carboxyl C–O bond, as expected for L-amino acids in a right-handed helix. The orientation of the C–O bonds also determines the sense of the chain, so the amino and carboxyl ends may readily be identified.

The distribution of the amino acid residues among the lengths of α-helix and the "corners" between them is shown in Fig. 27. Three of the corners are

References p. 267

sharp, with only one residue uncoupled from the α-helix, but there is one region of eight residues in which the backbone arrangement is not at all regular. At the present time the reasons for the formation of these corners are not known. The only residue which would necessarily break the regularity of the α-helix is proline, but there are only four prolines in myoglobin, and certainly seven corners. One proline appears to be the sole "hinge" at a sharp corner, but two others which have been identified take part in quite long non-α-helical sections[49]. One might hope to find the raison d'être in some particularly elegant scheme of interaction between the side chains at the corner, or between some side chains and atoms of the backbone, forming hydrogen bonds which would compensate for the loss of those involved in the helix. Alternatively, the main compensation might be seen in terms of interaction between the helical lengths as units, a true scheme of tertiary structure. Unfortunately, the identification of side chains in myoglobin is not yet complete, and we must wait for details of interactions between them to be elucidated.

Apart from this detailed picture of the polypeptide chain, the 2 Å map of myoglobin gives us a fascinating view of the business end of the molecule, the haem group. Fig. 28 shows a section of the electron density taken through the haem plane with a skeleton of the expected atomic positions superimposed. The orientation of the haem plane relative to the crystal axes agrees very closely with measurements made by means of the anisotropy in electron

0 1 2 3 4 Å

Fig. 28. Section of the electron density map through the haem plane with a skeleton of the expected atomic positions superimposed. (From Kendrew *et al.*[47].)

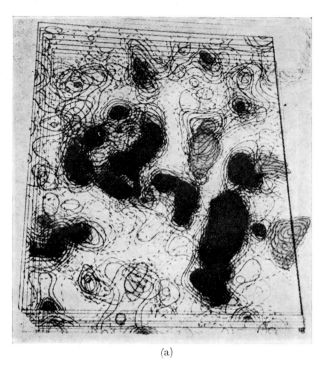

(a)

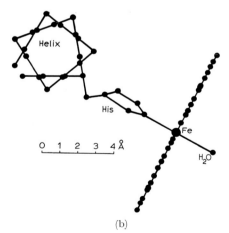

(b)

Fig. 29. Electron density in the region of the haem iron atom of myoglobin, showing the histidine link to the polypeptide chain and a presumptive water molecule on the opposite side of the haem plane.

spin resonance for the iron atom[50]. The way in which the attachment is made to the protein part is also shown clearly in the map (Fig. 29): as had long been believed on chemical grounds, the iron appears to be coordinated to a histidine side chain, while the sixth coordination position, presumably occupied by the oxygen molecule in oxymyoglobin, is here, in metmyoglobin, filled by a water molecule.

Many of the treasures buried in this electron density map have yet to be dug out. In particular there is the prospect of deriving the full sequence of amino acids by correlating the peptide structures derived chemically with the spacial arrangement of the most easily identified side chains. However, the potentialities of the diffraction pattern are not exhausted: measurable reflections are found out to 1.5 Å spacing, at which resolution individual carbon, nitrogen and oxygen atoms should be distinguishable, and the difficulties of identifying the smaller side chains should be overcome.

All this detailed work was carried out with crystals of myoglobin from the sperm whale. It has also been shown that the main chain configuration is similar in myoglobin from the common seal, which crystallises in a different form[51]. This was done by working out the signs of a set of real reflections, using three isomorphous replacements, and then comparing the corresponding electron density projection with the same projection taken from the three dimensional map of sperm whale myoglobin. The task of orienting the sperm whale molecule in the seal unit cell was greatly helped by electron spin resonance measurements of the haem orientation in both cells. The two projections of the electron density agree very closely in all the features which can be ascribed to the main polypeptide chain and the haem group. Also it is particularly interesting that the projected positions of two of the heavy atoms, $AuCl_4^-$ and HgI_4^{2-}, are the same for sperm whale and seal.

(b) Haemoglobin

There have surely been more studies of haemoglobin, the red blood pigment, than of any other single protein. Many of the recent ones have been aimed at questions of structure and configuration, and it would be impossible to do justice to them all: here one can only describe the picture of the molecule obtained recently by Perutz and his co-workers using the isomorphous replacement method of X-ray analysis, and mention the more immediate correlations or disagreements with results won by other techniques.

The molecular weight of this protein is 67,000, and there are four haem groups, each of which can bind reversibly one molecule of oxygen. After some controversy, it has become clear that the chemical results on normal adult human haemoglobin are consistent with there being four polypeptide chains of roughly equal size, which are identical in pairs, one pair being characterised by the N-terminal sequence valyl-leucyl- (α chain), and the other pair by the sequence valyl-histidyl-leucyl- (β chain)[52]. A similar result has been obtained for horse haemoglobin, where the N-terminal sequences are valyl-leucyl- and valyl-glutaminyl-[53], and it seems probable that all vertebrate haemoglobins are alike in having four polypeptide chains of two different types.

Almost the whole sequence of amino acids in both α- and β-chains of human haemoglobin has been determined by Braunitzer et al.[54]. Though several short regions are clearly homologous between the chains, and a balance of charged side chains is maintained, the overall differences are much greater than might have been expected from the species differences earlier found in insulin. Also, occasionally, one, or a small group of residues is omitted from one chain or the other, with the β chain some eight residues longer altogether. As we shall see, one of the largest gaps, where apparently five residues are missing from the α chain, has been since correlated with a well marked feature in the electron density map. The sequence of the first 31 residues from the N-terminus of the β chain which was first published includes those amino acids at which specific and genetically determined exchanges take place in some of the pathological haemoglobins, for example the replacement of a glutamic acid residue by one of valine in sickle cell haemoglobin[38].

The content of free sulphydryl groups has been measured in several haemoglobins by amperometric titration with silver and mercuric ions. All the vertebrate haemoglobins investigated so far do have these groups, but the number varies considerably. With horse haemoglobin, which has been the source material for most of the crystallographic studies, the native molecule readily binds two mercuric ions or four silver ions[55]. Since, apparently, one cysteine residue may bind two silver ions[56], there are probably only two cysteine sulphydryls available in the native molecule. This picture is confirmed by the crystallographic results, which show two sulphydryl sites 21 Å apart[41].

The first isomorphous replacement was obtained by reacting these sulphydryl groups of horse haemoglobin with p-chloromercuribenzoic acid (PCMB), an experiment suggested by a report of the effect of PCMB on the oxygen dissociation curve[61]. The crystal form used was a centred monoclinic one (space group C2) with two molecules in the unit cell, but only half a molecule in the asymmetric unit of pattern. Two molecules of PCMB were bound to each molecule of haemoglobin, i.e. one per asymmetric unit, and it was later found that other mercurials could be bound at the same sites. An entirely different pair of sites was discovered by blocking the sulphydryl groups with iodoacetamide, and then crystallising the haemoglobin in the

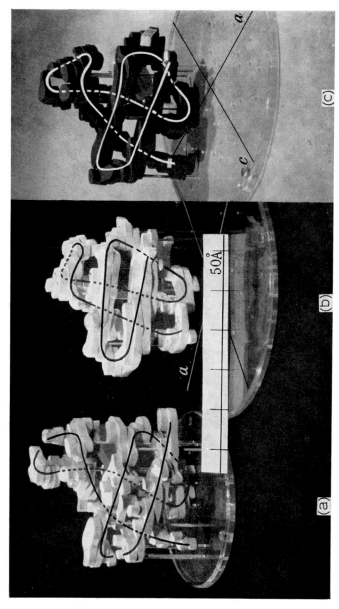

Fig. 30. The two different chains in the asymmetric unit of haemoglobin compared with myoglobin (left). (From Cullis et al.[58].)

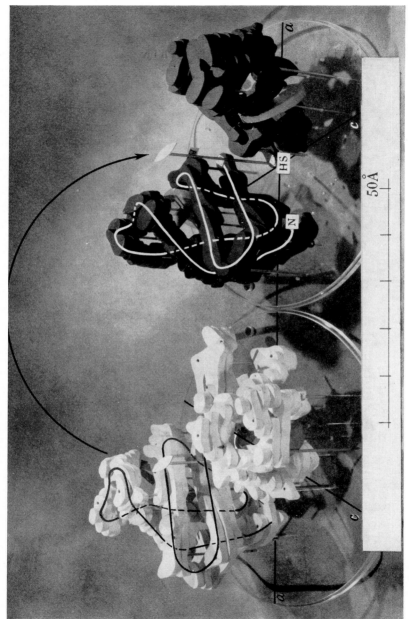

Fig. 31. Two pairs of chains from haemoglobin, symmetrically related by the dyad axis. The arrow shows how one pair is placed over the other to assemble the complete molecule. (From Perutz *et al.*[58].)

presence of two equivalents of mercuric acetate[57]. Altogether six different isomorphous heavy atom compounds, with the heavy atoms mostly attached through the sulphydryl groups, were used to determine the phases of the 1200 reflections in the diffraction pattern which have Bragg spacings greater than 5.5 Å[58].

The three-dimensional map of the electron density, produced after much calculation on an electronic computer, has a resolution slightly better than that of the first three-dimensional map for myoglobin, but provides essentially the same kind of information: the general run of the polypeptide chains, and the positions of the haem groups. In the result both of these features contain surprises.

The four polypeptide chains are revealed as four distinct sub-units, arranged tetrahedrally. These will be described first as separate entities, and later we shall see how they are assembled to make the complete molecule. From the crystal symmetry the sub-units must necessarily be identical in pairs, in agreement with the chemical studies, but the two unrelated types of chains are also very similar, and both resemble the conformation of the myoglobin chain closely. The comparison is shown in Fig. 30, where the chains have been built up from sections cut to the shapes of the higher contours of the electron density map. In the model the two types of chains have been made black and white; the white one is the valyl-leucyl-α-chain and the valyl-glutaminyl-β-chain is the black one[59]. Clearly there are some differences of detail between the black and white chains, and between either of them and the myoglobin chain but the overall similarity is outstanding. The most obvious difference can be seen at the top right-hand corner of each model in Fig. 30. Here the β chain is like myoglobin, probably having eight residues not coupled in α-helices (Fig. 27); while in the α chain this corner is cut off, showing a deletion from the amino acid sequence. This gap had already been found by Braunitzer et al. to be five residues long[54]. Each sub-unit carries one haem group in the same position and orientation relative to the polypeptide chain as in myoglobin. The orientations can be compared with some precision, for, although the haem planes are not very accurately defined in the electron density map, measurements of haem orientation relative to the crystal axes are available from electron spin resonance studies, as in the case of myoglobin[60]. There seem to be several possible points of attachment for the haems apart from the link to the iron atom, for the chain folds round to make a pocket in which the haem is snugly lodged.

The close similarity with myoglobin enables some of the detailed features which must be common to the two proteins, but cannot be seen in the map of haemoglobin at the present resolution, to be taken over from the map of myoglobin at 2 Å resolution. The sense of the chains must be the same, so the amino and carboxyl ends can be identified in haemoglobin too. Also, the manner of linking the haem is believed to be similar, so it is possible to decide which is the reactive side of the haem plane (labelled O_2 in the

Fig. 32. Haemoglobin model partially assembled, with one white chain to be added. (From Perutz *et al.*[58].)

figures), and see where the histidine residue would make the link across to the polypeptide chain.

The quaternary structure, or manner of associating the four sub-units to form the complete molecule is shown in Figs. 31, 32 and 33. One cannot do better than quote Perutz's account[58]. "The first step in the assembly of the molecule is the matching of each chain by its symmetrically related partner (Fig. 31). It will be noted that there is comparatively little contact between the members of each pair, suggesting rather tenuous linkages. In the next step the white pair is inverted and placed over the black pair as

References p. 267

indicated by the arrow. Fig. 32 shows one white chain placed over the pair of black ones, and Fig. 33 shows the molecule completely assembled. The resulting arrangement is tetrahedral and has almost, but not quite, the orthorhombic point group symmetry 222. It contains two *pseudo dyads* which lie approximately at right angles to each other and to the true dyad. This means that, to a first approximation, each sub-unit can be generated by a rotation of 180° from any of its neighbours. Figs. 31, 32 and 33 also show that the surface contours of the white chains exactly fit those of the black, so that there is a large area of contact between them. This structural complementarity is one of the most striking features of the molecule".

Fig. 33. Haemoglobin model completely assembled. The haem groups are indicated by the grey discs. (From Perutz *et al.*[58].)

Perhaps the most surprising thing about the molecule is the arrangement of the haem groups, shown diagramatically in Fig. 34. From the shape of the oxygen dissociation curve of haemoglobin, which is sigmoid, not hyperbolic, or from the rates at which the molecules of oxygen are bound, which increase with each successive addition, it is apparent that there is some scheme of interaction between the haem groups. It was thought that this

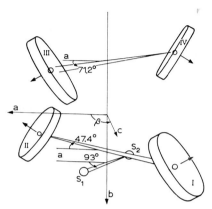

Fig. 34. Arrangement of haem groups in haemoglobin. Arrows indicate the reactive side of each haem. (From Perutz et al.[58].)

might be a steric effect; if so, the haem groups should have been found close together. In fact, the shortest distance between iron atoms is 25.2 Å (pair unrelated by symmetry), while the symmetrically related iron atoms have distances of 33.4 and 36.0 Å between them. The observation that the haem–haem interaction is reduced by blocking the sulphydryl groups with mercurials[61] is also of great interest in relation to this picture of the structure, for the positions of the sulphydryls are clearly marked by heavy atoms. As shown in Fig. 34, they lie between two symmetrically related haems (on the black chains), with S—Fe distances of about 13 Å and 21 Å, and close to points of contact between the black and the white chains. The spacial arrangement is suggestive of a long path of interaction between haems on the black and the white chains, through the black chain histidine and cysteine to the white chain (Fig. 33), but the details must await an electron density map at higher resolution.

(c) Viruses

The discussion in this section will be very brief, and restricted to the small group of viruses which have been studied in some detail by X-ray diffraction methods. Particular emphasis will be placed on results which have come from the application of the isomorphous replacement technique.

The group includes tobacco mosaic virus (TMV) and some related strains, bushy stunt virus (BSV), turnip yellow mosaic virus (TYMV), and southern bean mosaic virus (SBMV), which are pathogenic in plants, and one small animal virus, that of poliomyelitis (poliovirus). All of these consist only of protein and ribonucleic acid (RNA). The absolute amount of RNA is approximately the same in all of them, some $2 \cdot 10^6$ molecular weight units per particle, but the amount of protein varies considerably: TYMV, for example, has approximately $6 \cdot 10^6$ molecular weight units of protein, while TMV has some $37 \cdot 10^6$ molecular weight units[62].

The first X-ray photographs of TMV, taken some twenty years ago by Bernal and Fankuchen[63], showed that the protein part of each virus particle was made up of sub-units arranged in a regular way; and the same has since been demonstrated not only for other viruses which are rod shaped like TMV, but also for some small spherical ones including BSV, TYMV, SBMV and poliovirus. This type of information can be obtained comparatively quickly by X-ray diffraction, for symmetry in the particle produces a corresponding symmetry in the diffraction pattern. In fact, the symmetry of the pattern is higher than that of the virus, for, as we have seen, natural protein-containing materials are asymmetric at the level of their component atoms, while the diffraction pattern necessarily has a centre of symmetry superimposed on any symmetry in the atomic arrangement of the specimen. Symmetry in the virus particle is most immediately obvious when it is incorporated into the infinite symmetry of a crystal through some fortunate orientation of the particles. This is the case with BSV, where the crystals have tetrahedral symmetry, *i.e.* three twofold axes and four threefold axes so related that they point along the edges and diagonals of a cube respectively[64]. Here the virus particles must also have this symmetry, and so be divisible into twelve asymmetric units which are interrelated by the twofold and threefold axes. There is, however, a further fivefold symmetry in the BSV particle which shows up in the diffraction pattern as a distribution of particularly strong reflections along certain directions which are not crystallographic axes[65].

The search for these non-crystallographic elements of symmetry was stimulated by the suggestion from Crick and Watson[66] that small spherical viruses were likely to be composed of identical sub-units arranged according the operations of cubic symmetry, which provide the only systematic way of making a complete spherical shell from units of arbitrary shape. The particular type of cubic symmetry which is most relevant is that of the icosahedron, which has fivefold, threefold and twofold axes: in this case sixty asymmetric units are required to complete the shell (Fig. 35). Fivefold symmetry can only be found in finite objects such as a single virus particle; it is impossible to extend the fivefold symmetry through the essentially infinite repetitions of a crystal lattice. This means that its effects must be looked for in the distribution of intense reflections in the diffraction pattern; they will not be revealed in any more straight-forward way.

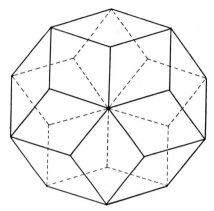

Fig. 35. Diagram of a rhombic triacontahedron, viewed down a fivefold axis. Two types of sub-units may be arranged at the threefold and fivefold vertices of such a figure to form the protein shell of turnip yellow mosaic virus. (From Huxley and Zubay[71].)

The appropriate fivefold "spikes" of strong reflections have been found in the patterns of BSV[67], TYMV[68], SBMV[69] and poliovirus[70]. The electron microscope pictures of TYMV, however, show 32 sub-units of similar size arranged, to a close approximation, at the vertices of a rhombic triaconta-hedron or a pentakis dodecahedron[71, 72]. Both of these semi-regular solids have the icosahedral symmetry required by the X-ray results, but, since the vertices are of two different kinds, twelve lying on fivefold axes and twenty on threefold axes, the morphological sub-units must also comprise two distinct sets. If each of these sets is made up of identical chemical sub-units, then there must be at least 60 of these in each set. At present the chemical evidence is not sufficiently precise to decide between the two most likely possibilities of 120 or 180 sub-units in all.

TMV is the only virus so far for which an isomorphous replacement has been achieved. It is therefore possible to discuss its structure in more detail, and, in particular, to say something about the relationship between the RNA and the protein. The molecular weight, as mentioned before, is $39 \cdot 10^6$, of which $2 \cdot 10^6$ is RNA; and the shape seen in the electron microscope is a straight rod 3,000 Å long and about 170 Å wide. Chemical methods have revealed that the protein is made up of some 2,100 sub-units of molecular

References p. 267

weight 17–18,000, while the nucleic acid is a single molecule, as shown by its sedimentation behaviour in the ultracentrifuge. For this rod-shaped virus the problem of arranging asymmetrical sub-units with similar contacts is solved, as for the regular polypeptide chain, by building a helix. The evidence for this will be discussed later, but we may note that since the operation of adding sub-units to a helix could go on indefinitely, it is

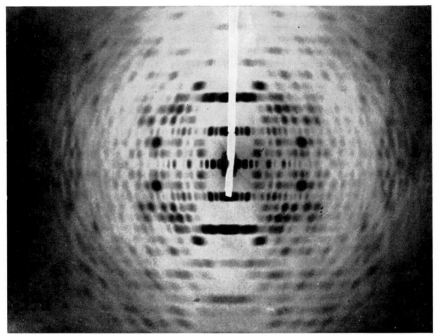

Fig. 36. X-ray diffraction diagram of an orientated gel of TMV, common strain, taken with a high-resolution focussing camera and crystal-monochromatized Cu Kα-radiation. (From Franklin et al.[67].)

probable that the length of the TMV rod is determined by the RNA component. The RNA contains approximately 6,400 nucleotides, and if fully extended would be some 48,000 Å long, some 16 times the length of the virus particle. Evidently, on the basis of mere numerology one cannot decide the configuration of the RNA: to take two extreme possibilities it might be folded in a perfectly regular way along the whole length, or it might be arranged in as many as sixteen equal strands running back and forth along the length of the rod. It is reasonable, though, to expect an answer from the X-ray studies.

One of the superb X-ray diffraction photographs of TMV taken by

Franklin is reproduced in Fig. 36. It must be emphasised that the specimen is not a crystal of TMV, but is a gel of the virus in water, placed in a capillary, where the long thin rods have become aligned parallel to the axis. The orientation of the rods about their axes is quite random, and the observed diffraction is that of a single virus particle. The well marked layer lines correspond to an axial repeat of 69 Å, and it was shown by Watson[74] that the other striking feature, the presence of strong diffraction close to the meridian on every third layer line, and its absence on the other low order layer lines, was consistent with a helical arrangement of $(3n+1)$ sub-units in three turns, the pitch of the helix being 23 Å. The number n has only recently been determined with certainty, first from isomorphous replacement studies and later from an interpretation of the parts of the diffraction pattern due to the outside structure of the virus: it was found to be 16, *i.e.* 49 sub-units in three turns[73]. The total number of X-ray sub-units in the whole virus particle is thus $49/69 \times 3000 = 2130$, in very close agreement with the number of chemical sub-units determined by end-group analysis.

The isomorphous derivative used in determining n was one prepared by Fraenkel-Conrat, which has a methyl mercury group bound to the single cysteine residue of each sub-unit. It appears that this cysteine sulphydryl group is not accessible to larger mercurials such as PCMB. Another derivative, in which lead is bound at two positions on each sub-unit, had been prepared previously by Caspar, and was used by him to obtain the first direct picture of the electron density in TMV[75].

As with the globular proteins, the effects of the heavy atom have been interpreted first in the regions of the diffraction pattern where the phase is restricted to 0° or 180°. For the TMV pictures only the equatorial diffraction is known to be "real", and it is only here that sign determination can be successfully carried out. The first set of signs came from the lead derivative, and was completely confirmed with the methyl mercury compound. It was then possible to compute a picture of the radial variation in electron density for a cylindrically averaged particle, *i.e.* one in which any variation in electron density around the axis at a fixed radius has been averaged out. The result is shown in Fig. 37. Two important features of the structure are immediately obvious: first, the virus rod has a hole of 35–40 Å diameter extending along the axis, and, second, the maximum diameter of the rod is about 180 Å. The significance of the maxima at 25, 40, 66 and 78 Å will be discussed later. The existence of the hole has been beautifully confirmed by Huxley[76], who succeeded in staining the inside surface of the rod with phosphotungstate and so making the hole visible in the electron microscope. Confirmation of the maximum diameter comes from Franklin's studies of the binding of osmium to TMV, where the effects on the diffraction pattern showed the osmium atoms to be bound at a radius of 90 Å. This maximum diameter of 180 Å is greater than one would have expected from the inter-particle spacing of 152 Å measured in dried gels, but this apparent anomaly is explained by the presence of a deep helical groove in the outer surface of the virus which enables neighbouring particles to intermesh when the intervening water is removed[77].

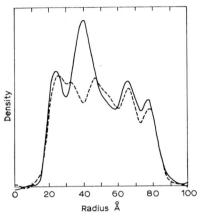

Fig. 37. The cylindrically averaged radial distribution of electron density in TMV (full curve) and repolymerised, nucleic acid-free TMV protein (dotted curve). (From Franklin *et al.*[67].)

The key to the location of the RNA comes from a similar radial density map computed for a "dummy" virus composed of the protein part without the RNA. The virus can be broken down by treatment with dilute alkali into degraded RNA and a protein component of low molecular weight (A-protein)[78]. When the RNA has been removed, readjusting the pH allows the A-protein to re-polymerise into rods which can be oriented in a capillary in much the same way as the complete virus. Such a specimen gives a dif-fraction pattern sufficiently similar to that of the complete virus to ensure that the sub-units in the repolymerised protein are arranged in a very similar, and possibly identical, way[79]. There are, however, important changes in the intensities in various parts of the diffraction pattern. In particular, along the equator, where the phases were known from isomorphous replace-ment, it was possible to use the new amplitudes to compute a radial electron density distribution for the RNA-free rod. This also is shown in Fig. 37. It can be seen that the structural similarity surmised from the general appearance of the photographs is revealed in some detail by this picture: the only feature which is significantly changed is the large peak at 40 Å radius for the whole virus, which now appears as a shallow trough. Clearly, this large peak represents the electron density due to the RNA, with its comparatively *heavy* phosphorus atoms, and, indeed, a calculation of the integrated electron density difference agrees well with the known composition of 5 % RNA. No interpretation has yet been given for the smaller peaks at 25, 66 and 78 Å.

Other information about the configuration of the RNA will come from the remaining part of the diffraction pattern, but the phases have not yet been determined by isomorphous replacement. There is, therefore, not the same degree of certainty about any further conclusions which may be drawn, but an impressive body of evidence can be assembled to support the idea that the RNA is in the form of a single thread following the same helix of 23 Å pitch as the protein sub-units.

There seems to be little doubt that all the RNA is in one strand with a single sugar-phosphate backbone. Evidence of the single backbone comes from kinetic studies of the degradation of the isolated RNA by ribonuclease[80]. If several strands of nucleotides were aligned parallel to one another with cross-links between them, a break in one of the strands would not break the whole RNA; only a series of cleavages at approximately the same position could achieve this. The degradation kinetics of double-stranded DNA is of this kind[81], but RNA is degraded like a single strand of nucleotides, since upon incubation with ribonuclease, degradation proceeds immediately, with the highest rate at the beginning of the reaction. Also, in electron microscope observations of TMV which had been treated with hot detergent for various short times, Hart found that the virus rods became degraded by removal of the protein from the ends (frequently from only one end) exposing the RNA as a single fibre of greatly extended form[82]. Apparently, on being "uncovered" the RNA could unfold to at least 11 times its length in the virus. The minimum length for the RNA from a completely degraded rod would thus be 33,000 Å, which may be compared with the estimated 48,000 Å for a fully extended single chain of that molecular weight. Clearly, anything other than a single chain could not stretch to such a length, and the observation that even slightly degraded rods can show RNA extended to the same degree apparently precludes any "looping" of this single chain from one end of the virus to the other.

The perfection of the diffraction pattern of TMV suggests that the RNA, like the protein, has a helical structure. Moreover, the radial density distribution shows the RNA embedded in protein, suggesting an intimate connection in which its configuration is determined by the arrangement of protein sub-units, rather than being self-determined and independent of the protein. Also, since the sub-units are identical, as far as the present evidence goes, one must suppose that the scheme of interaction between protein and RNA is perfectly regular from one sub-unit to the next. There are very few ways of arranging this, as there are probably only three nucleotides per sub-unit:

References p. 267

one way has the RNA chain following the same helix of 23 Å pitch as the sub-units, the other ways all require the RNA to be looped from one end of the virus to the other and back again several times. Taking all the evidence together, it seems that the RNA must be wound along this one simplest helical path, of 40 Å radius and 23 Å pitch, running without reversal of direction from one end of the virus to the other. The length of this path is 33,000 Å, in perhaps fortuitously good agreement with Hart's estimate from partially degraded TMV.

There is a great deal more information in the diffraction pattern which will, in time, be "unlocked" by further applications of isomorphous replacement. Technical difficulties limit the resolution of the pattern to about 4.5 Å, but it appears likely that any remaining uncertainties about the general configuration of the RNA will be dispelled within a comparatively short time. Also, one may look forward to significant contributions to the picture of the RNA–protein relationship, which will be essential to an understanding of the mechanisms of assembly of the virus and of infection.

ACKNOWLEDGEMENTS

I wish to thank Drs. M. F. Perutz, J. C. Kendrew and A. Klug for helpful comments on parts of the manuscript; also Miss J. A. Mason and Mr. R. M. Simmons for help in preparing the diagrams.

REFERENCES

[1] P. DESNUELLE, in H. NEURATH AND K. BAILEY (Eds.), *The Proteins*, Vol. IA, Academic Press, New York, 1953, p. 87.

[2] T. HAHN, *Z. Krist.*, 109 (1957) 438.

[3] J. TROMMEL AND J. M. BIJVOET, *Acta Cryst.*, 7 (1954) 703.

[4] D. P. SHOEMAKER, J. DONOHUE, V. SCHOMAKER AND R. B. COREY, *J. Am. Chem. Soc.*, 72 (1950) 2328.

[5] J. DONOHUE AND K. N. TRUEBLOOD, *Acta Cryst.*, 5 (1952) 419.

[6] B. M. OUGHTON AND P. M. HARRISON, *Acta Cryst.*, 12 (1959) 396.

[7] H. L. YAKEL AND E. W. HUGHES, *Acta Cryst.*, 7 (1954) 291.

[8] J. PETERSON, L. K. STEINRAUF AND L. H. JENSEN, *Acta Cryst.*, 13 (1960) 104.

[9] L. PAULING, R. B. COREY AND H. R. BRANSON, *Proc. Natl. Acad. Sci. U.S.*, 37 (1951) 205.

[10] W. B. WRIGHT, *Acta Cryst.*, 11 (1958) 632.

[11] J. C. KENDREW AND M. F. PERUTZ, *Ann. Rev. Biochem.*, 26 (1957) 327.

[12] R. B. COREY AND J. DONOHUE, *J. Am. Chem. Soc.*, 72 (1950) 2899.

[13] J. DONOHUE, *J. Phys. Chem.*, 56 (1952) 502.

[14] L. PAULING AND R. B. COREY, *Advances in Protein Chem.*, 12 (1957) 133.

[15] W. L. BRAGG, J. C. KENDREW AND M. F. PERUTZ, *Proc. Roy. Soc. (London)*, A, 203 (1950) 321.

[16] J. DONOHUE, *Proc. Natl. Natl. Acad. Sci. U.S.*, 39 (1953) 470.

[17] L. BROWN AND I. F. TROTTER, *Trans. Faraday Soc.*, 52 (1956) 537.

[18] M. F. PERUTZ, *Nature*, 167 (1951) 1053.

[19] A. ELLIOTT AND B. R. MALCOLM, *Proc. Roy. Soc. (London)*, A, 249 (1959) 30.

[20] L. PAULING AND R. B. COREY, *Nature*, 171 (1953) 59.

[21] F. H. C. CRICK, *Acta Cryst.*, 6 (1953) 689.

[22] L. PAULING AND R. B. COREY, *Proc. Natl. Acad. Sci. U.S.*, 37 (1951) 729; 39 (1953) 253.

[23] R. E. MARSH, R. B. COREY AND L. PAULING, *Biochim. Biophys. Acta*, 16 (1955) 1.

[24] R. E. MARSH, R. B. COREY AND L. PAULING, *Acta Cryst.*, 8 (1955) 710.

[25] P. M. COWAN, A. C. T. NORTH AND J. T. RANDALL in *Fibrous Proteins and their Biological Significance, Symposium Soc. Exptl. Biol.*, IX, Cambridge University Press, 1955.

[26] G. N. RAMACHANDRAN AND G. KARTHA, *Nature*, 174 (1954) 269.

[27] F. H. C. CRICK AND A. RICH, *Nature*, 176 (1955) 780.

[28] A. RICH AND F. H. C. CRICK, *Nature*, 176 (1955) 915.

[29] M. DIXON AND E. C. WEBB, *Enzymes*, Longmans, Green & Co., London, 1958.

[30] A. P. RYLE, F. SANGER, L. F. SMITH AND R. KITAI, *Biochem. J.*, 60 (1955) 541.

[31] C. H. W. HIRS, S. MOORE AND W. H. STEIN, *J. Biol. Chem.*, 235 (1960) 633; D. H. SPACKMAN, W. H. STEIN AND S. MOORE, *J. Biol. Chem.*, 235 (1960) 648.

[32] F. A. ANDERER, H. UHLIG, E. WEBER AND G. SCHRAMM, *Nature*, 186 (1960) 922; A. TSUGITA, D. T. GISH, J. YOUNG, H. FRAENKEL-CONRAT, C. A. KNIGHT AND W. M. STANLEY, *Proc. Natl. Acad. Sci. U.S.*, 46 (1960) 1463.

[33] J. C. KENDREW AND J. KRAUT, in F. H. C. CRICK AND J. C. KENDREW, *Advances in Protein Chem.*, 12 (1957) 133.

[34] J. BOYES-WATSON, E. DAVIDSON AND M. F. PERUTZ, *Proc. Roy. Soc. (London) A*, 191 (1947) 83.

[35] R. ASCHAFFENBURG AND J. DREWRY, *Nature*, 176 (1955) 218.

[36] D. W. GREEN, A. C. T. NORTH AND R. ASCHAFFENBURG, *Biochim. Biophys. Acta*, 21 (1956) 583.

[37] M. F. PERUTZ, A. M. LIQUORI AND F. EIRICH, *Nature*, 167 (1951) 929.

[38] V. M. INGRAM, *Nature*, 180 (1957) 326.

[39] J. C. KENDREW, *Progr. in Biophys. and Biophys. Chem.*, 4 (1954) 244.

[40] E. J. COHN, *Nucleus*, 25 (1948) 263.

[41] D. W. GREEN, V. M. INGRAM AND M. F. PERUTZ, *Proc. Roy. Soc. (London)*, A, 225 (1954) 287.

[42] W. L. BRAGG AND M. F. PERUTZ, *Proc. Roy. Soc. (London)*, A, 225 (1954) 315.

[43] D. M. BLOW AND F. H. C. CRICK, *Acta Cryst.*, 12 (1959) 794.

[44] G. BODO, H. M. DINTZIS, J. C. KENDREW AND H. W. WYCKOFF, *Proc. Roy. Soc. (London), A*, 253 (1959) 70.

[45] M. M. BLUHM, G. BODO, H. M. DINTZIS AND J. C. KENDREW, *Proc. Roy. Soc. (London), A*, 246 (1958) 369.

[46] J. C. KENDREW, G. BODO, H. M. DINTZIS, R. G. PARRISH, H. W. WYCKOFF AND D. C. PHILLIPS, *Nature*, 181 (1958) 662.

[47] J. C. KENDREW, R. E. DICKERSON, B. E. STRANDBERG, R. G. HART, D. R. DAVIES, D. C. PHILLIPS AND V. C. SHORE, *Nature*, 185 (1960) 422.

[48] W. L. BRAGG, *Acta Cryst.*, 11 (1958) 70.

[49] H. C. WATSON AND J. C. KENDREW, *Nature*, 190 (1961) 670.

[50] D. J. E. INGRAM AND J. C. KENDREW, *Nature*, 178 (1956) 905.

[51] H. SCOULOUDI, *Proc. Roy. Soc. (London), A*, 258 (1960) 181.

[52] H. S. RHINESMITH, W. A. SCHROEDER AND N. MARTIN, *J. Am. Chem. Soc.*, 80 (1958) 3358.

[53] S. WILSON AND D. B. SMITH, *Can. J. Biochem. and Physiol.*, 37 (1959) 405.

[54] G. BRAUNITZER, N. HILSCHMANN, V. RUDLOFF, K. HILSE, B. LIEBOLD AND R. MULLER, *Nature*, 190 (1961) 480; W. KONIGSBERG, G. GUIDOTTI AND R. J. HILL, *J. Biol. Chem.*, 236 (1961) PC 55.

[55] V. M. INGRAM, *Biochem. J.*, 59 (1955) 653.

[56] A. C. ALLISON AND R. CECIL, *Biochem. J.*, 69 (1958) 27.

[57] A. F. CULLIS, H. M. DINTZIS AND M. F. PERUTZ, *I.U.P.A.C. Symposium on Protein Structure*, Butterworth, London, 1958, p. 50.

[58] A. F. CULLIS, H. MUIRHEAD, A. C. T. NORTH, M. F. PERUTZ AND M. G. ROSSMANN, *Proc. Roy. Soc. (London), A*, 265 (1962) 161.

[58a] M. F. PERUTZ, M. G. ROSSMANN, A. F. CULLIS, H. MUIRHEAD, G. WILL AND A. C. T. NORTH, *Nature*, 185 (1960) 416.

[59] D. B. SMITH AND M. F. PERUTZ, *Nature*, 188 (1960) 406.

[60] D. J. E. INGRAM, J. F. GIBSON AND M. F. PERUTZ, *Nature*, 178 (1956) 906.

[61] A. F. RIGGS AND R. A. WOLBACH, *J. Gen. Physiol.*, 39 (1956) 585.

[62] W. FRISCH-NIGGEMEYER, *Nature*, 178 (1956) 307.

[63] J. D. BERNAL AND I. FANKUCHEN, *J. Gen. Physiol.*, 25 (1941) 111.

[64] C. H. CARLISLE AND K. DORNBERGER, *Acta Cryst.*, 1 (1948) 194.

[65] D. L. D. CASPAR, *Nature*, 177 (1956) 475.

[66] F. H. C. CRICK AND J. D. WATSON, *Nature*, 177 (1956) 473.

[67] R. E. FRANKLIN, D. L. D. CASPAR AND A. KLUG, *Plant Pathology, Problems and Progress*, University of Wisconsin Press, 1959, p. 447.

[68] A. KLUG AND J. T. FINCH, *J. Molecular Biol.*, 2 (1960) 201.

[69] B. E. MAGDOFF, *Nature*, 185 (1960) 673.

[70] J. T. FINCH AND A. KLUG, *Nature*, 183 (1959) 1709.

[71] H. E. HUXLEY AND G. ZUBAY, *J. Molecular Biol.*, 2 (1960) 189.

[72] H. L. NIXON AND A. J. GIBBS, *J. Molecular Biol.*, 2 (1960) 197.

[73] R. E. FRANKLIN AND K. C. HOLMES, *Acta Cryst.*, 11 (1958) 213.

[74] J. D. WATSON, *Biochim. Biophys. Acta*, 13 (1954) 10.

[75] D. L. D. CASPAR, *Nature*, 177 (1956) 928.

[76] H. E. HUXLEY, *Proc. Stockholm Conf. on Electron Microscopy*, Almqvist and Wiksell, Stockholm, 1959, p. 260.

[77] R. E. FRANKLIN AND A. KLUG, *Biochim. Biophys. Acta*, 19 (1956) 403.

[78] G. SCHRAMM, *Z. Naturforsch.*, 2b (1947) 108.

[79] R. E. FRANKLIN, *Biochim. Biophys. Acta*, 18 (1955) 313.

[80] A. GIERER, *Z. Naturforsch.*, 13b (1958) 477.

[81] V. N. SCHUMAKER, E. G. RICHARDS AND H. K. SCHACHMAN, *J. Am. Chem. Soc.*, 78 (1956) 4230.

[82] R. G. HART, *Biochim. Biophys. Acta*, 28 (1955) 457.

[83] E. MARGOLIASH, *J. Biol. Chem.*, 237 (1962) 2161.

SUBJECT INDEX

DATE DUE

DATE DUE			
MR 16 68			

GAYLORD   PRINTED IN U.S.A.